SALICYLATES

An International Symposium

SALICYLATES

An International Symposium
sponsored by the
EMPIRE RHEUMATISM COUNCIL
with the support of the
NICHOLAS RESEARCH INSTITUTE LTD.

Postgraduate Medical School of London
13th-15th September, 1962

Edited by

A. St. J. DIXON   B. K. MARTIN

M. J. H. SMITH   P. H. N. WOOD

With 43 Figures and 8 Plates

J. & A. CHURCHILL LTD.
104 Gloucester Place, London, W.1.
1963

The costs of production of this book were subsidized by the Nicholas Research Institute Ltd.

Set in 10/11 pt. Imprint type and
Printed in Great Britain

PREFACE

THIS symposium was the first occasion on which were gathered together those specifically interested in the salicylates. The variety of topics discussed and the different scientific disciplines represented at the meeting reflected the impact of these relatively simple drugs on many fields of research. The salicylates possess serious claims to scientific attention because they are among the most ancient of remedies and yet have stood the test of time, because they have a remarkable resilience as chemotherapeutic agents, and because of the range and diversity of their useful and toxic actions.

During the eighty years since the introduction and widespread use of synthetic preparations a voluminous literature has accumulated. Nevertheless it has not been possible to formulate precise ideas either about the mode of action of salicylates or to explain the exact manner in which they produce their toxic effects. It was hoped that this meeting would provide the opportunity to take stock of our present knowledge and thus to focus attention on those aspects that seemed of importance for future advances in this field.

Under the sponsorship of the Empire Rheumatism Council, with the support of the Nicholas Research Institute Ltd., the main responsibility for the meeting lay in the hands of an Organizing Committee, who have also acted as the Editorial Committee for this report. The Committee is grateful to the Postgraduate Medical School of London for the excellent facilities made available at the Wolfson Institute, and to the Arthritis and Rheumatism Foundation of America and to a number of pharmaceutical companies for grants for travelling expenses for some of the overseas participants. The Committee is also indebted to the Nicholas Research Institute Ltd. for a subsidy towards the costs of production of this report.

The proceedings of the symposium have been edited in order to present the material in a form more suitable for publication as a book. It is hoped also that the report may serve as an up-to-date bibliographic review of the subjects discussed. The committee have endeavoured to see that full references are cited. Where no reference is quoted, the inference to be drawn is that the work has not been published. Where work is referred to in the discussions by the author's name only, the full reference will be found in the bibliography at the end of the papers immediately preceding that discussion. Reference to work mentioned during the symposium is made only by designation of the author's name in capital letters; page references are not given, but can be found easily from the Contributor Index. When reference is made to the work of someone who happened to be present but who had not presented this work at the symposium, this convention does not apply.

In general the use of proprietary names has been avoided, although if the proprietary name is used it is treated as a proper noun. Preference has been given to B.P., B.P.C., or Approved Names, or to standard chemical nomenclature. The only instance in which this nomenclature may not be universally understood occurs with Paracetamol, the chemical name of which is N-acetyl-p-aminophenol (Acetaminophen, U.S.A.N.). For proprietary products that were referred to frequently we have used certain synonyms that most people already understand:

Disprin and Solprin (Reckitt & Sons Ltd.).	soluble aspirin
Bufferin (Bristol-Myers Company) .	buffered aspirin
Alka-Seltzer (Miles Laboratories Ltd.) .	effervescent aspirin
Paynocil (Beecham Research Laboratories Ltd.).	aspirin-glycine
Calurin (Dorsey Laboratories) . .	calcium aspirin urea
Enseal and Nuseal coatings (Eli Lilly & Company Ltd.) . . .	enteric-coated aspirin or sodium salicylate (unless coating specified otherwise)
Trafuril (Ciba).	thurfyl nicotinate cream

These terms are used with these specific meanings in the singular; when used in the plural their meaning is more general, e.g. soluble aspirins include any preparation that is dissolved readily in water.

The Committee is indebted to Miss Beryl Howard and Miss Pamela Coates for much assistance, to Messrs. Harry Cooper for transcribing the proceedings of the symposium, to Miss D. F. Atkins for checking the references, and to Mr. David Banks for redrawing most of the figures. The Committee also wish to thank Mr. M. C. G. Andrews, General Secretary of the Empire Rheumatism Council, for his support and help.

CONTENTS

FIFTH SESSION—THE TOXICITY OF SALICYLATES

I*

CONCLUDING SESSION

PARTICIPANTS

List of those presenting papers or contributing to the discussions

STEWART S. ADAMS . . Research Department, Biology Division, Boots Pure Drug Company, Nottingham

W. DONALD ALEXANDER . University Department of Medicine, Gardiner Institute, Western Infirmary, Glasgow.

K. W. ANDERSON . . Biochemist, Nicholas Research Institute Ltd., Slough, Bucks.

BARBARA M. ANSELL . . Consultant Physician, Rheumatism Unit, Canadian Red Cross Memorial Hospital, Taplow, Bucks.

K. FRANK AUSTEN . . Associate in Medicine, Massachusetts General Hospital and Harvard Medical School, Boston, Mass., U.S.A.

DANIEL M. BACHMAN . Associate Professor of Medicine and Head, Division of Rheumatology, University of Oregon Medical School, Portland, Oregon, U.S.A.

THEODORE B. BAYLES. . Director of Research, Robert Breck Brigham Hospital, and Clinical Associate in Medicine, Harvard Medical School, Boston, Mass., U.S.A. (Vice-President, American Rheumatism Association).

D. M. BROWN . . Head, Department of Pharmacology and Chemotherapy, Beecham Research Laboratories, Betchworth, Surrey.

G. A. H. BUTTLE . . Professor of Pharmacology, School of Pharmacy, University of London.

E. G. L. BYWATERS . E.R.C. Professor of Rheumatology, Postgraduate Medical School of London, and Director, M.R.C. Rheumatism Research Unit, Canadian Red Cross Memorial Hospital, Taplow, Bucks.

JOHN J. CALABRO . . Associate Professor of Medicine and Director, Division of Rheumatology, Seton Hall College of Medicine and Dentistry, Jersey City, N.J., U.S.A.

H. CAMPBELL . . . Medical Statistician, General Register Office, Somerset House, London.

H. VAN CAUWENBERGE . Professor of Medicine, University of Liège, Belgium.

R. COBB . . . . Research Department, Biology Division, Boots Pure Drug Company, Nottingham.

N. F. COGHILL . . Consultant Physician, West Middlesex Hospital, Isleworth, Middlesex.

H. O. J. COLLIER . . Director of Pharmacological Research, Parke, Davis and Company, Hounslow, Middlesex.

R. CONSDEN . . . Biochemist, M.R.C. Rheumatism Research Unit, Canadian Red Cross Memorial Hospital, Taplow, Bucks.

W. S. C. COPEMAN . . Senior Physician, Arthur Stanley Institute of Rheumatic Diseases, Middlesex Hospital, and Physician-in-charge, Department of Rheumatic Diseases, West London Hospital, London. (Chairman, Empire Rheumatism Council).

BRIAN CREAMER . . Consultant Physician and Lecturer in Medicine, St. Thomas's Hospital, London.

D. N. CROFT . . . Department of Medicine, St. Thomas's Hospital, London.

GORDON CUMMING . . Lecturer in Medicine, University of Birmingham.

A. J. CUMMINGS . . Biochemist, Nicholas Research Institute Ltd., Slough, Bucks.

CLARKE DAVISON . . Associate Professor of Pharmacology, George Washington University School of Medicine, Washington, D.C., U.S.A.

FRANK DICKENS . . Professor of Biochemistry, Courtauld Institute of Biochemistry, Middlesex Hospital Medical School, London.

ALLAN ST. J. DIXON . . Consultant Physician, Chelsea and Kensington Group Rheumatism Unit, St. Stephen's Hospital, London.

R. DOMENJOZ . . . Professor of Pharmacology, Friedrich-Wilhelms University, Bonn, Federal German Republic.

ALAN K. DONE . . Associate Research Professor of Pediatrics, University of Utah College of Medicine, Salt Lake City, Utah, U.S.A.

J. J. R. DUTHIE . . Senior Lecturer, Department of Medicine, University of Edinburgh, and Consultant Physician, Rheumatic Diseases Unit, Northern General Hospital, Edinburgh.

K. FREMONT-SMITH . . Visiting Physician, Robert Breck Brigham Hospital, and Assistant, Department of Medicine, Harvard Medical School, Boston, Mass., U.S.A.

L. E. GLYNN . . . Consultant Pathologist, M.R.C. Rheumatism Research Unit, Canadian Red Cross Memorial Hospital, Taplow, Bucks.

A. W. G. GOOLDEN	Consultant Radiotherapist, Hammersmith Hospital, London.
J. A. HICKLIN	First Asistant, The Medical Unit, The London Hospital, London.
PETER R. HOLT	Head, Gastroenterology Laboratory, St. Luke's Hospital, New York, N.Y., U.S.A.
A. K. HUGGINS	John Wyeth Fellow in Pharmacology, E.R.C. Research Unit on Drug Metabolism, Department of Chemical Pathology, King's College Hospital Medical School, London.
J. H. HUMPHREY	Head, Division of Immunology, National Institute for Medical Research, Mill Hill, London.
J. W. HURLEY	Visiting Physician, Elkhart Clinic, Elkhart, Indiana, U.S.A.
F. AVERY JONES	Consultant Physician, Department of Gastroenterology, Central Middlesex Hospital, Park Royal, London.
E. KELEMEN	Docent, Postgraduate Medical School, Budapest, Hungary.
JACK R. LEONARDS	Associate Professor of Biochemistry, Western Reserve University School of Medicine, Cleveland, Ohio, U.S.A.
GERHARD LEVY	Associate Professor of Pharmacy and Biopharmaceutics, State University of New York at Buffalo, Buffalo, N.Y., U.S.A.
G. P. LEWIS	Department of Physiology and Pharmacology, National Institute for Medical Research, Mill Hill, London.
R. K. S. LIM	Medical Sciences Research Laboratory, Miles Laboratories Inc., Elkhart, Indiana, U.S.A.
DAVID A. LONG	Chief Medical Adviser and Head, Medical Research Department, The Wellcome Foundation, London.
A. I. MACDOUGALL	Department of Medicine, Stobhill General Hospital, Glasgow.
ALASTAIR G. MACGREGOR	Professor of Materia Medica and Therapeutics, University of Aberdeen.
B. K. MARTIN	Deputy Director of Research, Nicholas Research Institute Ltd., Slough, Bucks.
A. ASHLEY MILES	Professor of Experimental Pathology, University of London, and Director, Lister Institute of Preventive Medicine, London.
MALCOLM D. MILNE	Professor of Medicine, Westminster Medical School, London.

ANDREW MUIR . . . Consultant Physician, South Lanarkshire Group, Law Hospital, Carluke, Lanarkshire.

T. R. NIEDERLAND . . Professor of Pharmacobiochemistry, Komensky University Medical School, Bratislava, Czechoslovakia.

C. OSORIO . . . M.R.C. Experimental Radiopathology Research Unit, Hammersmith Hospital, London.

D. J. PARRY . . . Department of Medicine, West Middlesex Hospital, Isleworth, Middlesex.

F. M. PARSONS . . Consultant in Clinical Renal Physiology, Renal Research Unit, The General Infirmary, Leeds.

R. S. BRUCE PEARSON . Consultant Physician, King's College Hospital, London.

ERNEST R. PITMAN . . Visiting Physician, City Hospital at Elmhurst, Elmhurst, New York, N.Y., U.S.A.

JAMES L. A. ROTH . . Professor of Clinical Gastroenterology and Director, Division of Gastroenterology, Graduate School of Medicine, University of Pennsylvania, Philadelphia, Pa., U.S.A.

D. G. RUSHTON . . Lecturer in Forensic Pathology, King's College Hospital Medical School, London.

J. E. SCOTT . . . E.R.C. Research Fellow in Biochemistry, M.R.C. Rheumatism Research Unit, Canadian Red Cross Memorial Hospital, Taplow, Bucks.

J. T. SCOTT . . . Lecturer in Medicine (Rheumatology), Hammersmith Hospital and Postgraduate Medical School, London.

STANTON SEGAL . . Clinical Endocrinology Branch, National Institute of Arthritis and Metabolic Diseases, National Institutes of Health, Bethesda, Maryland, U.S.A.

B. SHAW . . . . Senior Biochemist, Biochemistry Section, Boots Pure Drug Company, Nottingham.

G. HOWARD SMITH . . Biochemistry Department, Wellcome Research Laboratories, Beckenham, Kent.

M. J. H. SMITH . . Director, E.R.C. Research Unit on Drug Metabolism, and Reader in Chemical Pathology, King's College Hospital Medical School, London.

W. G. SPECTOR . . Professor of Pathology, Medical College of St. Bartholomew's Hospital, London.

WINIFRED L. STAFFORD . Research Assistant in Biochemistry, Department of Experimental Medicine, Guy's Hospital, London.

J. M. Stowers . . Consultant Physician, Royal Infirmary and City Hospital, Aberdeen.

L. Th. F. L. Stubbé . Physician, University Hospital, Leiden, The Netherlands.

H. F. West . . . Director, Rheumatism Research Unit, Nether Edge Hospital, Sheffield.

Michael W. Whitehouse . Staines Medical Research Fellow, Exeter College, and Lecturer, Department of Biochemistry, University of Oxford.

L. F. Wiggins . . Director of Research, Nicholas Research Institute, Slough, Bucks.

G. Wilhelmi . . Pharmacologist, J. R. Geigy SA, Basle, Switzerland.

D. A. Willoughby . . Research Fellow, Department of Pathology, Medical College of St. Bartholomew's Hospital, London.

C. V. Winder . . . Senior Research Pharmacologist, Parke, Davis and Company, Ann Arbor, Michigan, U.S.A.

Robert W. Winters . Professor of Pediatrics, Columbia University College of Physicians and Surgeons, New York, N.Y., U.S.A.

Philip H. N. Wood . . Department of Medicine (Rheumatology), Postgraduate Medical School of London.

Victor Wynn. . . Reader in Metabolism, St. Mary's Hospital Medical School, London.

INTRODUCTION

W. S. C. Copeman

Physician, Arthur Stanley Institute,
Middlesex Hospital, London

As Chairman of the Empire Rheumatism Council, which has helped to sponsor this meeting, it is my pleasant duty to welcome you here today. Those who know our Council will forgive me if I remind others that it is the body which, above others in this country, has put the subject of rheumatology on the map in the past 25 years. Its objects are to foster research into all aspects of rheumatic diseases. The Council also encourages teaching, both lay and medical, within this field, and it tries to stimulate such public authorities as are susceptible to stimulation to provide better treatment both in this country and in the Commonwealth. One of the Council's more recent activities has been sponsoring symposia such as this. We have organized six so far, the subjects including genetics, auto-immunity, and certain aspects of orthopaedics. Symposia are always arranged by invitation and therefore the people who are wanted are present. I believe I am right in saying that we have practically never so far had a refusal from anyone whom we have invited. I think, therefore, that the workers in these various fields must feel that these symposia form a useful contribution.

The idea, of course, is to bring together workers in a specified field who might not otherwise have these contacts, and today there are assembled clinicians, medical men engaged in research, and pharmaceutical experts, some qualified medically and some not.

I am sure that you are not under the delusion that the salicylates form a new subject. I should like to remind you that the great Thomas Sydenham, who was called the English Hippocrates, in the seventeenth century initiated the fashion for the barks of trees as sources for medicinal compounds because the Peruvian or Jesuit's bark, which yielded quinine, had just been introduced and found to be of great medicinal use in an England where malaria was still endemic. Consequently barks of indigenous trees were explored, including the genus *Salix*. The barks of the willow and poplar trees were found to yield a substance which was an antipyretic and useful as a bitter—and bitters were popular in those days for medicinal purposes. (Until the world-shattering invention of angostura bitters, during the last century, the poplar bark was also used for flavouring drinks, salicin being the active principle—as quinine is, I believe, of its successor.)

Then in 1838 Piria discovered salicin and in 1876, in the lifetime of people still living, this was used for the treatment of rheumatic disease by Maclagan of Glasgow. Next year the German Professor, Senator, suggested that salicylic acid, which had recently been synthesized, might prove less irritant. This was found to be so, and that was the real beginning of salicylate therapy as we know it today.

This may well prove to have been an historic assembly from the point of view of this subject, which has not previously been discussed in its entirety by experts. It is a pleasure to welcome Professor Niederland from Czechoslovakia, Professor Domenjoz from Germany, Dr. Wilhelmi from Switzerland, Dr. Kelemen from Hungary, Professor van Cauwenberge from Belgium, and Dr. Stubbé from The Netherlands, in addition to a number of distinguished workers from the United States. I feel sure that you will advance knowledge, and I hope that you will have a pleasant three days.

SALICYLATES IN THE BODY

Chairman E. G. L. BYWATERS

OPENING ADDRESS

THE HISTORY OF SALICYLATES

E. G. L. BYWATERS

Medical Research Council Rheumatism Research Unit Taplow, Buckinghamshire, and Postgraduate Medical School of London

THE willow, old English sallow, Latin *Salix*, hence salicylate, grows, as you all know, by waters, and thus it was I who was asked to open this Symposium. Some years ago I found a book by Wilkinson published in 1803. Wilkinson came from Sunderland—he was obviously a hard-headed Northern businessman who promoted willow bark as a commercial proposition, for all his advocacy of what he called 'that branch of the healing art termed Medical Surgery'. We were then in the middle of the Napoleonic wars with our backs to the wall and had no Peruvian bark, but Wilkinson, perforce, cultivated his garden and found something just as good.

However, apart from the ancients, Hippocrates, Pliny, Celsus, Dioscorides, and Galen, it was really the Rev. Edward Stone who drew the attention of the emergent scientific world to the willow in his communication to the Royal Society in 1763. He, like Maclagan a hundred years later (1876), was led to this partly by the Doctrine of Signatures, which reads the cure from the cause. As he said,

'As this tree delights in a moist or wet soil, where agues chiefly abound, the general maxim that many natural maladies carry their cures along with them or that their remedies lie not far from their causes was so very apposite to this particular case that I could not help applying it; and that this might be the intention of Providence here, I must own, had some little weight with me.'

In 1798 an apothecary in Bath, Mr. William White, was able to save at least £20 a year for the charity by substituting willow bark for Peruvian

3

bark, and Wilkinson, though rather apprehensive of the commercial reaction, at least endorsed its efficacy. However he, Stone, James (1792), White, and their followers used willow bark mainly for agues, fevers, abscesses, and fluxes—chiefly, therefore, as an antipyretic and only very rarely and, as it were, by accident is a case of rheumatism included. Right through the first half of the nineteenth century acute rheumatism was being treated by purgatives and, as Bouillaud (1840) recommended, by repeated blood-letting. It was left to Maclagan in 1876 to discover the specific value of salicin in acute rheumatism. It is interesting that Maclagan also invoked the Doctrine of Signatures:

' It seemed to me that a remedy for that disease would most hopefully be looked for among those plants and trees whose favourite habitat presented conditions analogous to those under which the rheumatic miasma seemed most to prevail. A low-lying damp locality, with a cold rather than warm climate, gives the conditions under which rheumatic fever is most readily produced. On reflection, it seemed to me that plants whose haunts best corresponded to such a description were those belonging to the natural order Salicaceae, the various forms of willow. Among the Salicaceae, therefore, I determined to search for a remedy for acute rheumatism. The bark of many species of willow contains a bitter principle called salicin. This principle was exactly what I wanted.'

Like a careful man, he took the powder himself before giving it to his first patient, William R., aged 48, seen on the fourth day of his second attack of rheumatic fever, and the powder worked. Perhaps we should pay more attention to the Doctrine of Signatures today.

Since the time of Maclagan, salicylates have never looked back. Stricker and Riess both introduced salicylic acid in 1876, and aspirin was produced some 20 years later. Briefly summarized, therefore, the chronology is:

Ancient History
Hippocrates, Celsus, Pliny, Dioscorides, Galen, down to Boerhaave in 1751 (Gross & Greenberg, 1948)

The Bark

Salix alba	1763	Rev. Edward Stone, of Chipping Norton
Salix latifolia	1792	Samuel James, Surgeon, of Hoddesdon, Hertfordshire
	1798	William White, Apothecary, of Bath
	1803	G. Wilkinson, of Sunderland

Pharmacological Properties

Antipyretic	1763	Stone
Antirheumatic	1874–1876	Maclagan and Stricker
Uricosuric	1877	Sée

Chemical Structure

Salicin	1826–1829	Leroux
Salicylic acid	1835–1838	Löwig and Piria
—synthesized	1860	Kolbe & Lautemann

Aspirin introduced 1899

The programme appears to provide no particular session dealing with pain. It is therefore worth emphasizing that salicylate has analgesic power, not only anti-inflammatory but also anti-nociceptive (Winder, 1959). The millions of aspirins consumed each year are consumed primarily for pain. To emphasize this rather neglected aspect of the Symposium, therefore, I will end with a picture of the weeping willow which, like the modern type of symposium, tends to suffer somewhat from gravity.

REFERENCES

Bouillaud, J. P. (1840). 'Traité clinique du Rhumatisme Articulaire.' Paris: Baillière.

Gross, M., & Greenberg, L. A. (1948). 'The Salicylates, a critical bibliographic review', p. 1. New Haven: Hillhouse Press.

James, S. (1792). 'Observations on the Bark of a particular species of Willow, showing its superiority to the Peruvian and its singular efficacy in the cure of agues, etc.' London: Johnson.

Kolbe, H., & Lautemann, E. (1860). *Justus Liebigs. Ann. Chem.*, **115**, 157.

Leroux, H. (1930). *J. Chim. méd.*, **6**, fol. 341. (quoted by Gross and Greenberg, 1948).

Löwig, cited by Tschirch, A. (1917). 'Handbuch der Pharmakognosie.' Leipzig: Tauchnitz.

Maclagan, T. J. (1876). *Lancet*, **i**, 342.

Piria, R. (1838). *C.R. Acad. Sci. Paris*, **6**, 338.

Riess, L. (1876). *Berl. klin. Wschr.*, **13**, 86.

Sée, G. (1877). *Bull. Acad. Méd. (Paris)*, **26**, 689.

Stone, E. (1763). *Phil. Trans.*, **53**, 195.

Stricker, S. (1876). *Berl. klin. Wschr.*, **13**, 15, 99.

White, W. (1798). 'Observations and Experiments on the Broadleaved Willow Bark.' Bath: Hazard.

Wilkinson, G. (1803). 'Experiments and Observations on the Cortex *Salicis latifoliae* or Broad-leafed Willow Bark.' Newcastle-upon-Tyne: Walker.

Winder, C. V. (1959). *Nature (Lond.)*, **184**, 494.

SIGNIFICANT FACTORS IN THE HISTORY OF ASPIRIN

B. K. MARTIN

The Nicholas Research Institute Ltd.
Slough, Buckinghamshire

THE popular or more romantic aspects of the history of aspirin are well recorded (Hecht, 1935; Gross & Greenberg, 1948; Eichengrün, 1949; Schlenk, 1950; Galmiche, 1957; Hochwalt, 1957). It would, I believe, be of greater value to select and comment on what I consider to be some of the more significant factors in the history of aspirin. The term significant is used in a wide sense to include that which was considered significant at the time, and that which may only now have become significant in the light of our present knowledge.

Acetylsalicylic acid was introduced in 1899 by the Bayer Company of Germany under the trade-name 'Aspirin', as a substitute or replacement for sodium salicylate. Now, 63 years later, we can see that it not only succeeded in that respect, but also greatly extended the use of the salicylates. In Germany and certain other countries 'Aspirin' remains a trade-mark, but in others, Great Britain, France and the United States, it is no longer a trade-mark and the name aspirin may now be freely used.

Salicylic acid, or more accurately its sodium salt, had been accepted for many years as the treatment of choice for rheumatic conditions. However, sodium salicylate possessed certain unpleasant side effects, notably gastric disturbance, whilst many patients developed a strong aversion to the taste. The scene was therefore set for the introduction of a derivative which might be free from these disadvantages. Aspirin was not the first synthetic derivative of salicylic acid introduced with this objective in mind. Salol, phenetsal, and salicylamide had already been used clinically. It is worthy of note that these compounds all involved substitution on the carboxyl group of salicylic acid, whereas aspirin is substituted on the phenolic group.

Advantages of aspirin

How far was aspirin successful in overcoming the problems of gastric disturbance and taste? One can certainly accept that its taste is far more agreeable, whilst the fact that it was very soon formulated as a tablet— this was the era of tablets—further improved this aspect. Generally speaking, aspirin gave rise to fewer reports of gastrointestinal disturbance (Floeckinger, 1899; Witthauer, 1899; Wohlgemuth, 1899; Kétly, 1900;

Lehmann, 1900), although one can only wonder how much this may be attributed to its improved taste. Whilst bleeding from mucous membranes attributable to high dosage of the salicylates had been reported at that time (Wolffberg, 1876; Pullmann, 1889), this aspect played no role in the introduction of aspirin.

What was the rationale on which the superiority of aspirin was based? It was assumed that salicylic acid, liberated from sodium salicylate by the acid of the stomach, caused these symptoms by irritating the mucous membrane of the stomach (Binz, 1891; Wohlgemuth, 1899). The aim, therefore, was a compound that would release the active salicylic acid as soon as possible after being absorbed (Dreser, 1899). On the basis of various *in vitro* experiments in which a suspension of aspirin was found to be only slowly hydrolysed under acidic conditions, it was considered that aspirin passed through the stomach unchanged, to be absorbed from the intestine either as such or after hydrolysis (Dreser, 1899; Wohlgemuth, 1899).

In the light of our present knowledge we can amplify these views somewhat. We now know aspirin is absorbed very largely as such. We are also aware that the blood and other tissues possess enzymes capable of greatly increasing the rate of hydrolysis of aspirin to many times that of the simple chemical hydrolysis at physiological pH (Smith, Hand & Madden, 1947; Mulinos & Ardam, 1950; Edwards, 1952). Even so, appreciable quantities of aspirin persist in the blood for up to two hours after a single oral dose (Lester, Lolli & Greenberg, 1946; Mandel, Cambosos & Smith, 1954; Smith, 1956; Sleight, 1960; Leonards, 1962), but far more important, 'aspirin passes through the stomach unchanged' (Kétly, 1900); that is so, but in the limits of their knowledge at that time they naturally did not consider absorption from the stomach. Now I believe that absorption from the stomach is very significant.

I have mentioned that the early workers on aspirin viewed salicylic acid, which resulted from the hydrolysis of aspirin, as the active agent (Dreser, 1899). Over the years the opinion has sometimes been expressed that aspirin possesses superior therapeutic properties, particularly as an analgesic (*Lancet*, 1955). Stockman (1913) was of that opinion. In the absence of any convincing evidence on this point, it is worthy of note that the two views are not entirely incompatible. Aspirin and salicylic acid differ appreciably in their physico-chemical characteristics; aspirin is slightly more soluble, is a weaker acid, and shows a lower degree of protein-binding. These changes are capable of giving rise to considerable biochemical differences in the absorption and distribution characteristics of the two substances. Aspirin may well provide salicylic acid at the desired site, at the optimum concentration, over a suitable period of time, and so provide a superior clinical effect.

REFERENCES

Binz, C. (1891). 'Vorlesungen ueber Pharmakologie', 2nd Ed., p. 579. Berlin: Hirschwald.
Dreser, H. (1899). *Pflüg. Arch. ges. Physiol.*,76, 306.
Edwards, L. J. (1952). *J. chem. Soc.*, p. 4114.
Eichengrün, A. (1949). *Pharmazie*, 4, 582.
Floeckinger, F. C. (1899). *Med. News (N. Y.)*, 75, 645.
Galmiche, P. (1957). *Presse méd.*, 65, 303.
Gross, M., & Greenberg, L. A. (1948). 'The Salicylates, a critical bibliographic review', p. 6. New Haven: Hillhouse Press.
Hecht, G. (1935). *Münch. med. Wschr.*, 538.
Hochwalt, C. A. (1957). *Aust. J. Pharm.*, 38, 771.
Kétly, L. (1900). *Heilkunde*, 4, 14.
Lancet, (1955). *Lancet*, i, 550.
Lehmann, O. (1900). *Ther. d. Gegenw.*, 41, 190.
Leonards, J. R. (1962). *Proc. Soc. exp. Biol. (N. Y.)*, 110, 304.
Lester, D., Lolli, G., & Greenberg, L. A. (1946). *J. Pharmacol., exp. Ther.*, 87, 329.
Mandel, H. G., Cambosos, N. M., & Smith, P. K. (1954). *J. Pharmacol. exp. Ther.*, 112, 495.
Mulinos, M. G., & Ardam, I. (1950). *J. Pharmacol. exp. Ther.*, 98, 23.
Pullmann, (1889). *Berl. klin. Wschr.*, 26, 604 (quoted by Binz, C. [1891]).
Schlenk, O. (1950). *Pharmazie*, 5, 411.
Sleight, P. (1960). *Lancet*, i, 305.
Smith, M. J. H. (1956). *J. Pharm. Pharmacol.*, 3, 409.
Smith, P. K., Hand, H. A., & Madden, R. J. (1947). *Fed. Proc.*, 6, 373.
Stockman, R. (1913). *Brit. med. J.*, i, 597.
Witthauer, K. (1899). *Heilkunde*, 3, 396.
Wohlgemuth, J. (1899). *Ther. Mh. (Halbmh.)*, 13, 276.
Wolffberg, quoted by Myers, A. B. R. (1876). *Lancet*, ii, 676.

BIOPHARMACEUTICAL ASPECTS OF THE
GASTROINTESTINAL ABSORPTION OF SALICYLATES

Gerhard Levy

Biopharmaceutics Laboratory, School of Pharmacy
State University of New York at Buffalo, Buffalo, N.Y., U.S.A.

The clinical administration of salicylates is almost always by mouth, and thus it is appropriate to examine the factors which govern their absorption from the gastrointestinal tract. It will be shown that the chemical properties of the particular salicylate derivative used, as well as its pharmaceutical formulation, can significantly modify the rate and extent of absorption of an administered dose, and apparently also the intensity and incidence of associated gastrointestinal irritation.

Absorption kinetics

The absorption of salicylates occurs predominantly by passive diffusion of undissociated drug molecules across gastrointestinal membranes (Schanker et al., 1958). Such a diffusion process can be described by Fick's Law:

$$-dN = D.A.\frac{dc}{dx}.dt \tag{I},$$

where N is the amount of diffusible drug in a given volume of gastrointestinal fluids, D is a diffusion rate constant, A is the surface area of the membrane barrier, dc/dx is the concentration gradient of diffusible drug across the membrane, and t is time.

The salicylate concentration on the serosal side of the gastrointestinal membranes is very much lower than that in gastrointestinal fluids during the more important phases of absorption and so the concentration gradient, dc/dx in equation (I), may be replaced by C, the concentration of unionized drug in gastrointestinal fluids *at the mucosal surface*. This latter qualification is important because the pH at the membrane surface is not necessarily the same as the pH of the gastrointestinal fluids, and C is a function of pH. A simplified and slightly modified form of equation (I) is

$$-dC = K.C.dt \tag{II},$$

which upon integration yields

$$\log C = \log C_0 - \frac{K}{2 \cdot 3}.t \tag{III},$$

9

where C is the concentration of diffusible drug in gastrointestinal fluids at time t, C_0 is the initial concentration of drug in gastrointestinal fluids, and K is a constant incorporating surface area, volume of gastrointestinal fluids, membrane thickness, and the diffusion rate constant D. Equation (II) indicates that absorption of salicylates is a first-order kinetic process, and that if pH, volume, and absorptive surface area are constant, a graph of the logarithm of unabsorbed drug against time should yield a straight line. Hogben and co-workers (1957) have determined the absorption of salicylic acid (SA) and acetylsalicylic acid (ASA) from the human stomach under conditions that satisfy these requirements. Their data, plotted in semilogarithmic form, do indeed yield straight lines for each drug (Levy, Gumtow & Rutowski, 1961). The difference in the slopes of these lines reflects the different values of the diffusion rate constant D which, in the context of the present dicussion, is more properly referred to as a specific absorption rate constant. D normally reflects the rate of penetration of the drug through the gastrointestinal membrane, but under certain circumstances it may indicate the rate of diffusion of the drugs through gastrointestinal fluids rather than through the membrane.

The specific absorption rate constant of salicylic acid is about twice that of acetylsalicylic acid. This means that SA is absorbed twice as rapidly as ASA when the drugs are ionized to the same degree. Though both drugs are weak acids, ASA is the weaker of the two. It is less ionized than SA at any pH. Considering equimolar concentrations of the two drugs, the ratio of undissociated ASA concentration to undissociated SA concentration changes from slightly above 1 at pH 1·0 to about 3 at pH 5·0. Thus while SA intrinsically is absorbed more rapidly than ASA, this difference tends to disappear at a higher pH (Levy, Gumtow & Rutowski, 1961).

In the absorption of dissolved drug from the gastrointestinal tract, diffusion through gastrointestinal membranes is usually rate-limiting unless the viscosity of gastrointestinal fluids is increased, when diffusion through these fluids may become the rate-limiting process. The retarding effect of high viscosity on salicylate absorption has been demonstrated in rats by comparative studies with two per cent methylcellulose (Davison et al., 1961).

Dissolution of drug solids

An additional factor is introduced if the salicylate is administered in solid form. Drug solids must dissolve before they can be absorbed. In the sequence:

Dissolution→Diffusion to the gastrointestinal membrane→Diffusion
through the membrane;
the dissolution step is the slowest, and is therefore absorption rate

determining. This is shown by the more rapid absorption of salicylate
when the drug is administered in solution rather than when administered
in tablet form (Levy, Gumtow & Rutowski, 1961). The kinetics of the
dissolution process can be described by the Noyes-Whitney Law:

$$\frac{da}{dt} = K.S.(C_s - C_b) \quad \cdot \quad \text{(IV)},$$

where the dissolution rate da/dt is the product of the specific dissolution
rate constant K, surface area S, and the difference between drug concentration in the diffusion layer, C_s, and the concentration in the bulk of
the solution, C_b, at time t. The value of C_s is essentially equal to the
solubility of the drug in the dissolution medium.

We have determined the dissolution rate of a number of salicylates in
0·1 N hydrochloric acid under conditions that have been described

DISSOLUTION RATES OF VARIOUS SALICYLATES AT 37° C

Compound	Dissolution rate		in pH 8·0 buffer (Sørensen, double strength)	pH of diffusion layer in buffer
	in 0·1 N HCl			
	Stirring speed			
	355 r.p.m.	560 r.p.m.	560 r.p.m.	
	(as mg. salicylic acid/hr./cm.²)			
Salicylic acid	38	46	350	3·8
Acetylsalicylic acid	49	68	350	4·2
Aluminium acetylsalicylate*	7·7			
Aspirin anhydride	< 0·5			
Sodium salicylate	5,200			
Sodium acetylsalicylate	4,900			

* Commercially available aluminium aspirin is chemically impure and exhibits
some lot-to-lot variation of dissolution rate. The value quoted is a representative
one.

previously (Levy & Sahli, 1962). Dissolution rates for various salicylates
are shown in the Table, and include compounds that dissolve rapidly
(NaSA, NaASA), slowly (SA, ASA), and very slowly (Aluminium ASA,
ASA Anhydride). Based on the respective dissolution rates, it is apparent
that salicylate absorption should be much more rapid after oral administration of the sodium salts in solid form than after administration of
the acids in solid form, provided all other factors remain constant.
However, certain other factors can diminish these differences or over-
shadow them entirely.

The effect of pH on the dissolution rate of weak acids such as SA and

ASA may be shown by suitable modification of the Noyes-Whitney equation. The solubility, C_s, of a weak acid is a function of hydrogen ion concentration, $[H^+]$:

$$C_s = C_0\left[1 + \frac{K_a}{[H^+]}\right] \qquad (V),$$

where C_0 is the solubility of the undissociated acid and K_a is its dissociation constant. If $[H^+]$ is much less than K_a, (pH $> 4\cdot5$ in the case of SA and ASA),

$$C_s = C_0\frac{K_a}{[H^+]} \qquad (VI),$$

which can be expressed in logarithmic form as

$$\log C_s = \log C_0 - pK_a + pH \qquad (VII).$$

Substituting (VII) in the logarithmic form of equation (IV) under conditions where C_s is very much greater than C_b, so that C_b can be neglected (this applies to drugs dissolving in gastrointestinal fluids where the concentration of dissolved drug remains low due to continuous absorption),

$$\log\frac{da}{dt} = \log K + \log S + \log C_0 - pK_a + pH \qquad (VIII).$$

When constant surface area of drug is maintained,

$$\log\frac{da}{dt} = K^* + pH \qquad (IX),$$

where

$$K^* = \log K + \log S + \log C_0 - pK_a \qquad (X).$$

Thus the logarithm of dissolution rate is a function of the pH; this is the pH of the diffusion layer surrounding the drug solids, and not necessarily the pH of the bulk solution. In the case of highly soluble salts of SA and ASA, deviations from (IX) will occur due to cation and viscosity effects (Nelson, 1957).

The increase in dissolution rate of SA and ASA at higher pH is shown in the Table. The data suggest one possible reason why administration of salicylates in enteric-coated tablets leads to less gastrointestinal bleeding than administration of conventional tablets; dissolution is more rapid at the relatively high pH of intestinal fluids than at the low pH of gastric fluids. The time of contact between salicylate solids and mucosa is therefore considerably shorter in the intestine than in the stomach.

The dissolution rate of ASA in gastric fluids may be increased by alkaline substances which raise the pH of gastric fluids. However, the higher pH also increases ionization of dissolved drug and thereby tends to decrease the rate of absorption. Another technique, which does not interfere with absorption, is to mix solid drug with sufficient antacid to raise the pH in the immediate environment of the drug solids, as in the so-called buffered aspirin preparations. Their relative efficacy depends on the buffering agent used and on the ratio of drug to buffering agent, amongst other factors.

Studies in our laboratory also have identified tablet compression pressure, type and concentration of lubricant and disintegrant, particle size, granule size, and other pharmaceutical formulation factors as having significant effects on dissolution rate (Levy et al., 1963a, b, c). Thus different formulations of aspirin tablets may cause their active ingredient to dissolve at different rates, and therefore these formulations may differ in the rate of absorption of aspirin. We have recently demonstrated a linear relationship between absorption, as reflected by urinary excretion, and the *in vitro* dissolution rate of aspirin from different brands of compressed tablets (Levy, 1961). However, there is no correlation between dissolution rate and tablet disintegration time (Levy & Hayes, 1960). For example, it is not too difficult to prepare compressed tablets from ground glass particles in such a manner that the tablets disintegrate in ten seconds; yet the glass particles are insoluble and certainly are not absorbed from the human gastrointestinal tract.

The variability in absorption rate of aspirin from different brands of tablets makes it unfeasible to use these as a standard of comparison for evaluating the absorption or irritant properties of other salicylates. For this purpose aqueous solutions of aspirin should be used, because these are not subject to most of the formulation effects described.

The importance of physico-chemical form

Both SA and ASA have limited solubility in water, and their water-soluble salts must be used in the preparation of dosage forms for administration in solution. The most rapid absorption is achieved by the use of these solutions, and there is evidence that administration of salicylates in solution results in the least incidence and severity of gastrointestinal bleeding (Khalil, 1960; Levy & Hayes, 1960; Pierson et al., 1961; Leonards, 1962). Unfortunately, solutions of salts of SA are unpalatable and solutions of salts of ASA are also unstable. Economic considerations and inconvenience often militate against the use of solutions for salicylate therapy.

Compressed tablets of the freely water-soluble sodium and calcium salts of ASA have been marketed in the hope that more rapid absorption and a reduction of gastrointestinal irritation might be achieved. Such hopes have been realized only in part. The major problem, apart from cost, is related to the hygroscopic nature of these salts. They attract moisture, hydrolyse, and in time form a highly compact 'cemented' tablet which dissolves very slowly and can prove to be extremely irritating.

However, if these preparations are well formulated and protected from moisture by adequate single-unit packing, and if the cost is no problem, they may be used advantageously whenever ASA therapy is indicated.

If possible, compressed tablets of ASA should be administered dispersed in a glass of water. When mixed with buffering agents, the tablets can actually be *dissolved* in moderate volumes of water. This may also be accomplished with sodium citrate, sodium bicarbonate, or similar alkaline substances in conjunction with plain aspirin. It is advisable, however, to limit the quantity of these substances to approximately stoicheiometric amounts, because ingestion of large quantities of base may raise urinary pH, increase salicylate excretion rate, and thereby decrease the biological half-life of salicylate. The small amounts of alkaline substances in the usual buffered ASA combinations are ordinarily insufficient to modify urinary pH significantly.

The use of certain sparingly-soluble salicylate compounds has been advocated because of their presumed greater palatibility, stability, and freedom from irritation. Aluminium ASA is the most widely employed of these. Because of the very low dissolution rate of this substance, we examined its absorption rate and availability (Levy & Sahli, 1962). The absorption pattern of aluminium ASA is quite unusual. Despite slow and incomplete absorption, peak blood levels occur as rapidly as with ASA. The reason for the early absorption peak despite incomplete absorption becomes apparent only after consideration of the dissolution of aluminium ASA in media of pH 6·0 and above. This is accompanied by deposition of a film of a water-insoluble basic aluminium compound on the remaining drug solids, which retards any further dissolution (Levy & Procknal, 1962). The dissolution rate, and therefore the absorption rate, of this drug is at its maximum during the early post-ingestion period when the drug solids are in an acidic environment where no film formation takes place. We have also studied the gastrointestinal absorption of ASA anhydride. Despite predictions to the contrary (Garrett, 1959), we have shown that ASA anhydride is not only absorbed very slowly but also incompletely (Levy & Gagliardi, 1963).

Salicylates are often combined with other substances that are claimed to have absorption-enhancing effects. In reviewing certain published studies of such combinations, it becomes apparent that the investigators have failed to consider one or more important variables. The more important mechanisms determining salicylate blood levels after the administration of different salicylate combinations are:

    (i) dissolution rate;
    (ii) gastric emptying time;
    (iii) intrinsic absorption rate;
    (iv) serum protein binding;

(v) rate and extent of biotransformation;

(vi) excretion rate.

Clearly an additive can increase salicylate blood levels by mechanisms other than enhancement of intrinsic absorption rate.

Salicylate elimination kinetics

In a rational dosage regime for salicylate therapy in acute rheumatic fever the aim is plasma levels that are high enough to achieve maximum anti-inflammatory effect, but that are below toxic levels. The range between effective and toxic concentrations is only about 10 mg. per 100 ml. Careful dosage adjustment is necessary to maintain concentrations in this narrow range, and must be based on the following considerations:

(i) the magnitude of salicylate plasma concentration fluctuations (peak and valley effects) is decreased by administering the drug at shorter time intervals;

(ii) maintenance dosage must be established on the basis of the biological half-life of salicylate, as determined for each individual patient.

We have been able to maintain relatively constant salicylate levels by use of this approach, as shown by urinary excretion data (Levy & Sahli, 1962). This was accomplished by administering a priming dose, followed by maintenance doses at three-hour intervals. Dosage was adjusted according to the half-life of salicylate. A half-life of six hours is the average value found in healthy subjects taking single usual doses of a salicylate, but half-lives as short as 4·7 hours and as long as 9·0 hours have been observed (Brodie, Burns & Weiner, 1959). Maintenance doses based on a 4·7 hour half-life are considerably higher than those based on a 9·0 hour half-life.

The half-life of salicylate is dose-dependent to some degree and increases markedly when high doses are administered. Half-lives of as high as 19 hours have been reported when the administered dose exceeded 10 g. of sodium salicylate per day (Swintosky, 1956). Half-life may be affected also by certain disease conditions, particularly if hepatic or renal involvement is present, and by alterations of serum protein composition. A urinary pH above 7·0 causes more rapid excretion. Thus salicylate half-life should be determined in each patient on intensive salicylate therapy, and should be repeated at the various stages of his illness. In this manner it is possible to adjust dosage to changes in salicylate elimination rate (half-life) that may accompany changes in the condition of the patient. Maintenance of constant salicylate concentration in fluids of distribution should promote the attainment of a salicylate diffusion equilibrium between the various body compartments, including target sites. Thus it is possible that a correct dosage regime will not only prevent drug accumulation and thereby reduce the likelihood of toxic reactions, but also will increase the effectiveness of salicylate therapy.

SUMMARY

The gastrointestinal absorption of salicylates, given in solid form, is rate-limited by the dissolution process. The rate of dissolution of a salicylate is a function of its intrinsic dissolution rate, pH, and the physico-chemical properties of its pharmaceutical dosage form, amongst other factors. The absorption pattern of different salicylate compounds can be correlated with *in vitro* dissolution rate data and other physico-chemical parameters. It is desirable that salicylate dosage regimes be based upon a consideration of kinetic factors, in order to prevent accumulation and to reduce the likelihood of toxicity.

REFERENCES

Brodie, B. B., Burns, J. J., & Weiner, M. (1959). *Med. Exp. (Basel)*, 1, 290.
Davison, C., Guy, J. L., Levitt, M., & Smith, P. K. (1961). *J. Pharmacol. exp. Ther.*, **134**, 176.
Garrett, E. R. (1959). *J. Amer. pharm. Ass., sci. Ed.*, **48**, 676.
Hogben, C. A. M., Schanker, L. S., Tocco, D. J., & Brodie, B. B. (1957). *J. Pharmacol. exp. Ther.*, **120**, 540.
Khalil, H. A. (1960). *Alexandria med. J.*, **6**, 38.
Leonards, J. R. (1962). *Fed. Proc.*, **21**, 452.
Levy, G. (1961). *J. pharm. Sci.*, **50**, 388.
Levy, G. (1963a). *J. pharm. Sci.*, in press.
Levy, G., Antkowiak, J. M., Procknal, J. A., & White, D. C. (1963b). *J. pharm. Sci.*, in press.
Levy, G., & Gagliardi, B. A. (1963). *J. pharm. Sci.*, in press.
Levy, G., & Gumtow, R. H. (1963c). *J. pharm. Sci.*, in press.
Levy, G., Gumtow, R. H., & Rutowski, J. M. (1961). *Canad. med. Ass. J.*, **85**, 414.
Levy, G., & Hayes, B. A. (1960). *New Engl. J. Med.*, **262**, 1053.
Levy, G., & Procknal, J. A. (1962). *J. pharm. Sci.*, **51**, 294.
Levy, G., & Sahli, B. A. (1962). *J. pharm. Sci.*, **51**, 58.
Nelson, E. (1957). *J. Amer. pharm. Ass., sci. Ed.*, **46**, 607.
Pierson, R. N. Jr., Holt, P. R., Watson, R. M., & Keating, R. P. (1961). *Amer. J. Med.*, **31**, 259.
Schanker, L. S., Tocco, D. J., Brodie, B. B., & Hogben, C. A. M. (1958). *J. Pharmacol. exp. Ther.*, **123**, 81.
Swintosky, J. V. (1956). *J. Amer. pharm. Ass., sci. Ed.*, **45**, 395.

DISCUSSION

WINTERS: What sort of additives affect the intrinsic absorption rate?
LEVY: Anything that would change the nature of the barrier of the gastrointestinal tract would modify the intrinsic rate of absorption of drugs. Surface-active agents are an example; this is primarily a detergent

and spreading effect. In high concentrations such agents can damage the mucosa.

WEST: What is a tablet lubricant? Is biological half-life determined by a biological assay, or is it a chemical half-life measured by metabolites?

LEVY: Tablets have to be expelled from the die following compression. In order to reduce friction and prevent breakage one uses small amounts of lubricants, such as mineral oil or stearates.

Biological half-life can be expressed in two ways. I have spoken of biological half-life in terms of the rate of decrease of the amount of drug in the body. In the case of certain drugs whose pharmacological effect can be measured quantitatively, one can also consider a pharmacological half-life in terms of the rate of decrease of drug activity.

ANDERSON: LEVY had two salicylate preparations, one which was absorbed rapidly and one with poor dissolution in the stomach, aluminium salicylate, and yet he found no significant difference in the blood level peaks. Does he think that absorption from the gastric lumen is not a significant factor in producing the plasma level?

LEVY: There was a significant difference in the height of the peak, but not in the time of its occurrence. When a drug is slowly absorbed one would expect the peak to be delayed, but this was not so. I believe gastric absorption does play a significant role in the absorption of salicylates. However, I think the intestine is the major site of absorption, if only because of the large surface area. Solid drugs may remain in the stomach for a long time and may be totally absorbed there. Solutions usually pass rapidly into the intestine, which is where they are absorbed.

DUTHIE: Clinicians are familiar with the clinical advantage of aspirin over sodium salicylate. I understand that aspirin is rapidly hydrolysed after absorption. Is there any pharmacological explanation for this difference in clinical effect?

LEVY: There is considerable evidence that aspirin is more effective as an analgesic (Lasagna, L. [1961]. *Amer. J. med. Sci.*, **242**, 620), but whether it is a better anti-inflammatory agent I am not so sure. On the basis of available information there is little difference between the tissue distribution of aspirin and of salicylic acid at a given time. Distribution has not been studied over a period of time and, since the hydrolysis of aspirin in the body has a half-life of about half an hour, there is ample opportunity for such differences to occur.

COLLIER: In the guinea-pig intravenous aspirin is 32 times as active as is sodium salicylate in antagonizing bradykinin bronchoconstriction, which agrees with the clinical observations. Given by the intraduodenal route this difference is not nearly so evident.

THE EXCRETION OF SALICYLATE AND ITS METABOLITES

M. D. Milne

Department of Medicine, Westminster Medical School
London

The metabolism and excretion of salicylate has probably been investigated more than that of any other drug, and much detailed information is therefore available. In 1878 Blanchier and Bochefontaine found that sodium salicylate given by mouth appeared in the urine within 15–18 minutes, and that the excretion was completed in 22 hours after doses of 1–2 g. and in 44 hours after 4–5 g. About 30 years ago it was well known that sodium bicarbonate diminished the toxicity of salicylates, and the two drugs were usually prescribed together. A more scientific approach was made by Coburn (1943), who recommended that dosage should be controlled by plasma levels. Smull, Wegria and Leland (1944) first showed that sodium bicarbonate reduced plasma levels in patients on fixed repeated doses of salicylates. Two years later Smith and co-workers (1946) proved that this was due to increased urinary output of salicylate in alkaline urine, a finding that has been confirmed and elaborated by many later workers (Williams & Leonards, 1948; Parker, 1948; Davis & Smith, 1951; Dalgaard-Mikkelsen, 1951; Macpherson, Milne & Evans, 1955; Gutman, Yü & Sirota, 1955; Schachter & Manis, 1958; Weiner, Washington & Mudge, 1959).

From the point of view of practical pharmacology the following information is of direct importance in salicylate therapy. Sodium salicylate is converted by hydrochloric acid in the stomach to sodium chloride and free salicylic acid. The free acid is lipid-soluble and therefore diffuses across the gastric mucosa, and salicylate can be detected in the blood less than 30 minutes after ingestion. Peak blood levels after a single dose are reached in about two hours and are followed by a gradual logarithmic fall. Salicyl compounds cannot be detected in blood or urine after about 48 hours from the last dose of the drug. Conjugates of salicylic acid are only in low concentration in plasma (Schachter & Manis, 1958) and therefore crude estimations of salicyl compounds give a reasonably accurate value of salicylic acid in blood, but not in urine. The ratio of free salicylate to conjugates in plasma is about 70 at peak blood levels two hours after salicylate ingestion, but only 15 twenty-four hours after ingestion.

Salicylate is 50–80 per cent bound to plasma proteins; the percentage bound decreases with rise of plasma concentration, indicating partial saturation of protein receptor bonds at high plasma levels. Almost all ingested salicylate is eliminated in the urine within 48 hours. After administration of the ^{14}C-labelled compound to rats (Alpen, Mandel & Smith, 1951) no radioactivity could be detected in the CO_2 of the expired air. Only trace amounts of salicylate are present in sweat, bile, and faeces. The rate of urinary excretion is such that reasonably stable plasma levels of the drug can be maintained by doses spread at intervals of 4–6 hours. To produce concentrations of over 35 mg. per 100 ml., doses of 10 g. or more of salicylate per day must be prescribed. Acetylsalicylic acid is rapidly hydrolysed by plasma and tissue esterases; plasma levels of acetylsalicylic acid are therefore always very low, and never exceed 2 mg. per 100 ml. at ordinary therapeutic doses (Mandel, Cambosos & Smith, 1954).

Regulation of salicylate excretion

The rate of urinary excretion of free salicylate is influenced by four separate factors: glomerular filtration rate (GFR), rate of proximal tubular secretion of salicylate, the rate of urine flow, and the pH of the urine. Plasma levels at any given dose are increased by renal failure, with fall of glomerular filtration rate and rise of the blood urea. Renal failure also reduces the rate of proximal tubular secretion because of progressive atrophy of nephrons and reduction of the proximal tubular mass. Proximal tubular secretion of salicylate is reduced by inhibitors that compete for the available tubular transport system, for example, probenecid, p-aminobenzoic acid, p-aminohippurate, and acetazolamide. Polyuria increases the rate of salicylate output, and oliguria correspondingly reduces it.

Urinary pH is particularly important in the pH range of 7·0–8·0. If the urine is acid there is only negligible change in salicylate clearance, but in alkaline urine the mean clearance is about four times as great at pH 8·0 as at pH 7·0. The clearance is well above the glomerular filtration rate at pH 8·0, but considerably below the GFR in acid urine (Gutman, Yü & Sirota, 1955). Sodium bicarbonate should not be prescribed with salicylate for at least two reasons: many patients given salicylates have serious heart disease, and therefore excess sodium is undesirable; in addition, the rate of change of clearance with pH is greater in alkaline than acid urine. Small changes in the pH of alkaline urine will considerably alter the salicylate clearance, and thus it is more difficult to produce stable plasma levels of the drug.

The effect of acetazolamide on salicylate excretion is particularly complex. This drug slightly lowers GFR and also competes with salicylate for proximal tubular secretion, both factors tending to reduce excretion. It also causes a polyuria because of its diuretic action, and an alkaline urine by inhibition of renal carbonic anhydrase, both tending to increase excretion. In practice salicylate output is increased by acetazolamide, but not so much as by sodium bicarbonate or by hyperventilation (Macpherson, Milne & Evans, 1955; Weiner, Washington & Mudge, 1959).

Of the metabolites of salicylic acid, gentisic acid is excreted similarly to free salicylate (Batterman & Sommer, 1953). The excretion of con-jugates of salicylic acid is reduced by fall in GFR and in proximal tubular secretion, but is unaffected by change of urine flow and of urine pH. Plasma levels of salicylate are also modified by variations in the rate of conjugation of the drug. Thus large oral doses of p-aminobenzoic acid increase plasma salicylate concentrations not only by competition for proximal tubular secretion, but also by competition for enzymic reactions that conjugate both drugs with glycine, to p-aminohippurate and salicyluric acid respectively (Salassa, Bollman & Dry, 1948).

Excretion of free salicylate

Salicylic acid is a weak acid of pK_a 3·0. This means that unbound salicylate in plasma is almost entirely in the ionized water-soluble form, only a very small percentage being unionized and lipid-soluble. Both fractions diffuse freely across the glomerulus, the concentration in glomerular filtrate being equal to that of non-protein-bound salicylate in plasma. Almost all foreign organic acids are secreted by the proximal tubule, whatever the pK_a of the acid, and the process appears to depend merely on acidic properties and not on the chemistry of the molecule. All such acids, including uric acid as an example of a naturally occurring weak acid, compete for the available transport system. Since very strong organic acids with pK_a values of 2·0 or less, sulphonic acids for example, are secreted by the tubular cells it seems reasonable to assume that the water-soluble ionized fraction rather than the unionized portion is actively secreted.

In the distal tubule the physical properties of the weak acid determine its actual excretion rate. In some cases, p-aminohippuric acid for example, neither ionized nor unionized fractions diffuse across the distal tubule cells, and therefore the amount excreted is quantitatively equal to the sum of the amount filtered at the glomerulus and that secreted by proximal tubule cells. The excretion rate does not vary with alteration of urine flow and change of urine pH, and consequently such acids can be used to determine the rate of renal plasma flow or, at higher concent-rations with saturation of proximal tubular secretion, maximal tubular secretory activity, Tm_{PAH}.

Salicylic acid is an example of an acid in which the unionized lipid-soluble fraction is highly diffusible, whereas diffusion of the ionized portion is negligible. If the distal tubular urine is highly alkaline the proportion of unionized salicylate in the tubular fluid is extremely small and in fact is less than that in peritubular blood, which is at a lower pH of about 7·4. Salicylate therefore tends to diffuse from the blood into the tubular fluid, but very little can actually diffuse in this direction because a large fraction of the salicylate has already been secreted as the blood bathes the proximal tubule cells. Conversely, if the urine is highly acid the concentration of the unionized fraction within the tubular fluid is high, and therefore a considerable amount of the drug diffuses back into the peritubular blood, with reduction in the rate of salicylate output and a corresponding fall in salicylate clearance. If the rate of urine flow is high there will be less time available for back-diffusion to occur, and therefore polyuria increases salicylate excretion. In the case of some other organic acids the difference between the diffusibility of the ionized and the unionized fractions is not so extreme, and both components can diffuse across the distal tubule cells. In such cases, variation in urinary pH will have little or no effect on the clearance of the acid, but the excretion rate will still be greatly influenced by the rate of urine flow. Many organic bases behave in the opposite manner to salicylic acid, their clearance being increased in acid urine. The Table gives the acids and bases at present known to be affected by non-ionic diffusion or ion-trapping, and therefore showing the phenomenon of pH-dependent excretion.

Metabolism of salicylic acid

The three chief metabolic products of salicylates are the conjugate with glycine to form salicyluric acid (Bertagnini, 1856), the ether or phenolic glucuronide (SPG), and the ester or acyl glucuronide (SAG) (Fig.). The

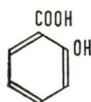

Salicylic Acid

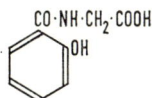

Salicyluric Acid

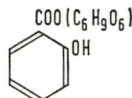

Salicylic Acyl Glucuronide

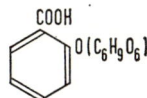

Salicylic Phenolic Glucuronide

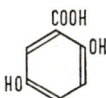

Gentisic Acid

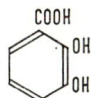

2 : 3 – Dihydroxybenzoic Acid

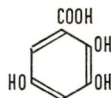

2 : 3 : 5 -Trihydroxybenzoic Acid

Structural Formulae of Salicylic Acid and its Metabolites

DRUGS SHOWING pH-DEPENDENT EXCRETION

Name of drug	Metabolites not showing pH-dependent excretion	Species investigated	Reference
ACIDIC DRUGS—URINARY OUTPUT GREATER IN ALKALINE URINE			
Salicylic acid	Salicyluric acid and acyl and phenolic glucuronides	Man	Smith et al., 1946
		Dog and Rabbit	Weiner, Washington & Mudge, 1959
Gentisic acid	Ethereal sulphate and glucuronide	Man	Batterman & Sommer, 1953
Phenobarbitone	p-Hydroxyphenobarbitone	Man and Dog	Waddell & Butler, 1957a
5:5-Dimethyl-2:4--oxazolidinedione*	probably excreted unchanged	Man and Dog	Waddell & Butler, 1957b
Indolylacetic acid and other indolic acids	∝ no. of C atoms in side chain: even—indolylacetylglutamine odd —indolylacrylglycine	Man, Dog and Rat	Milne et al., 1960
Phenylbutazone	Hydroxyl derivatives (both phenol and alcohol hydroxylation)	Man and Dog	Gutman et al., 1960
Probenecid	Ester glucuronide	Dog	Weiner, Washington & Mudge, 1960
Nitrofurantoin	unknown metabolites	Dog	Woodruff, Malvin & Thompson, 1961

BASIC DRUGS—URINARY OUTPUT GREATER IN ACID URINE

Drug	Metabolite	Species	Reference
Mepacrine and other acridine derivatives	Demethylated product and other metabolites	Man	Jailer, Rosenfeld & Shannon, 1947
Chloroquine and other derivatives of aminoquinoline	unknown metabolites	Man	Jailer, Rosenfeld & Shannon, 1947
Quinine	Derivatives by oxidation	Man Dog	Haag, Larson & Schwartz, 1943 Torretti, Weiner & Mudge, 1962
Nicotine	Nornicotine and γ-(3-pyridyl)-γ-methylaminobutyric acid	Man	Haag & Larson, 1942
Procaine	p-Aminobenzoic acid and diethylaminoethanol	Dog and Rabbit	Terp, 1951
Mecamylamine	probably excreted unchanged	Man, Dog and Rat	Baer et al, 1956 Milne et al, 1957
Pempidine	probably excreted unchanged	Man Dog	Harington, Kincaid-Smith & Milne, 1958 Torretti, Weiner & Mudge, 1962
Tolazoline	probably excreted unchanged	Dog	Torretti, Weiner & Mudge, 1962
Meperidine and normeperidine	Meperidinic and normeperidinic acids and conjugates	Man	Asatoor, London, Milne & Simenhoff, unpublished data
5-Hydroxytryptamine	5-Hydroxyindolylacetic acid, N-acetyl-5-hydroxytryptamine and glucuronide	Rat	Sandler & Spector, 1961

* Metabolic product of troxidone.

glucuronide conjugation was first recognized by Quick (1933), and the differentiation into the two glucuronides by Alpen and co-workers (1951). In addition, a small fraction is oxidized to gentisic or 2:5-dihydroxybenzoic acid (Roseman & Dorfman, 1951), and traces of 2:3-dihydroxybenzoic acid (Bray, Thorpe & White, 1950) and 2:3:5-trihydroxybenzoic acid (Dumazart & Ouachi, 1954). Alpen and co-workers (1951) administered [^{14}C]salicylate and found the partition in the urine in man was as follows:

Free salicylate	10–85 per cent	(mean 61 per cent)
Salicyluric acid	0–50 per cent	(mean 8 per cent)
SPG	12–30 per cent	(mean 22 per cent)
SAG	0–10 per cent	(mean 5 per cent)
Gentisic acid	1 per cent	(mean 1 per cent)

Excretion of free salicylate is extremely variable and is chiefly dependent on urine pH. In alkaline urine up to 85 per cent will be eliminated as free salicylate, whereas in acid urine this may be as low as 10 per cent of the dose (Parker, 1948; Macpherson, Milne & Evans, 1955). The figures are therefore of greatest use as indicating the proportion excreted as various metabolites, and obviously salicyluric acid and SPG are quantitatively most important. Considerable species differences occur in salicylate metabolism. The dog produces no SAG (Alpen et al., 1951), and both dogs and mice oxidize a higher proportion of the dose to gentisic acid (Roseman & Dorfman, 1951).

Peak plasma levels of SAG and salicylurate occur at the same time as that of free salicylate, two hours after an oral dose, but the peak level of SPG is usually delayed to eight hours after ingestion. The highest concentrations of SPG, expressed in μmole per litre, are always considerably higher than those of salicylurate and SAG. Probably the conjugation takes place in many tissues, including intestinal mucosa, liver, kidney, urinary bladder, spleen, and lung (Schachter & Manis, 1958). Conjugation of salicylate is a relatively slow process in man. The maximum observed excretion of salicyluric acid is 5 μmole per minute, which is only one-twentieth the rate of possible output of benzoylglycine (hippuric acid). Similarly, after ingestion of p-methoxybenzoate the rate of maximal acyl glucuronide excretion can be six times that of SAG, and after salicylamide the rate of output of phenolic glucuronide may be 20 times that of SPG. This may be of importance in salicylate poisoning, as metabolism cannot be relied upon to convert free salicylate rapidly to less toxic and more easily excreted conjugates. In addition, glycine conjugation of salicylic acid can be easily reduced by competitive inhibition, such as by administration of p-aminobenzoic acid (Salassa, Bollman & Dry, 1948). Oxidation to gentisic acid and other polyhydroxy aromatic acids is due to non-specific oxidative enzymes, and is within normal limits in phenylketonurics who lack phenylalanine hydroxylase (Roseman & Dorfman, 1951).

Excretion of metabolites

Gentisic acid is excreted like free salicylic acid (Batterman & Sommer, 1953). This acid and other polyhydroxy aromatic acids excreted in trace amounts after salicylate ingestion undergo spontaneous oxidation in alkaline urine and therefore, as in alkaptonuria, there may be darkening of the urine due to formation of complex aromatic pigments.

The conjugates of salicylic acid with glycine and glucuronic acid are water-soluble organic acids that do not easily diffuse back across the renal tubular cells. Their excretion therefore resembles that of p-amino-hippurate, being dependent only on glomerular filtration and proximal tubular secretion; consequently their clearance is not affected by variation in urine flow or in urinary pH. Excretion parallels plasma levels of the conjugates, and therefore salicyluric acid and SAG are the main metabolites in urine for about three hours after salicylate ingestion, whereas SPG predominates in later specimens. Clearances of salicyluric acid and SAG approximate to that of p-aminohippurate, being many times higher than the GFR. The clearance of SPG is somewhat lower, possibly due to the extensive plasma-protein binding of this conjugate, which may interfere with proximal tubular secretion and certainly reduces the proportion filtered at the glomerulus. Probenecid greatly reduces the clearances of salicyluric acid and SAG by competition for proximal tubular secretion, but has less consistent and less quantitative effects on the lower clearance of SPG. The higher clearances of the conjugates as compared to that of free salicylic acid account for the fact that, whilst salicyl compounds in plasma can be assumed to be free salicylate without significant error, analysis in urine requires refined and elaborate methods of separation of the large number of metabolites actually excreted.

Recent results obtained by Weiner and co-workers (1961) suggest that the differentiation between the diffusibility of salicylic and salicyluric acids may not be so absolute as previously thought. Although it is not easy to demonstrate pH-dependent excretion of salicyluric acid at ordinary plasma levels, this occurred at concentrations of 20–70 mg. per 100 ml., with saturation of the proximal tubular transport system. Clearances changed from values indicating net tubular secretion to those of net tubular reabsorption at plasma salicylurate levels of 20 mg. per 100 ml. with an acid urine, but not until values of 70 mg. per 100 ml. had been reached with an alkaline urine. These results indicate that at very high plasma and urinary levels significant back-diffusion of salicylurate does in fact occur, and that the lipid-soluble unionized fraction is significantly more diffusible than the water-soluble ionized component.

2*

SUMMARY

Salicylate clearance is lowered by reduction of glomerular filtration rate, by inhibition of proximal tubular secretion as after probenecid, by oliguria, and by acidification of the urine. Clearances indicate net tubular secretion in highly alkaline urine, but prove net tubular reabsorption by distal tubular back-diffusion of unionized salicylate in acid urine. The mechanisms of pH-dependent excretion are discussed in detail. The conjugates of salicylic acid are less diffusible across cell membranes and therefore have a higher clearance than salicylic acid both in acid and in alkaline urine.

REFERENCES

Alpen, E. L., Mandel, H. G., Rodwell, V. W., & Smith, P. K. (1951). *J. Pharmacol. exp. Ther.*, **102**, 150.
Alpen, E. L., Mandel, H. G., & Smith, P. K. (1951). *J. Pharmacol. exp. Ther.*, **101**, 1.
Baer, J. E., Paulson, S. F., Russo, H. F., & Beyer, K. H. (1956). *Amer. J. Physiol.*, **186**, 180.
Batterman, R. C., & Sommer, E. M. (1953). *Proc. Soc. exp. Biol. (N.Y.)*, **82**, 376.
Bertagnini, C. (1856). *Justus Liebigs Ann. Chem.*, **97**, 248.
Blanchier, [P. A.], & Bochefontaine, —. (1878). *C. R. Soc. Biol. (Paris)*, **30**, 287.
Bray, H. G., Thorpe, W. V., & White, K. (1950). *Biochem. J.*, **46**, 271.
Coburn, A. F. (1943). *Bull. Johns Hopk. Hosp.*, **73**, 435.
Dalgaard-Mikkelsen, S. (1951). *Acta Pharmacol. (Kbh).*, **7**, 243.
Davis, P. L., & Smith, P. K. (1951). *Arch. int. Pharmacodyn.*, **86**, 303.
Dumazart, C., & Ouachi, M. E. (1954). *Ann. pharm. franç.*, **12**, 723.
Gutman, A. B., Dayton, P. G., Yü, T. F., Berger, L., Chen, W., Sicam, L.E., & Burns, J. J. (1960). *Amer. J. Med.*, **29**, 1017.
Gutman, A. B., Yü, T. F., & Sirota, J. H. (1955). *J. clin. Invest.*, **34**, 711.
Haag, H. B., & Larson, P. S. (1942). *J. Pharmacol. exp. Ther.*, **76**, 235.
Haag, H. B., Larson, P. S., & Schwartz, J. J. (1943). *J. Pharmacol. exp. Ther.*, **79**, 136.
Harington, M., Kincaid-Smith, P., & Milne, M. D. (1958). *Lancet*, **ii**, 6.
Jailer, J. W., Rosenfeld, M., & Shannon, J. A. (1947). *J. clin. Invest.*, **26**, 1168.
Macpherson, C. R., Milne, M. D., & Evans, B. M. (1955). *Brit. J. Pharmacol.*, **10**, 484.
Mandel, H. G., Cambosos, N. M., & Smith, P. K. (1954). *J. Pharmacol. exp. Ther.*, **112**, 495.
Milne, M. D., Crawford, M. A., Girão, C. B., & Loughridge, L. W. (1960). *Clin. Sci.*, **19**, 165.
Milne, M. D., Rowe, G. G., Somers, K., Muehrcke, R. C., & Crawford, M. A. (1957). *Clin. Sci.*, **16**, 599.
Parker, W. A. (1948). *Quart. J. Med.*, N.S. **17**, 229.
Quick, A. J. (1933). *J. biol. Chem.*, **101**, 475.
Roseman, S., & Dorfman, A. (1951). *J. biol. Chem.*, **192**, 105.
Salassa, R. M., Bollman, J. L., & Dry, T. J. (1948). *J. Lab. clin. Med.*, **33**, 1393.
Sandler, M., & Spector, R. G. (1961). *Nature (Lond.)*, **189**, 839.

Schachter, D., & Manis, J. G. (1958). *J. clin. Invest.*, **37**, 800.
Smith, P. K., Gleason, H. L., Stoll, C. G., & Ogorzalek, S. (1946). *J. Pharmacol. exp. Ther.*, **87**, 237.
Smull, K., Wegria, R., & Leland, J. (1944). *J. Amer. med. Ass.*, **125**, 1173.
Terp, P. (1951). *Acta pharmacol. (Kbh).*, **7**, 259.
Torretti, J., Weiner, I. M., & Mudge, G. H. (1962). *J. clin. Invest.*, **41**, 793.
Waddell, W. J., & Butler, T. C. (1957a). *J. clin. Invest.*, **36**, 1217.
Waddell, W. J., & Butler, T. C. (1957b). *Proc. Soc. exp. Biol. (N.Y.)*, **96**, 563.
Weiner, I. M., Garlid, K. D., Romeo, J. A., & Mudge, G. H. (1961). *Amer. J. Physiol.*, **200**, 393.
Weiner, I. M., Washington, J. A. Jr., & Mudge, G. H. (1959). *Bull. Johns Hopk. Hosp.*, **105**, 284.
Weiner, I. M., Washington, J. A. Jr., & Mudge, G. H. (1960). *Bull. Johns Hopk. Hosp.*, **106**, 333.
Williams, F., & Leonards, J. R. (1948). *J. Pharmacol. exp. Ther.*, **93**, 401.
Woodruff, M. V., Malvin, R. L., & Thompson, I. M. (1961). *J. Amer. med. Ass.*, **175**, 1132.

OBSERVATIONS RELATING TO THE
DISTRIBUTION AND EXCRETION OF SALICYLATES

A. J. CUMMINGS

The Nicholas Research Institute Ltd.
Slough, Buckinghamshire

THE relationship between plasma salicylate concentrations and the rates at which salicylate is excreted in the urine has been studied in men who received a single oral dose of aspirin.

The equivalent of 0·65 g. of aspirin was administered orally to two groups of eight men as tablets of plain aspirin or of aloxiprin (aloxiprin is the Approved Name for a polymeric condensation product of aluminium oxide and aspirin). Aloxiprin provides a form of aspirin that appears to be less rapidly absorbed than plain aspirin from the gastrointestinal tract, the difference being most marked in the acid environment of the stomach. Blood and urine specimens were collected from the test subjects at 0, 1, 2, 3, 5, and 7 hours after dosage, and their total salicylate content determined after hydrolysis by the method of Brodie, Udenfriend and Coburn (1944).

The mean rates of salicylate excretion in the urines of the two groups both attained very similar maxima (Fig. 1), although the maximum rate of excretion in the group that received aloxiprin was achieved later. However, if allowance is made for the initially slow rate of absorption, the excretion pattern of aloxiprin is not very different from that of plain aspirin. As the maximum rates of excretion were similar it was anticipated that the maximum plasma salicylate concentrations would also be approximately in the same ratio, although the maximum level after aloxiprin might occur later. In fact, the plasma salicylate concentrations obtained were very different, the maxima in the group receiving plain aspirin being appreciably higher. The mean plasma salicylate levels shown in Fig. 1 tend to minimize the differences at the first hour after dosage, when the results obtained with plain aspirin deviated from the mean to a greater extent than those obtained with aloxiprin (Cummings & Martin, 1962).

The possibility was considered that, due to the slower rate of absorption of aloxiprin aspirin from the gastrointestinal tract, lower but longer-sustained plasma salicylate levels would be obtained. This was obviously not so; in fact, a comparison of the respective plasma salicylate concentrations shown in Fig. 1 appears to indicate that the whole of the aspirin content of aloxiprin is not being absorbed. However, no marked difference was found in the total amount of salicylate excreted in the urine in 24 hours by four subjects who received equivalent doses of plain aspirin and aloxiprin in a cross-over experiment, indicating that the aspirin of aloxiprin is absorbed to much the same extent.

After doses of up to 1 g. of plain aspirin most individuals achieve a maximum plasma salicylate level after about one hour, whereas the

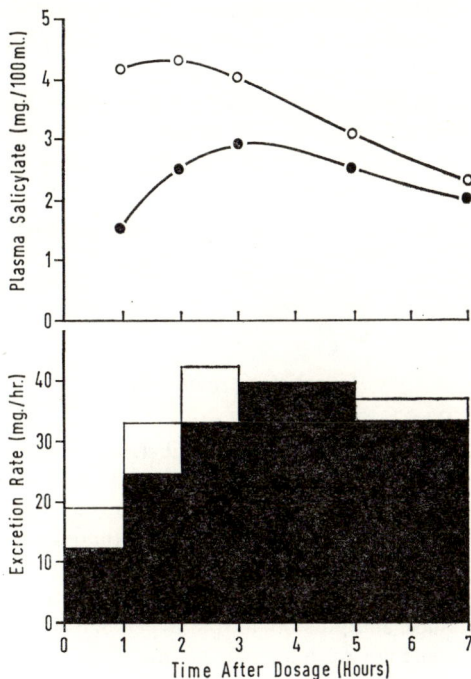

FIG. 1 PLASMA SALICYLATE CONCENTRATIONS AND RATES OF URINARY EXCRETION AFTER PLAIN ASPIRIN AND ALOXIPRIN

A single dose of 0·65 g. of aspirin or aloxiprin was administered orally to two groups of eight men. The mean values from the two groups of subjects are plotted, plain aspirin as open symbols and aloxiprin as closed symbols.

excretion of salicylate in the urine becomes maximal only after three or more hours. The greater part of the urine salicylate is present as metabolites, and these together may account for 90 per cent or more of the urine salicylate. On the other hand almost all the plasma salicylate is present as salicylate ion, either in free solution or bound to protein (Schachter & Manis, 1958). Since the plasma appears to be unable to metabolize salicylate, most of the urine salicylate must first have passed from the plasma to the body tissues concerned with this metabolism, and

must cross at least one cell membrane. Thus the rate of salicylate metabolism, and hence its rate of removal from the plasma, may be limited by
the physical processes involved in reaching the metabolizing site or by
the chemical rate of reaction of the metabolic process. Once formed the
metabolites are assumed to be rapidly eliminated. These pathways of
salicylate distribution and excretion are summarized in Fig. 2, which is
an adaptation of a scheme first proposed by Teorell (1937).

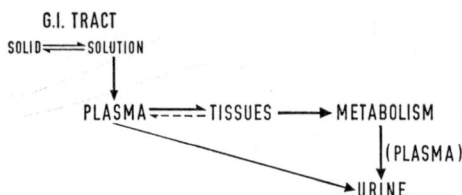

G.I. TRACT
SOLID⇌SOLUTION

PLASMA⇌TISSUES ⟶ METABOLISM

(PLASMA)

URINE

FIG. 2. PATHWAYS OF DISTRIBUTION AND
EXCRETION OF SALICYLATE

Plasma-tissue equilibrium

We consider that during the initial period after the administration of
a dose of aspirin, the plasma and tissue salicylate concentrations are not
necessarily in equilibrium and that it is the tissue concentration that
governs the rate of salicylate excretion in the urine. Thus after plain
aspirin administration the later attainment of maximum rates of excretion
in the urine, compared with the time of attainment of maximum plasma
salicylate levels, is due to the rate of transfer from the plasma to the
metabolizing tissues, and possibly to tissues generally, being lower than
the rate of salicylate absorption from the gut. This might be expected
from the different concentration gradients between the various body
compartments. Consequently the plasma salicylate rises rapidly to a
disproportionately high level compared with the tissue salicylate concentration, and the plasma and tissue concentrations only attain equilibrium in three or more hours after dosage.

The aspirin of aloxiprin is absorbed more slowly from the gut and the
rates of entry of salicylate into the plasma, and of its removal from plasma
by distribution to the tissues, are more comparable than the corresponding rates obtained with plain aspirin. That is, with aloxiprin the
plasma and tissue concentrations are never far from equilibrium, and in
this instance the urinary excretion rates correspond more closely to the
plasma salicylate concentrations. It is of interest to note that individuals
who absorbed plain aspirin from the gut at a slow rate, who achieved a
maximum plasma salicylate level more than one hour after dosage, gave
results similar to those obtained with aloxiprin.

We therefore suggest that when aspirin is slowly absorbed a greater proportion of the salicylate enters the tissues and is metabolized during the first 2–3 hours than is the case when it is rapidly absorbed. This would seem to suggest that the removal of salicylate from the plasma and its metabolism in the tissues approximates to a zero-order process; that is, the rate of metabolism is in part independent of the body salicylate concentration.

There is some evidence to suggest that when the plasma salicylate level exceeds a certain value the main metabolite of salicylic acid, salicyluric acid, is formed and hence excreted by a zero-order process. The ester glucuronide of salicylic acid, however, may be formed by a predominantly first-order process. A study of the total excretion of salicylate in the urine, irrespective of the form in which it is excreted, reveals that during the period of approximately 2–6 hours after a 1 g. oral dose of aspirin the rate of excretion appears to be described by zero-order reaction kinetics. Thereafter the rate of excretion seems to approach a first-order process. Similar findings have been reported by Bray and his collaborators (1955) with respect to the excretion of benzoic acid metabolites in the urine of rabbits.

SUMMARY

Plasma salicylate concentrations and urinary salicylate excretion rates have been studied simultaneously after single oral doses of plain aspirin and of aloxiprin. Maximum plasma levels were usually attained at about one hour after dosage with plain aspirin, but not until about three hours after a dose of aloxiprin. Maximum excretion rates were not achieved until the third hour or later.

This suggests that there may be a delay in equilibration between concentrations in plasma and in the tissues after plain aspirin. After slow-release preparations urinary excretion rates vary more closely with plasma salicylate concentrations.

REFERENCES

Bray, H. G., Humphris, B. G., Thorpe, W. V., White, K., & Wood, P. B. (1955). *Biochem. J.*, **59**, 162.
Brodie, B. B., Udenfriend, S., & Coburn, A. F. (1944). *J. Pharmacol. exp. Ther.*, **80**, 114.
Cummings, A. J., & Martin, B. K. (1962). *Nature (Lond.)*, **195**, 1104.
Schachter, D., & Manis, J. G. (1958). *J. Clin. Invest.*, **37**, 800.
Teorell, T. (1937). *Arch. int. Pharmacodyn.*, **57**, 205.

DISCUSSION

CLARKE DAVISON (*Department of Pharmacology, George Washington University School of Medicine, Washington, D.C., U.S.A.*):

The enhanced urinary excretion of ionized salicylate in alkaline urine has always been something of a puzzle to me. Most of us are aware that in alkaline urine there is less passive back-diffusion of unionized salicylate, presumably because the ionized salicylate does not pass through a lipid membrane in the renal tubule. However, as MILNE has pointed out, the greatest effect is seen in the pH range 7·0 to 8·0. Salicylate is a fairly strong organic acid with a pK_a of 3·0. In the region of pH 7·0 it is essentially 99·99 per cent ionized; if the pH rises to 8·0 only an additional 0·01 per cent is ionized. How can such a small change in ionization account for such a marked change in the excretion of free ionized salicylate?

A practical point brought out by LEVY is the effect of bulk and viscosity upon absorption of salicylate and, undoubtedly, of other drugs. I would also add that diet can markedly affect the urinary pH. I have become increasingly aware of the need for rigid control of diet in drug studies on human volunteers. This is a trite point, but one which some investigators have overlooked. They have not attempted to control diet, and some have even been unaware whether the subjects had taken food or not.

CONSDEN: One factor that contributes to the different excretion rate according to urinary pH may be connective tissue protein-binding of salicylate. Salicylate is bound rather strongly to some proteins. We have observed that, by exposing the tissue to salicylate solutions, large amounts of the drug are bound to collagen, but that salicylate can be washed out easily by bicarbonate. A change of pH from 7·0 to 8·0 is sufficient to release salicylate from the tissue and may perhaps contribute to the observed large increase in urinary salicylate.

MILNE: I doubt that protein-binding contributes to pH-dependent excretion. What matters is the pH of the plasma, where the protein is, and not the pH of the urine. Quite small doses of sodium bicarbonate or ammonium chloride that do not alter plasma pH to any measurable degree still have gross effects on urinary pH. In addition, proximal tubular secretion is not influenced by protein-binding because it is the *free* drug that is secreted. This causes rapid dissociation of the protein-drug complex, with which it is in equilibrium.

Back diffusion depends not so much on the absolute amount of unionized salicylate within the lumen as on the gradient of hydrogen ions between lumen and peritubular blood. The peritubular blood is at pH 7·4; a change of pH from 7·0 to 8·0 straddles that figure and thus explains the great effect of this change on the excretion of ionized salicylate.

LEONARDS: Williams and I showed over ten years ago that the administration of sodium bicarbonate did not alter the binding of salicylate in blood.

STOWERS: Salicylates are known to affect the distribution of some drugs, such as sulphinpyrazone. Does the body distribution of salicylate suggest that it is entirely extracellular, or does it get into the cells also?

MILNE: The distribution is in whole body water, but it is uneven. A drug like salicylate is in lower concentration in cellular fluid because the latter is more acidic than plasma.

FREMONT-SMITH: We measured the volume of distribution of sodium salicylate in normal subjects and found it to average 148 ml. per kg. of body weight, ranging from 128 to 175 ml. We have also found that non-bound salicylate was in equilibrium between the plasma and the synovial fluid in 15 rheumatoid joints (Rosenthal, R. K., & Fremont-Smith, K. [1962]. *Arthr. and Rheum.*, **5**, 317).

DIXON: CUMMINGS followed the absorption of two forms of aspirin by plasma salicylate levels. We have been told that an appreciable amount of aspirin is absorbed as such, and that some circulates in this form as well. Couldn't this account for some of CUMMINGS's findings?

G. CUMMING: Can CUMMINGS give any information about the time relationships of the diffusion of salicylate into the body space?

A. J. CUMMINGS: We didn't determine the actual aspirin content of the plasma. I agree that this could partly explain the differences found.

We are doing more detailed work on the diffusion of salicylates between plasma and tissues, but the only results so far are those I have quoted.

Free aspirin

DIXON: How much aspirin does circulate as such? This may be relevant to DUTHIE's comment on the apparently superior clinical effect of aspirin.

M. J. H. SMITH: When giving small doses of aspirin, of the order of 1 g., one frequently gets at least 25 per cent as free aspirin (Smith, M. J. H. [1951]. *J. Pharm. Pharmacol.*, **3**, 409). A lot depends on how the salicylate and acetylsalicylate levels are measured.

MILNE: Mandel and his colleagues showed that at therapeutic salicylate concentrations of 30 mg. per 100 ml. or more the highest plasma acetyl-salicylate levels did not exceed 2·0 mg. per 100 ml. The only exception is when aspirin is given intravenously; then, of course, there could be a short-lived and very high level.

The main trouble with salicylate biochemistry has been the lack of specific chromatographic methods. Physical methods for separating these compounds are just as bad as salting-out methods for proteins and are quite useless. It used to be said that salicylate conjugates did not occur in blood. This is not true; the one-seventieth of total salicylate present at the peak level two hours after a dose is now readily seen to be conjugates by paper chromatography and fluorimetry. These methods give good separation, as shown by Schachter and Manis.

CONSDEN: Not only have many reported studies employed involved and laborious procedures; most investigators also have not dealt with all the five metabolites that account for the greater part of ingested salicylate. This may be the reason for the large discrepancies in the literature. Even in Schachter's methods there are a number of steps; these are too time-consuming to be suitable for experiments involving large numbers of samples, as in experiments on salicylate metabolism in health and disease. We use relatively simple paper-chromatographic methods similar to Schachter's which give good separation of the three acids and of the two glucuronides.

MILNE: I agree that the accuracy of the methods must be geared to the time available and how accurate the methods need to be. Nevertheless one should not delude oneself that crude separative measures give full separation of closely similar compounds that give the same colorimetric reaction.

DAVISON: I agree that in the first 5–15 minutes the percentage of plasma salicylate present as aspirin might perhaps be considerably higher than 25 per cent. In our routine analyses, which are by colorimetric or fluorimetric methods, we include an alkaline hydrolysis which breaks down aspirin but does not affect the conjugates. Thus we report total salicylate, not including the glucuronic acid and glycine conjugates. To determine free aspirin one omits the preliminary hydrolysis; with the newer fluorimetric instruments one can determine even a few μg. of aspirin.

LEONARDS: The percentage of aspirin depends a great deal on the rate at which it is absorbed. With slow absorption the amount of intact aspirin in the blood is very small, but if it is absorbed rapidly, as it is from solutions of the salts of aspirin, the proportion in the blood 10–20 minutes after ingestion can be 30–40 per cent of the total salicylate.

WINTERS: Does acetate have any effect on the secretory process in the proximal tubule? Also, does MILNE suggest that salicylate is not being secreted during acidosis, or is it being secreted in the stop-flow pattern and then diffusing back as it comes out of the kidney?

MILNE: I am sure the latter is correct. One of the defects of stop-flow techniques is that phenomena in the distal tubule obscure what is happening in the proximal tubule. This is not a disadvantage of micropuncture, but that is a much more difficult technique.

It is a very non-specific secretory process in the proximal tubule. Acetate has been shown to increase the secretion of p-aminohippuric and many other acids, and I am sure that it would also increase the secretion of salicylate.

RELATIONSHIP OF DOSAGE AND TYPE OF SALICYLATE THERAPY TO PLASMA LEVELS IN PATIENTS WITH RHEUMATOID ARTHRITIS

BARBARA M. ANSELL

Medical Research Council Rheumatism Research Unit
Taplow, Buckinghamshire

SALICYLATES remain the most widely used therapeutic agents in rheumatoid arthritis. The main aims of therapy are to relieve pain and reduce muscle stiffness; to do this effectively requires continued medication at a high dosage level, when gastric intolerance is often a problem. To overcome this numerous modifications of salicylate formulations have been devised, which fall into two types. One type contains glycine, carbonates, or citric acid, in various combinations with aspirin; the second comprises enteric-coated preparations. Most of the compound tablets contain 5 gr. (324 mg.) of aspirin, but aspirin–glycine contains 10 gr. in each tablet and the coated preparations contain 5 gr. of aspirin and 5 or 10 gr. of sodium salicylate. These latter are all big red tablets and are superficially indistinguishable. We tend to employ pure preparations, and also one locally-made compound tablet of aspirin and codeine without phenacetin.

To investigate the duration of effective plasma salicylate levels after a single oral dose, we administered 1·0 g. of each of the following preparations to fasting normal subjects: plain aspirin, aspirin–glycine, soluble aspirin, buffered aspirin, and enteric-coated aspirin. Plasma salicylate levels, determined by the method of Trinder (1954), were measured after two hours and then at one- or two-hourly intervals for a period of at least 12 hours. All the results quoted were obtained in this way and at a time when no other drug was being administered. All preparations other than enteric-coated aspirin produced similar plasma salicylate curves (Fig.), but with the latter effective levels did not develop until eight hours following ingestion. From this it seems obvious that in order to get continuously adequate levels administration of non-enteric-coated preparations must be at least four-hourly. In the interpretation of the plasma salicylate level it is important to know the type of preparation taken and the time of the last dose.

In practice we administer salicylate medication four-hourly except during the night, when there is an eight-hour interval. Blood salicylate levels are usually taken $2\frac{1}{2}$–3 hours after the fasting morning dose. Provided there is no gastric intolerance dosage is increased until adequate analgesia or salicylism occurs. The first sign of the latter is usually tinnitus, and this is quickly followed by deafness.

As would be expected, the plasma salicylate level rises with dosage. Children tolerate salicylate better than adults. For example, a girl of 15 years with severe Still's Disease (juvenile rheumatoid arthritis) was given increasing dosage in the usual way. She made no complaint of tinnitus at plasma salicylate levels in the region of 50 mg. per 100 ml. It was not until she was taking 8·0 g. per day, which gave a blood salicylate

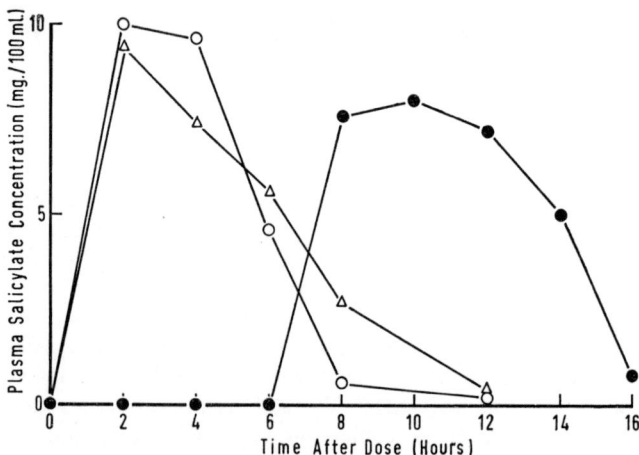

PLASMA SALICYLATE CONCENTRATIONS AFTER A SINGLE DOSE OF
VARIOUS ASPIRIN PREPARATIONS

1·0 g. of an aspirin preparation was administered to the same subject in the fasting state on three occasions. Each point represents the mean of these three sets of observations. Plain aspirin is depicted by open circles, enteric-coated aspirin by closed circles, and aspirin-glycine by open triangles. The observations after buffered aspirin and soluble aspirin are not shown because they were almost identical to those after plain aspirin.

level of 61 mg. per 100 ml., that she started to complain of tinnitus. When the dosage was reduced to 6·7 g. per day her tinnitus disappeared, even though the blood salicylate level was 57 mg. per 100 ml. However, we do not like to keep the plasma salicylate at these levels because we have observed that, even without prior tinnitus, some children show hyperventilation, nausea, and vomiting. On the whole, we have found that with children it is reasonable to try to maintain levels of 30–35 mg. per 100 ml., and with adults 25–30 mg. per 100 ml. However, in some children where pain has been a very real problem it has been found advisable to maintain levels ranging between 30 mg. and 40 mg. per 100 ml., without apparent untoward side effects. If intolerance develops when the plasma level is below 15 mg. per 100 ml. it is very unlikely that effective analgesia can be established using salicylate alone.

Our experience suggests that in any one individual equivalent doses of the various aspirin preparations give the same plasma salicylate levels after equilibrium has been obtained. However, there is considerable variation between individuals in the plasma level obtained by a given dose. This variation does not appear to correlate with the weight of the patient, nor with the activity of the disease process.

Fremont-Smith (1955) suggested that patients with rheumatoid arthritis tolerate buffered aspirin better than a plain preparation, but Batterman (1958) did not confirm this in relation to gastric intolerance. Our experience suggests that it is rare for patients to tolerate analgesic doses of plain aspirin over a long period of time, and that although dyspepsia is seen with soluble aspirin and aspirin–glycine, it is less frequent. However, occult bleeding still occurs with these latter formulations and so we have preferred enteric-coated preparations, which are well tolerated by most patients. As the enteric-coated preparation takes longer to become effective, regular administration is essential; this frequently causes improvement in morning stiffness, provided the last dose is taken late at night (see also Claudy & Sloan, 1958).

SUMMARY

The aim of salicylate therapy is to give effective relief of pain. The dosage required varies from individual to individual, but can be found by increasing the amount given until tinnitus occurs and then stabilizing the level at 10 gr. (648 mg.) per day less than this. In the majority of adults the plasma salicylate level will then be between 25 and 30 mg. per 100 ml. Should tinnitus develop with the level below 15 mg. per 100 ml. it is unlikely that adequate analgesia will be obtained with salicylate alone.

In patients with Still's Disease (juvenile rheumatoid arthritis) tinnitus is much less common. Children are able to tolerate a relatively greater dosage, but it is advisable to keep the plasma level in the region of 30 mg. per 100 ml.

REFERENCES

Batterman, R. C. (1958). *New Engl. J. Med.*, **258**, 213.
Claudy, E. K., & Sloan, C. (1958). *J. Arkansas med. Soc.*, **54**, 510.
Fremont-Smith, P. (1955). *J. Amer. med. Ass.*, **158**, 386.
Trinder, P. (1954). *Biochem. J.*, **57**, 301.

SALICYLATES AND URIC ACID EXCRETION

ALLAN ST. J. DIXON

Chelsea and Kensington Group Rheumatism Unit
St. Stephen's Hospital, London

SALICYLATES are thought not to affect the production, equilibrium distribution, or protein-binding of urate (Salteri, Cirla & Fasoli, 1958). Their action upon urate elimination is that of directly modifying renal urate clearance and of modifying the actions of other drugs, such as

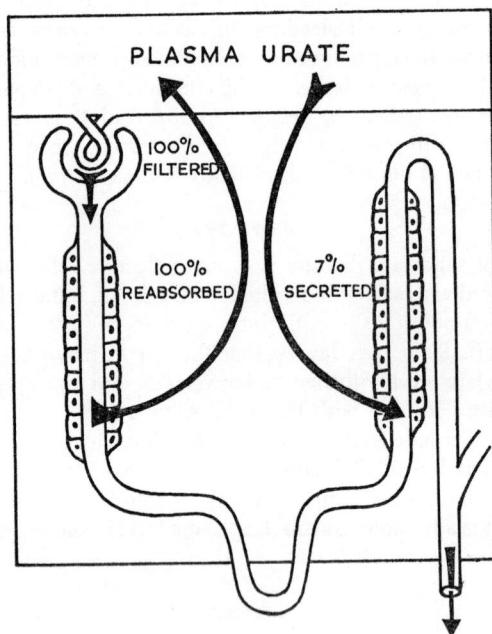

CIRCULATION OF URATE IN THE KIDNEY

probenecid, sulphinpyrazone, zoxazolamine, chlorothiazide, and pyrazinamide, which are known to affect the excretion of urate.

One can assume that the internal circulation of urate in the normal kidney is as depicted in the figure, in which urate is 100 per cent filtered at the glomerulus, 100 per cent reabsorbed in the proximal tubule, and a small fraction, about 5–10 per cent, is passed back into the urine lower

38

down the nephron. We do not think that this is in the loop of Henle because the 24-hour urate clearance is unaffected by urine concentration. The evidence for tubular secretion of urate lies in such experiments as those of Poulsen and Praetorius (1954) in rabbits and those of Gutman, Yü and Berger (1959) in man. These workers demonstrated that the clearance of urate could exceed the glomerular filtration rate (GFR) under experimental conditions.

Proximal tubular reabsorption of urate is likely because urate clearance is abnormally increased in inherited renal diseases with proximal tubular damage, notably Wilson's disease (hepatolenticular degeneration) (Bishop, Zimdahl & Talbott, 1954) and in the Fanconi Syndrome (Sirota, Yü & Gutman, 1952). In other chronic renal states selective retention of urate occurs. These states include the nephrocalcinosis of hyperparathyroidism (Dixon & Treadwell, 1961) and the nephropathy of chronic lead poisoning. In both these conditions frank gout may occur; one presumes that the renal damage is predominantly in the distal tubule, interfering with secretion. Finally, the actions and interactions of various drugs such as probenecid and pyrazinamide only make sense if one can assume that transfer of urate between blood and tubular lumen can take place at at least two different sites after filtration at the glomerulus.

The uricosuric action of salicylate

In a remarkable paper on salicylates in 1877, Sée reported a large number of observations, many of which we are still discussing 85 years later without much more elucidation. For example, he noted that salicylates were more rapidly eliminated with an alkaline diet; that a small, $0.9°$ C, antipyretic effect was observed even in normal people; and that salicylates might cause small erosions of the pharynx, oesophagus, and stomach. In gouty patients he noted that salicylates were analgesic, could decrease joint swelling, and caused increased elimination of uric acid in the urine. He reported a rise in urine uric acid from 0.8 to 3.0 g. per litre during three successive days of treatment, although unfortunately he did not record the total daily urine output. However, he did say that the patient's regime was not otherwise modified.

This uricosuric action of salicylate has been confirmed repeatedly and has been shown to be due to a steep rise in urate clearance. However, at low dosage of salicylate, less than 2.0 g. per day, there is a paradoxical reversal of this action and urate is retained (Yü & Gutman, 1959). High doses, 5–8 g. per day, such as were used by Sée and more recently by Marson (1955), are required for consistent uricosuria. Most gouty patients cannot tolerate the accompanying toxic effects on the stomach or ears and this treatment has been given up except in patients with both gout and renal disease, in whom salicylates may be more effective than probenecid. The uricosuric action of salicylate is enhanced if the urine is made alkaline, even though the blood level of salicylate is reduced (Goodman & Gilman, 1955; Graham, 1958). This effect may depend on the concentration of ionized salicylate in the tubular lumen (Yü & Gutman, 1959); alternatively, only unionized salicylate in the distal tubule may be capable of blocking distal tubular urate secretion.

Comparison of salicylate and probenecid

The reason why salicylate is comparatively more effective than probenecid in promoting urate excretion in renal failure (Yü & Gutman, 1951; Seegmiller, 1957) is of interest. We also have had the same experience.

Sulphinpyrazone is about 98 per cent, and salicylate and probenecid are about 70–80 per cent, bound to plasma albumin. The amount of urine protein produced in 24 hours by the gouty kidney, almost always less than 1·0 g. per 24 hours, is too small to cause significant intraluminal binding and hence inactivation of these drugs. Thus we must consider whether the comparative failure of probenecid in the face of tubular damage is due to the fact that probenecid normally blocks an active transport system, whereas salicylate blocks a passive transport system such as diffusion.

Kinter and Cline (1961) studied diodone, p-aminohippuric acid, chlorphenol red, probenecid, and bromcresol green, all drugs that are selectively concentrated by renal tubules. They allowed isolated goldfish tubules to accumulate [^{131}I]diodone from a medium. When transferred to a new medium, the loaded tubules could maintain the intraluminal concentration of diodone against the gradient, but required metabolic energy to do so. When the energy cycle was poisoned escape of diodone occurred, but even in these metabolically inert tubules the lipid-soluble probenecid and bromcresol green were found partially to inhibit the escape of the accumulated diodone. This must mean that certain lipid-soluble substances taking part in tubular transport can inhibit the transport of other substances by a purely physical non-energy-requiring system. Since unionized salicylate is lipid-soluble and ionized salicylate is not, it lends support to the idea that it is by a mechanism such as this that salicylate may interfere with distal tubular secretion of urate in an acid urine.

In comparing the actions of probenecid and salicylate on urate transport it appears that two types of interference are caused by both drugs. First, a blockage of energy-requiring transport. This is the main effect of probenecid in the human kidney and it affects the proximal tubule. Secondly, a passive interference with diffusion, an effect seen mainly at the distal tubule with unionized salicylate in an acid urine. Alkalinization of the urine removes unionized salicylate distally, which increases net clearance. In renal damage active tubular transport is decreased, but passive blocking of back-diffusion is relatively unaffected.

Antagonism of other uricosuric drugs

All uricosuric drugs have a similar, though less marked, paradoxical urate-retaining effect in low dosage. These include probenecid, sulphinpyrazone, phenylbutazone (Gutman, Yü & Sirota, 1955) and zoxazolamine; but while these drugs all enhance each other's action, salicylate is exceptional in that it antagonizes the uricosuric effect of all of them, again suggesting additional actions or an additional pathway. Yü and coworkers (1962) examined the problem of why sulphinpyrazone reduced salicylate uricosuria at the same time as salicylate reduced sulphinpyrazone uricosuria. By infusing both drugs at constant known rates they showed that salicylate antagonized sulphinpyrazone by releasing the latter to a wider space; in fact there was a 25 per cent fall in serum level without a change in sulphinpyrazone clearance. This was associated with an uncoupling of the protein-binding of sulphinpyrazone. They implied that this meant that there was less available to block tubular reabsorption of urate in the proximal tubule. On the other hand, they found that sulphinpyrazone blocked the clearance of salicylate due, they thought, to competition for tubular secretion.

Recently chlorothiazide has been called 'the uricosuric agent which never grew up', since Demartini and co-workers (1962) showed that larger doses of 500 mg. by intravenous infusion caused uricosuria. Salicylate has been studied in relation to the low-dosage urate-retaining action of chlorothiazide, which it reverses. Microdissection of nephrons has shown that the similar drug, hydrochlorothiazide, localizes in the central part of the proximal tubule and in the whole of the distal tubule (Darmady et al., 1962). This double site of localization is consistent with the theory that uricosuric drugs with paradoxical urate-retaining action in low dosage act both on proximal tubular urate reabsorption and on distal tubular urate secretion, the net effect reflecting the predominant process.

Pyrazinamide, the antituberculous antibiotic, has so far been shown to have only urate-retaining actions. It is metabolized in the body to pyrazinoic acid, which is rapidly excreted. In a dose of 2–4 g. per day it causes an immediate suppression of urate excretion and a steep rise in plasma urate to 15 mg. per 100 ml. or more. Scott, Treadwell and I have concluded that probenecid, sulphinpyrazone, and zoxazolamine are all less effective in antagonizing pyrazinamide hyperuricaemia than is salicylate in the usual therapeutic doses. We agree with Benedek (1961) that even small doses of salicylate, of the order of 1·0 g. per day, reduce established pyrazinamide hyperuricaemia. We did not find that salicylate altered the plasma pyrazinoate level.

SUMMARY

Urate excretion occurs by glomerular filtration, proximal tubular reabsorption, and distal tubular secretion. Uricosuric agents, including salicylate, block both reabsorption and secretion, the net effect reflecting the predominant process. Salicylate differs from other uricosuric drugs in that it antagonizes the actions of the others, which themselves are mutually synergistic; its uricosuric effect is pH-dependent; it remains effectively uricosuric despite certain forms of renal damage; and it is relatively more powerful in antagonizing pyrazinamide.

Possible reasons for the difference between these drugs are, firstly, salicylates may uncouple the protein-binding of the other drugs and release them to a wider space; secondly, there may be more than one way that a drug can block urate transport. It seems likely, that this is a process that may explain certain features of the effect of salicylates on urate excretion.

REFERENCES

Benedek, T. G. (1961). X Congr. Lega. int. Reum., 2, 621. Rome: Minerva Medica.
Bishop, C., Zimdahl, W. T., & Talbott, J. H. (1954). Proc. Soc. exp. Biol. (N.Y.), 86, 440.
Darmady, E. M., Mawles, T. T., Renzi, A. A., Sheppard, H., & Stranick, F. (1962). Clin. Sci., 22, 295.
Demartini, F. E., Wheaton, E. A., Healey, L. A., & Laragh, J. H. (1962). Amer. J. Med., 32, 752.
Dixon, A. St. J., & Treadwell, B. L. (1961). X Congr. Lega. int. Reum., 2, 645. Rome: Minerva Medica.
Graham, W. (1958). Canad. med. Ass. J., 79, 634.
Goodman, L. S., & Gilman, A. (1955). 'The Pharmacological Basis of Therapeutics', 2nd Ed., p. 288. New York: Macmillan.
Gutman, A. B., Yü, T. F., & Berger, L. (1959). J. clin. Invest., 38, 1778.
Gutman, A. B., Yü, T. F., & Sirota, J. H. (1955). J. clin. Invest., 34, 711.
Kinter, W. B., & Cline, A. L. (1961). Amer. J. Physiol., 201, 309.
Marson, F. G. W. (1955). Lancet, ii, 360.
Poulsen, H., & Praetorius, E. (1954). Acta pharmacol. (Kbh.), 10, 371.
Salteri, F., Cirla, E., & Fasoli, A. (1958). Science, 127, 85.
Sée, G. (1877). Bull. Acad. Méd. (Paris), 26, 689.
Seegmiller, J. E. (1957). Amer. J. Med., 22, 807.
Sirota, J. H., Yü, T. F., & Gutman, A. B. (1952). J. clin. Invest., 31, 692.
Yü, T. F., Dayton, P. G., Berger, L., & Gutman, A. B. (1962). Fed. Proc., 21, 175.
Yü, T. F., & Gutman, A. B. (1951). Amer. J. Med., 11, 768.
Yü, T. F., & Gutman, A. B. (1959). J. clin. Invest., 38, 1298.

DISCUSSION

THEODORE B. BAYLES (*Robert B. Brigham Hospital and Harvard Medical School, Boston, Massachusetts, U.S.A.*):

Plasma salicylate levels in rheumatoid arthritis

These two papers seem to call for little specific comment. I would like to take up the observation, which has been made by several observers, that some patients with rheumatoid arthritis appear to tolerate larger doses of salicylate than would be expected from experience with other patients and with normal subjects. There is a report in the older literature describing a similar phenomenon in acute rheumatic fever (Scott, R. W., Thoburn, T. W., & Hanzlik, P. J. [1917]. *J. Pharmacol. exp. Ther.*, 9, 217). Random plasma salicylate determinations on our patients seemed to support the possibility that the metabolism of this drug is altered in active rheumatoid arthritis.

We compared plasma salicylate concentrations in 17 patients with active rheumatoid arthritis with those in 11 patients with inactive disease (Fremont-Smith, K., Tenckhoff, H., Godfrey, R. G., Mednis, A., Baker, N., & Bayles, T. B. [1961]. X Congr. Lega. int. Reum., 2, 1342. Rome: Minerva Medica). All patients had been given aspirin, 15 mg. per kg. daily in equally divided doses, for prolonged periods. Patients with a urinary pH of 6·5 or higher at the time of study were omitted because an alkaline urine increases salicylate excretion and thus should decrease plasma levels. Plasma salicylate levels were determined by the method of Brodie, Udenfriend and Coburn ([1944]. *J. Pharmacol. exp. Ther.*, 80, 114). Two and a half hours after the evening dose of aspirin, which should be the peak for the day, the average plasma salicylate concentration in the patients with active rheumatoid arthritis was about half that of the inactive group; 12 hours after the evening dose it was even less.

To avoid the effect of variable gastrointestinal absorption we then gave a single dose of sodium salicylate, 20 mg. per kg. intravenously, to another group of subjects and obtained serial plasma and urine samples over the following six hours. We again found that plasma salicylate concentrations were lower in patients with rheumatoid arthritis than in control subjects; the mean plasma salicylate concentrations are shown in the figure. This is a semi-logarithmic plot, and the lines are almost straight from two hours on. The values for each individual study also yielded reasonably straight lines when plotted in this fashion. Thus it is possible to estimate graphically the rate of disappearance of salicylate from the plasma for each experiment, expressed as the half-life or $t_{\frac{1}{2}}$. The rate of disappearance appeared to be significantly faster in the rheumatoid patients than in the control subjects. However, the normal controls were fully active, whereas all the rheumatoid patients were at complete rest in bed. When the same studies were repeated in normal subjects at complete rest in bed the results clearly demonstrated that the half-life of salicylate in the plasma is not shorter in patients with rheumatoid arthritis. This also demonstrated that muscular activity or the erect posture decreases the rate of removal of salicylate from the plasma following intravenous administration to normal individuals.

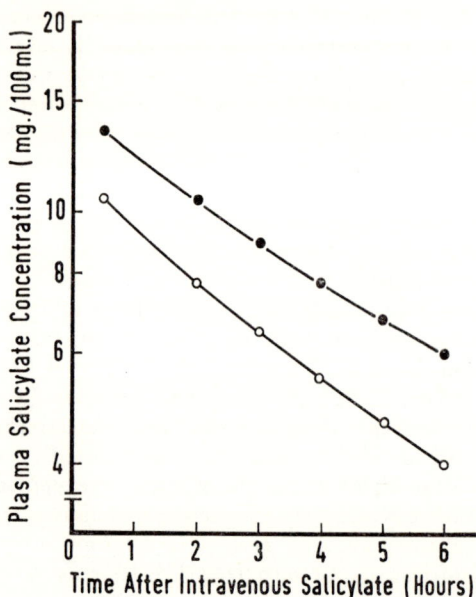

PLASMA SALICYLATE CONCENTRATIONS AFTER INTRA-
VENOUS SODIUM SALICYLATE

A single dose of sodium salicylate, 20 mg. per kg., was injected intravenously, and serial plasma and urine samples were collected in the ensuing six hours. Mean values are plotted, from seven patients with active rheumatoid arthritis (open circles) and from seven normal subjects (closed circles). The ordinate is marked on a logarithmic scale.

The lower plasma salicylate concentrations in rheumatoid subjects could be due to large amounts of conjugated salicylate, undetected by the Brodie method, in the rheumatoid plasma. This is unlikely because, by using both a method of hydrolysis under pressure (Ropes—personal communication) and Schachter and Manis's ([1958]. *J. clin. Invest.*, **37**, 800) spectrofluorimetric technique for the estimation of individual conjugates in the plasma, we found that the total of these conjugates in rheumatoid plasma does not amount to more than 10 per cent of the unconjugated salicylate, the same as in normal subjects. Another possible explanation could be chronic ingestion of salicylates. Studies in three individuals done before and after prolonged daily medication with aspirin seemed to rule this out; there was no change in plasma concentration or in urinary excretion following the intravenous test dose of sodium salicylate.

Alteration in the urinary excretion of salicylate conjugates could also account for the lower concentrations in the plasma. This is an unlikely explanation because over the six-hour test period 39·2 per cent of the infused salicylate appeared in the urine of the control subjects, either as free salicylate or in conjugated form; the corresponding value for the rheumatoid patients was 40·7 per cent. In both rheumatoid and control subjects salicylurate accounted for two-thirds of the total urinary salicylate, approximately one-fifth was in the form of glucuronides, and the remainder was unconjugated salicylate.

There remains one other possible explanation. The lower concentrations in rheumatoid subjects may be due to the hypoalbuminaemia that is often found in such patients with active disease.

OSORIO: Why is importance attached to the salicylate concentration in blood as an index of its toxic or therapeutic effect? It is generally accepted that salicylate is bound by the plasma proteins, and the concentration in the blood is meaningless unless one knows the extent of protein-binding. The free or non-protein-bound salicylate determines the concentration in the tissues. The shorter salicylate half-life in rheumatoid subjects may be due to a higher free salicylate, the consequence of decreased binding due to hypoalbuminaemia.

MILNE: I agree that, pharmacologically, free salicylate is the important thing to measure, but it is much more difficult to estimate than is the total concentration in plasma.

Certainly hypoalbuminaemia is an important factor in the differences in salicylate half-life between patients with rheumatoid arthritis and normal subjects, but this aspect will be dealt with in greater detail later on.

WIGGINS: In some of our studies of salicylate distribution we administered 1 g. of aspirin four times daily to 20 normal adults. After the seventh dose the plasma salicylate level had reached a steady state. There was a considerable difference between different individuals, but the salicylate levels appeared to vary inversely with body weight, ranging from 9 mg. per 100 ml. in the heaviest subject to 24 mg. per 100 ml. in the lightest. This emphasizes the need to consider body weight when starting patients on aspirin.

ANSELL: Certainly we have found a very marked individual variation. We used to try to administer salicylate on the basis of 1 gr. (60 mg.) per lb. body weight, but we found that this did not always form a satisfactory regime for dosage in children.

VAN CAUWENBERGE: Tinnitus seems to be a very individual symptom and doesn't necessarily correlate with the blood salicylate level. I am not convinced that this symptom can indicate a therapeutic limit.

ANSELL: I agree that patients who complain of tinnitus may have blood levels varying from 10 to 50 mg. per 100 ml. Nevertheless tinnitus is a useful guide as to whether one can get the patient to take an adequate dose of salicylate.

METABOLIC EFFECTS OF SALICYLATES

Chairman M. J. H. SMITH

SALICYLATES AND INTERMEDIARY METABOLISM

M. J. H. SMITH

Empire Rheumatism Council Research Unit on Drug Metabolism
King's College Hospital Medical School, London

DURING the last decade there has been an increasing amount of attention given to the effects of salicylates on cellular metabolism. One reason is that the drugs have been found to influence a variety of metabolic processes in man and in experimental animals (Smith, 1959a), and it is important that these actions should be defined as precisely as possible in biochemical terms. It has also been suggested by numerous authors that the actions of drugs may be explained by their ability to alter the functions of either an enzyme or of multi-enzyme systems. The purpose of the present article is to review the recent work on the effects of salicylates on intermediary metabolism and to attempt to discuss its implications with respect to some of the metabolic, clinical, and toxic actions of the drugs.

Oxidative phosphorylation

The first major action of salicylates on cellular metabolism to be demonstrated *in vitro* was the uncoupling action on oxidative phosphorylation reactions. Brody (1956) showed that salicylate decreased P/O ratios in respiring mitochondrial preparations, and his results have been confirmed by other workers (Penniall, Kalnitsky & Routh, 1956; Bosund, 1957; Packer, Austen & Knoblock, 1959; Jeffrey & Smith, 1959; Kirpekar & Lewis, 1960). The exact site at which salicylates interfere with the coupled processes of phosphorylation and oxidation has not been unequivocally defined.

One possible mechanism is that salicylates increase the breakdown of adenosine triphosphate (ATP), and Falcone (1959) has shown that the drugs stimulate mitochondrial adenosine triphosphatase. Charnock and

Opit (1962) reported that this effect occurred in freshly prepared but not in aged mitochondria. They suggested that an enhanced permeability of the mitochondrial membrane to ATP in the presence of salicylate could explain this stimulation of the adenosine triphosphatase *in vitro* and that the mitochondrial membrane itself is the site of salicylate action.

However, salicylates may act on one or more of the sequence of phosphorylation reactions that occur subsequent to the electron transport chain. The individual steps in this sequence have not yet been characterized and both phosphorylated and non-phosphorylated high-energy intermediates have been postulated. The phosphorylations associated with the entire respiratory chain appear to be uncoupled by salicylates (Jeffrey & Smith, 1959; Charnock, Opit & Hetzel, 1962), but Penniall (1958) has produced evidence that the terminal phosphorylation step, concerned with the oxidation of cytochrome *c*, may be more sensitive to the action of salicylate.

The effects of the uncoupling action

The implications of an uncoupling action on more general aspects of tissue metabolism have received some attention. Smith and Jeffrey (1956) showed that salicylates decreased the content of creatine phosphate and ATP and increased the amount of inorganic phosphate in isolated rat diaphragm muscle. A number of ATP-dependent reactions, including glutamine synthesis in guinea-pig brain cells (Messer, 1958), the acetylation of *p*-aminobenzoate by ox-kidney slices (Koivusalo & Luukkainen, 1959), and the acetylation of choline by guinea-pig brain (Kuriaki & Marumo, 1959), have been reported to be inhibited by salicylates. Smith and Moses (1960) found that the drugs considerably reduced the incorporation of radioactivity from labelled acetate into the soluble metabolic intermediates of chopped preparations of rat tissues, and Moses and Smith (1960) reported that in yeast suspensions salicylates inhibited the incorporation of ^{14}C from labelled glucose into compounds such as uridine diphosphoglucose and trehalose, which need ATP for their synthesis. Thus a number of effects that may be directly ascribed to the uncoupling action of salicylates have been shown to occur in more highly organized tissues than mitochondrial suspensions.

A further example is the increased oxygen uptake induced by salicylate in isolated tissues and whole animals. This is a theoretically expected result of an uncoupling action since there should be an increased rate of oxidation of endogenous and exogenous substrates to compensate for the relative inefficiency of the phosphorylating mechanisms. Salicylates have been shown to increase the oxygen consumption of isolated tissues (Sproull, 1954), of tissues removed from animals injected with the drug (Brody, 1956), of whole animals (Meade, 1954), and of man (Cochran, 1952). The results of Tenney and Miller (1955) are of particular relevance because they showed that the principal site of the increased oxygen uptake in the dog was the peripheral tissues.

Another expected result of an uncoupling action is an increased heat production at the tissue level because the energy normally used for the conversion of inorganic phosphate to ATP will be dissipated in other forms, principally as heat. The hyperpyrexia that is a prominent symptom of salicylate poisoning, especially in children (Segar & Holliday, 1958), is explicable on this basis. An important contributory factor may be the development of a state of water deficiency due firstly to the loss of substantial amounts of sweat as a result of the peripheral mechanisms concerned with heat loss, and secondly because the fluid intake of the patients was inadequate to compensate for this water loss.

The possible relation between an uncoupling action and other *in vivo* metabolic effects of salicylates is less clear. The severe depletion of liver glycogen observed in intact animals given salicylate (Lutwak-Mann, 1942) may be explained, at least in part, by a diminished rate of glycogen synthesis from carbohydrate precursors resulting from a decreased production of ATP. Some experimental evidence in favour of this view is that the injection of salicylate prevents the incorporation of radio-carbon from labelled acetate into liver glycogen in the rat (Smith, 1959b). However, other mechanisms such as adrenal medullary stimulation (Smith, 1955) and a delayed rate of gastric emptying (Smith & Irving, 1955) may also be concerned. The mechanism of the hypoglycaemic effect of salicylate in diabetic animals and man (Ingle, 1950; Dell'Aquila & Angarano, 1954) remains obscure. Some authors (Manchester, Randle & Smith, 1958; Randle & Smith, 1958; Horiuchi, 1959; Seltzer, 1962) have reported that uncoupling reagents, including salicylates, stimulate the glucose uptake of isolated rat diaphragm preparations, but their results have not been confirmed in other laboratories (Segal, Blair & Weinberg, 1960; Huggins & Smith, 1962).

It has also been suggested that there may be a connexion between the uncoupling action and the anti-inflammatory effects of salicylates (cf. Smith, 1959a). However, the more powerful uncoupling reagent, 2:4-dinitrophenol (DNP), appears to be devoid of experimental anti-inflammatory activity on the erythema induced by ultraviolet light (Adams & Cobb, 1958) and on the increased capillary permeability due to passive cutaneous anaphylaxis in the guinea-pig (Marks, Smith & Cunliffe, 1961), whereas salicylate is active in both test systems.

The uncoupling action of salicylate may therefore cause both an important physiological effect, an increased oxygen consumption, and one of the more serious toxic symptoms of the drug, hyperthermia, but it does not appear to be directly implicated in the experimental anti-inflammatory activity of the salicylates. It has therefore become necessary to search for other major actions of the drugs on enzyme systems.

Inhibition of transaminases

One recent method of approach has been the use of ^{14}C-labelled metabolic intermediates, such as glucose, pyruvate, and succinate, in conjunction with chromatographic and radioautographic techniques, to study the patterns of intermediary metabolism in isolated animal tissues and subcellular fractions. The tissue preparations are incubated with salicylates and any interference with the transfer of radiocarbon may be detected, localized at the enzyme systems involved, and studied on the isolated enzyme system *in vitro*. Huggins, Smith and Moses (1961) found that salicylate, but not DNP, caused an increased incorporation of radioactivity from [3-^{14}C]pyruvate into glutamic acid in chopped preparations of rat kidney. This result suggested that salicylate exerted an effect on glutamate metabolism distinct from its uncoupling action, and it was shown that salicylate inhibited rat serum glutamic–pyruvic transaminase activity *in vitro*. With the exception of thiosalicylic acid, only those congeners of salicylate that contain a phenolic hydroxyl in the *ortho* position to a carboxyl group possessed inhibitory activity against the enzyme (Steggle, Huggins & Smith, 1961).

Later work (Huggins, Bryant & Smith, 1961; Huggins & Smith, unpublished data) has shown that salicylate inhibits glutamic–pyruvic and glutamic–oxaloacetic transaminase activities in extracts of rat tissues, liver, kidney, brain, and diaphragm muscle. Two problems currently being investigated are the mechanism of the inhibition and whether it extends to other tissue transaminases. Experiments in whole animals and in man (Manso, Taranta & Nydick, 1956; Janota et al., 1960) have shown that the administration of salicylates actually increases the activities of transaminase enzymes in the blood. No information is available about the effect of the salicylates on the corresponding tissue enzymes, but it has been suggested (Mitidieri & Affonso, 1959) that the uncoupling action of salicylate may affect the permeability of many tissues, leading to an increased flow of soluble enzyme proteins into the circulation.

Some indirect evidence that salicylates inhibit transaminase enzymes *in vivo* was provided by Smith and Moses (1961). They found changes in the distribution of radioactivity from [^{14}C]glucose in liver preparations, isolated from rats receiving single or repeated injections of salicylates, that were consistent with an interference with glutamic–pyruvic transaminase. However, the physiological and pharmacological implications of a general inhibitory action of salicylates on cellular transaminases remain to be explored. Such an action could interfere with the interconversion of many amino acids and possibly influence the continued production of peptide substances, such as the kinins, which may be implicated in the maintenance of inflammatory reactions. Some anti-inflammatory drugs, including steroids and chloroquine, are inactive against rat serum glutamic–pyruvic transaminase *in vitro* (Steggle & Smith, unpublished data), but phenylbutazone resembles salicylates in inhibiting the enzyme activity (Pulver, Exer & Herrman, 1956) and both drugs also inhibit the transamidase that synthesizes glucosamine-6-phosphate from fructose-6-phosphate and glutamine in rat liver and connective tissue (Bollet, 1961).

Inhibition of dehydrogenases

A further group of important cellular enzymes affected by salicylates are the dehydrogenases. von Euler and Ahlstrom (1943) found that salicylate inhibited glucose and lactic dehydrogenases, and Kaplan, Kennedy and Davis (1954) reported that the drug caused multiple effects on the oxidative enzymes of the tricarboxylic acid cycle in rat kidney and liver homogenates. The enzymes inhibited to the greatest extent appeared to be α-ketoglutaric dehydrogenase and succinic dehydrogenase, but some evidence of interference with acotinase, isocitric dehydrogenase, and malic dehydrogenase was also obtained. More recent work (Bryant & Smith, 1962) has been concerned with the effects of salicylate on the transfer of radiocarbon from $[1:4-{}^{14}C]$succinate around the tricarboxylic acid cycle. Salicylates caused accumulations of the ${}^{14}C$ in malic and citric acids, suggesting that the drugs interfered with the further metabolism of these acids. It was found that salicylates inhibited malic and isocitric dehydrogenases *in vitro* and that the mechanism of the inhibition involved competition with the appropriate coenzyme, diphosphopyridine or triphosphopyridine nucleotide (Bryant, Smith & Hines, 1963). von Euler and Ahlstrom (1943) reported a similar mechanism for lactic dehydrogenase because the inhibitory action of salicylates was reversed by cozymase.

One obvious implication of these results is that any dehydrogenase enzyme that needs a pyridine nucleotide as cofactor may be inhibited by salicylate, and a considerable number of important enzymes, including glutamic dehydrogenase, α-glycerophosphate dehydrogenase, and glucose-6-phosphate dehydrogenase, belong to this category. The inhibitory action of salicylates on dehydrogenases may be even more widespread because xanthine oxidase, which does not require a pyridine nucleotide as a coenzyme, is also inhibited by salicylates *in vitro* and *in vivo* (Lutwak-Mann, 1942; Bergel & Bray, 1956; Mitidieri & Affonso, 1959). Succinic dehydrogenase is a further possible example, but any reported inhibitory action of salicylates on the enzyme activity in biologically complex systems, such as homogenates, must be interpreted with caution as it may be secondary to an interference with malic dehydrogenase.

Conclusions

The work of the last few years has made it clear that salicylates exert inhibitory effects on at least three vital groups of cellular enzymes, those concerned with oxidative phosphorylation, the transaminases, and the dehydrogenases. The relation of these actions at the tissue level to the known pharmacological, clinical, and toxic effects of the drugs poses intriguing questions. It appears that the uncoupling action of salicylates may explain certain metabolic effects, such as the increased oxygen consumption, and some of the disturbances of carbohydrate metabolism, and that it may be the initial cause of one of the serious symptoms, hyperpyrexia, that occurs in salicylate poisoning in children. However, it does not seem to be directly related to the experimental anti-inflammatory action of the salicylates. The physiological and pharmacological implications of the inhibitory action of salicylates on transaminases and dehydrogenases are subjects for speculation and further experiment.

It would be surprising if such fundamental biochemical lesions were not reflected in quite a widespread manner in the whole animal. One possible example is the well-known phase of metabolic acidosis that succeeds the initial transient phase of respiratory alkalosis in salicylate intoxication. An acidosis of this nature could be caused by an increased entry of keto and hydroxy acids into the circulation as a result of a failure of the tissues to oxidize and transaminate these acids in the presence of salicylates. There is some tentative evidence in favour of this view, because Dell'Aquila and Angarano (1956) found that the administration of salicylates increased the blood pyruvate concentration in both normal and diabetic human subjects.

One of the fascinations for all workers in the salicylate field is that these relatively simple drugs never fail to surprise. Their unexpected range and variety of actions on intermediary metabolism and on enzyme systems provide an almost *embarras de richesse* for everyone interested in correlating events at the cellular level with physiological and pathological effects. This should provide both a stimulating and rewarding area of research for experimental scientists of many different disciplines for some years to come.

SUMMARY

Recent work on the effects of salicylates on intermediary metabolism has revealed that the drugs influence the activities of at least three important groups of enzymes. Their uncoupling action on oxidative phosphorylation processes in mitochondrial preparations is now well established, but the exact site at which they act has not yet been defined. It appears that such an uncoupling action may cause the increased oxygen consumption and hyperthermia observed after salicylate administration in man, but that it may not be directly related to the anti-inflammatory properties of the drugs.

Salicylates inhibit certain transaminase enzymes, but the mechanism of inhibition and the extent to which the numerous tissue transaminases are affected has not been elucidated. Dehydrogenases are also inhibited by salicylates and the nature of the inhibition, competition with the appropriate coenzyme, strongly suggests that the drugs may produce very widespread effects on these vital cellular enzymes. It is concluded that the study of these actions of salicylates and their physiological and pharmacological implications provides a stimulating and rewarding area of research.

The author is grateful to the Empire Rheumatism Council for their continued support and encouragement over many years, and in particular for their generosity in establishing a Research Unit on the effects of drugs on metabolism.

REFERENCES

Adams, S. S., & Cobb, R. (1958). *Nature (Lond.)*, **181**, 773.
Bergel, F., & Bray, R. C. (1956). *Nature (Lond.)*, **178**, 88.
Bollet, A. J. (1961). *Arthr. and Rheum.*, **4**, 624.
Bosund, I. (1957). *Acta chem. scand.*, **11**, 541.
Brody, T. M. (1956). *J. Pharmacol. exp. Ther.*, **117**, 39.
Bryant, C., & Smith, M. J. H. (1962). *Biochem. J.*, **84**, 67P.
Bryant, C., Smith, M. J. H., & Hines, W. J. W. (1963). *Biochem.J.*, **86**, 391
Charnock, J. S., & Opit, L. J. (1962). *Biochem. J.*, **83**, 596.
Charnock, J. S., Opit, L. J., & Hetzel, B. S. (1962). *Biochem. J.*, **83**, 602.
Cochran, J. B. (1952). *Brit. med. J.*, **ii**, 964.
Dell'Aquila, M. D., & Angarano, D. (1954). *Folia endocr. (Roma)*, **7**, 5.
Dell'Aquila, M. D., & Angarano, D. (1956). *Policlinico, Sez. med.*, **63**, 53.
von Euler, H., & Ahlstrom, L. (1943). *Hoppe-Seylers Z. physiol. Chem.*, **279**, 175.
Falcone, A. B. (1959). *J. clin. Invest.*, **38**, 1002.
Horiuchi, K. (1959). *J. Fac. Sci. (Tokyo Univ.)*, **8**, 505.
Huggins, A. K., Bryant, C., & Smith, M. J. H. (1961). *J. Pharm. Pharmacol.*, **13**, 654.
Huggins, A. K., & Smith, M. J. H. (1962). *Biochem. J.*, **85**, 394.
Huggins, A. K., Smith, M. J. H., & Moses, V. (1961). *Biochem.J.*, **79**, 271.
Ingle, D. J. (1950). *Proc. Soc. exp. Biol. (N.Y.)*, **75**, 673.
Janota, I., Wincey, C. W., Sandiford, M., & Smith, M. J. H. (1960). *Nature (Lond.)*, **185**, 935.
Jeffrey, S. W., & Smith, M. J. H. (1959). *Biochem. J.*, **72**, 462.
Kaplan, E. H., Kennedy, J., & Davis, J. (1954). *Arch. Biochem.*, **51**, 47.
Kirpekar, S. M., & Lewis, J. J. (1960). *Brit. J. Pharmacol.*, **15**, 175.
Koivusalo, M., & Luukkainen, T. (1959). *Acta physiol. scand.*, **45**, 283.
Kuriaki, K., & Marumo, H. (1959). *Jap. J. Pharmacol.*, **8**, 96.
Lutwak-Mann, C. (1942). *Biochem. J.*, **36**, 706.
Manchester, K. L., Randle, P. J., & Smith, G. H. (1958). *Brit. med. J.*, **i**, 1028.
Manso, C., Taranta, A., & Nydick, I. (1956). *Proc. Soc. exp. Biol. (N.Y.)*, **93**, 84.
Marks, V., Smith, M. J. H., & Cunliffe, A. C. (1961). *J. Pharm. Pharmacol.*, **13**, 218.

54   M. J. H. SMITH

Meade, B. W. (1954). *Ann. rheum. Dis.*, **13**, 60.
Messer, M. (1958). *Aust. J. exp. Biol. med. Sci.*, **36**, 65.
Mitidieri, E., & Affonso, O. R. (1959). *Nature (Lond.)*, **183**, 471.
Moses, V., & Smith, M. J. H. (1960). *Biochem. J.*, **76**, 585.
Packer, L., Austen, F. K., & Knoblock, E. C. (1959). *Proc. Soc. exp. Biol.*
    (N.Y.), **100**, 239.
Penniall, R. (1958). *Biochim. biophys. Acta (Amst.)*, **30**, 247.
Penniall, R., Kalnitsky, G., & Routh, J. I. (1956). *Arch. Biochem.*, **64**, 390.
Pulver, R., Exer, B., & Herrmann, B. (1956). *Schweiz. med. Wschr.*, **86**,
    1080.
Randle, P. J., & Smith, G. H. (1958). *Biochem. J.*, **70**, 490.
Segal, S., Blair, A., & Weinberg, A. (1960). *Metabolism*, **9**, 1033.
Segar, W. E., & Holliday, M. A. (1958). *New Engl. J. Med.*, **259**, 1191.
Seltzer, H. S. (1962). *J. clin. Invest.*, **41**, 289.
Smith, M. J. H. (1955). *Brit. J. Pharmacol.*, **10**, 110.
Smith, M. J. H. (1959a). *J. Pharm. Pharmacol.*, **11**, 705.
Smith, M. J. H. (1959b). *J. biol. Chem.*, **234**, 144.
Smith, M. J. H., & Irving, J. D. (1955). *Brit. J. Radiol.*, **28**, 39.
Smith, M. J. H., & Jeffrey, S. W. (1956). *Biochem. J.*, **64**, 589.
Smith, M. J. H., & Moses, V. (1960). *Biochem. J.*, **76**, 579.
Smith, M. J. H., & Moses, V. (1961). *Biochem. J.*, **79**, 275.
Sproull, D. H. (1954). *Brit. J. Pharmacol.*, **9**, 262.
Steggle, R. A., Huggins, A. K., & Smith, M. J. H. (1961). *Biochem.*
    Pharmacol., **7**, 151.
Tenney, S. M., & Miller, R. M. (1955). *Amer. J. Med.*, **19**, 498.

SOME EFFECTS OF SALICYLATES UPON CONNECTIVE TISSUE METABOLISM

M. W. Whitehouse

Department of Biochemistry
University of Oxford

' If by some magic solution one could dissolve all the connective tissues of the body, all that would remain would be a mass of slimy epithelium, quivering muscle, and frustrated nerve cells.'

Arcadi (1952)

THE object of these studies was to find out what action salicylates have on connective tissue that might explain the beneficial effects of these drugs in such conditions as rheumatic fever and arthritis. Connective tissues contain as characteristic constituents one or more sulphated mucopolysaccharides. The polysaccharide sulphate content varies from about 2–3 per cent of the dry weight of such tissues as heart valves and cornea to about 20–30 per cent of such tissues as cartilage. Investigations have been carried out to determine the effect of salicylates and chemically related compounds upon the biosynthesis of mucopolysaccharide sulphates by representative connective tissues in three different types of experiment.

Experimental procedures

Groups of four male rats weighing 150–200 g. were injected intra-peritoneally with 20–100 mg. per kg. of sodium salicylate or related compounds, simultaneously with 10 mc per kg. of sodium [^{35}S]sulphate. The animals were killed 24 hours later and their rib cages removed. Radioactive mucopolysaccharide [^{35}S]sulphates were isolated from the rib cartilage and the specific radioactivity of this fraction determined for each animal (Boström & Whitehouse, unpublished data).

In other experiments cartilage was induced to form from a non-cartilaginous tissue, chick embryonic somites, in tissue cultures to which salicylate was added. The formation and growth of such cartilage takes five days. This process was followed microscopically, and also radio-chemically by measuring the incorporation into chondroitin sulphate of ^{35}S from sodium [^{35}S]sulphate in the culture medium. The latter is synthesized by the cartilage, but not by the original somite tissue (Lash, Holtzer & Whitehouse, 1960).

Experiments to assess the short-term effect of these drugs were only of one to four hours duration. The experimental material was obtained immediately after slaughter from oxen ranging in age from two days to ten years, and consisted of tracheal, costal, and nasal cartilage slices cut mechanically to a thickness of o·5 mm.; of circular tissue sections punched out from cornea and semilunar heart valves; and of sliced tissues cut free-hand in various ways from knee articular cartilage and from atrioventricular heart valves. The tissue slices were incubated with radioactive substrates in a Krebs-Ringer type phosphate or tris (2-amino-2-hydroxymethylpropane-1:3-diol) buffer medium at pH 7·4, with and without sodium salicylate or its congeners added at concentrations in the range 5×10^{-5} to 5×10^{-3} M (Whitehouse & Boström, 1961, 1962; Whitehouse, unpublished data). The following metabolic processes were studied as indices of the biosynthetic and catabolic activities of the tissues:

(i) incorporation of radioactivity from [1-^{14}C]acetate, [^{14}C]glucose, and sodium [^{35}S]sulphate into the mucopolysaccharide sulphates subsequently isolated from the tissues after papain digestion (Scott, 1960);

(ii) oxidation to [^{14}C]carbon dioxide of [1-^{14}C]octanoate, [^{14}C]glucose, [1-^{14}C]acetate, [2-^{14}C]pyruvate, and [1-^{14}C]lactate;

(iii) uptake and incorporation of sodium [^{32}P]phosphate into various organic polyphosphate fractions extracted from the tissues. These were separated by precipitation at pH 9·2, and then partially fractionated by precipitation with organic bases such as Rivanol (2:5-diamino-7-ethoxyacridine lactate) or mepacrine.

Only the biosynthesis of mucopolysaccharide sulphates was studied with cornea; this is primarily a biochemical activity of the corneal stroma, not shared with corneal epithelium and endothelium.

Salicylate and its analogues were also tested for their effects upon the hydrolysis of adenosine triphosphate (ATP) by rat liver mitochondria (Charnock & Opit, 1962), and upon phosphorylation coupled to succinate oxidation in rat liver mitochondria (Charnock, Opit & Hetzel, 1962).

Experimental results

The experiments in whole animals clearly showed that 100 mg. per kg. of sodium salicylate inhibited the incorporation of ^{35}S into cartilage polysaccharide sulphates *in vivo*. The same dose of sodium benzoate or 4-hydroxybenzoate had no effect. 2:4-Dinitrophenol, 20 mg. per kg., which is a potent uncoupler of oxidative phosphorylation in brain, kidney, liver, and heart muscle, also inhibited ^{35}S incorporation. Its structural isomer, 2:5-dinitrophenol, which does not uncouple oxidative phosphorylation in liver mitochondria at a concentration of o·05 mM, had much less effect upon ^{35}S incorporation into rib cartilage. The results showed that salicylate affected some aspect of cartilage metabolism in the whole animal, but it was not clear whether salicylate depressed the turnover of a pre-formed cartilage constituent or whether it inhibited the biosynthesis of cartilage mucopolysaccharide sulphates.

The tissue culture experiments established that potassium salicylate, at concentrations of 5 mM and greater, inhibited both the formation of cartilage tissue *de novo* and the biosynthesis of the constituent mucopolysaccharide sulphates. Cartilage biogenesis was not affected when potassium benzoate, potassium thiosalicylate, or phenol were present in the culture medium at the same concentration (Whitehouse & Lash, 1961). Cortisone and other anti-inflammatory steroids also inhibited cartilage biogenesis *in vitro* when present in the medium at rather lower concentrations, 0·1 mM. These experiments showed that both corticosteroids and salicylates could each independently influence the growth of this particular type of connective tissue. They offered no support for those theories that attribute the antirheumatic activity of salicylates solely to their ability to stimulate either the pituitary or the adrenal cortex (Needleman, 1961).

The short-term experiments with tissue slices fully confirmed these findings. Salicylates depress the *in vitro* biosynthetic activities of heart valves, cornea, and all four types of cartilage used in these experiments. Corticosteroids also depress cartilage and cornea metabolism. The results of these experiments are fully discussed elsewhere (Whitehouse & Boström, 1962; Boström, Moretti & Whitehouse, 1963), but the following conclusions may be drawn:

(i) The action of salicylate is reversible. Tissues pre-incubated with these drugs for periods up to three hours at 37° C and then transferred to a fresh medium containing no salicylate incorporated [^{14}C]glucose and [^{35}S]sulphate into the tissue polysaccharide sulphates to the same extent as tissues pre-incubated without salicylate. Charnock, Opit and Hetzel (1962) reported that salicylate had no irreversible effect upon oxidative phosphorylation by rat liver mitochondria.

(ii) The drug action is rapid. Mucopolysaccharide biosynthesis was significantly depressed within 20 minutes of adding the drugs to the incubation medium.

(iii) The concentration of salicylate required to inhibit the incorporation of each of radioactive glucose, acetate, and sulphate by at least 20 per cent is 2 mM, which is close to the plasma salicylate level necessary for effective therapy in rheumatic fever, 20–30 mg. per 100 ml. This is also the concentration at which SMITH has shown that salicylate is a potent uncoupler of oxidative phosphorylation in rat liver and ox heart mitochondria.

(iv) Even at 5 mM concentration salicylate did not inhibit the oxidation of glucose, acetate, pyruvate, or octanoate by the tissue slices. The yield of radioactive carbon dioxide after incubation with [2-^{14}C]pyruvate or

3*

[1-^{14}C]octanoate was even increased by 4 mM salicylate. 2:4-Dinitro-phenol, 0·05 mM, also stimulated the oxidation of these substrates by cartilage slices.

(v) Salicylate inhibited both the uptake of sulphate ions by the tissues and the utilization of the intracellular sulphate (Whitehouse & Boström, 1961). It also inhibited both the uptake of phosphate ions and the incorporation of the intracellular phosphate into organic phosphates. 2:4-Dinitrophenol likewise inhibited the uptake and incorporation of inorganic sulphate and phosphate.

(vi) These general effects were independent of the magnesium ion content of the medium.

Implications

Oxidative phosphorylation in connective tissues. The simplest explana-tion of these various phenomena is that salicylate uncouples oxidative phosphorylation within such tissues as cartilage, cornea, and heart valves. The process termed oxidative phosphorylation couples the principal energy-yielding oxidative reactions of animal cells to an energy-harnessing reaction, namely the phosphorylation of AMP and ADP. If the interrelationship between these two chemical activities is dislocated or uncoupled, then many dependent endergonic processes within the cells or within tissues maintained by the cells' activities would be severely impaired. These would include ion transport and tissue biosynthesis. It is not difficult to see how tissue swelling and the inflammatory response might also be retarded by salicylates if these processes are indeed energy-consuming and normally derive their energy from the hydrolysis of high-energy nucleoside di- and tri-phosphates synthesized by the fibroblasts and other mesenchymal cells.

These arguments hinge on the assumption that oxidative phosphoryla-tion does occur in the connective tissue cells and that it has the same characteristics as in mitochondria, including its sensitivity to salicylates. Some experimental support for this assumption has been obtained. The incorporation of inorganic phosphate into organic phosphates by connective tissue slices was dependent upon cellular oxidation and respiration. It was inhibited by carrying out incubation in an atmosphere of nitrogen or in the presence of 1 mM iodoacetate. Furthermore, the stimulation of cellular oxidation by connective tissues with 2:4-dinitro-phenol and sodium salicylate parallels the known actions of these two drugs upon phosphorylating preparations of liver and heart mito-chondria. Their respective isomers, 2:5-dinitrophenol and 4-hydroxy-benzoate, which have no effect on mitochondrial respiration since they do not uncouple oxidative phosphorylation, did not stimulate oxidative metabolism in cartilage.

Relationship of structure to activity. The effect of several other salicylate congeners upon cartilage and corneal metabolism paralleled their effect upon oxidative phosphorylation and respiration of rat liver mitochondria. A number of salicylate analogues were considerably more potent than salicylic acid as uncouplers of oxidative phosphorylation in mitochondria, as stimulators of liver mitochondrial adenosine triphosphatase, and in their effect upon the metabolism of cartilage, cornea, and heart valves. These congeners are characterized by two properties: they are more lipophilic than the salicylate ion at pH 7·4; and, like salicylic acid, they can form complexes with a number of metal ions, notably ferric and cuprous ions, in non-aqueous media (Whitehouse, 1962).

We can see how truly marginal is the activity of salicylic acid as an uncoupling agent by comparing it with its amide and with its 5-hydroxy derivative, gentisic acid. Both these compounds are virtually inactive towards oxidative phosphorylation in liver mitochondria (Brody, 1956) and towards oxidation, phosphorylation, and mucopolysaccharide biosynthesis in cartilage. Gentisate has been reported to be effective for treating rheumatic fever (Meyer & Ragan, 1948), but its usefulness as a drug for rheumatoid arthritis has been questioned (Rosenberg, Krevsky & Kagan, 1952). All attempts to demonstrate an unequivocal salicylate-like effect of gentisate upon the metabolism of ox heart valves have so far been quite unsuccessful. More lipophilic analogues of salicylamide and gentisate, such as salicylanilide and gentisaldehyde, were found to be moderately potent drugs *in vitro*. These findings certainly indicate that the presence of an ionized carboxyl group is not essential for conferring uncoupling activity upon salicylate analogues. Furthermore, there is apparently no simple relationship between potency as an uncoupling agent and the carboxylic acid dissociation constants of salicylic acid, pK_a 3·95, its inactive analogues 4-hydroxybenzoic acid, pK_a 5·66, and gentisic acid, pK_a 3·95, and several congeners and their inactive isomers, such as 2-hydroxynaphth-3-oic acid, pK_a 3·57, 2-hydroxynaphth-6-oic acid, pK_a 5·92 (inactive), and 5-phenylsalicylic acid, pK_a 3·91. These pK_a values are for solutions, determined by potentiometric titration with sodium hydroxide in 50 per cent (v/v) aqueous ethanol, to permit strict comparison between salicylic acid and its less water-soluble derivatives.

Only a few discrepancies were noted between the relative effect of a compound upon cartilage or corneal metabolism and upon oxidative phosphorylation in liver mitochondria. However, one of these is of especial interest, O-acetylphenyl salicylate, indicating that acetylsalicylic acid itself may not have any direct effect upon isolated connective tissues and that an unsubstituted phenolic group is the prime determinant of drug action. Many other phenols, such as pentachlorphenol and 2:4-dinitrophenol, are known to be powerful uncouplers of oxidative phosphorylation, but few if any simple aromatic acids are uncouplers; thus 2-methoxybenzoic acid is not an uncoupling agent and has no effect upon cartilage metabolism at a concentration of 4 mM. The acid dissociation constants of certain *ortho* substituted benzoic acids are certainly much higher than that of salicylic acid, e.g. acetylsalicylic acid, pK_a 5·1, and 2-methoxybenzoic acid, pK_a 5·6.

o-Hydroxyaldehydes were more potent than the corresponding acids in their effects upon the connective tissues, but not towards oxidative phosphorylation in liver mitochondria or in stimulating liver mitochondria. This was not due solely to rapid and complete oxidation of the aldehydes by the liver mitochondria; rather it suggests that these aldehydes pass more readily than the acids across the outer cell membranes into the tissue slices. *p*-Hydroxyaldehydes did not affect either mitochondrial or tissue slice metabolism.

Other possible effects of salicylate. So far I have discussed how salicylates might influence the activity and reactivity of connective tissue by cutting off part of the normal energy supply available to cells in these tissues derived from cellular oxidation. From the viewpoint of tissue biodynamics this may well be the most important property of salicylates, but there is at least one other possible effect of salicylates upon the connective tissues. Mucopolysaccharide biosynthesis may be governed by the supply of glutamine, which provides the amino group for the constituent amino sugars, glucosamine and galactosamine. Bryant and Smith (1962) have demonstrated that glutamine synthesis by liver preparations is depressed by salicylate and also by other anti-inflammatory drugs. It appears that the connective tissues are not entirely self-sufficient in being able to supply their own glutamine requirement. Under certain conditions exogenous glutamine greatly stimulates mucopolysaccharide biosynthesis in such tissues as cartilage, cornea, and nucleus pulposus (Rodén, 1956). The principal source of this glutamine in the whole animal would be the liver. If the supply of glutamine became the 'pacemaker', then any impairment of hepatic biosynthesis by salicylates might depress at least one biosynthetic process in extrahepatic tissues. Bollet (1961) has reported that salicylates inhibit glucosamine biosynthesis from glucose-6-phosphate and glutamine by granuloma tissue.

We begin to perceive what far-reaching consequences these modest events might entail when we consider that mucopolysaccharides, including hyaluronic acid, are being continuously turned over, even in such seemingly inert tissues as tendons and cartilage. Being polyanions, these polysaccharides can function as natural cation exchangers and so might profoundly influence the retention or movement of cations and their associated water, not only within but also through the tissues. There is some evidence that these acidic mucopolysaccharides influence the orientation and deposition of collagen-like proteins in the connective tissues. Thus any action of salicylates which inhibits mucopolysaccharide biosynthesis might reduce the movement of fluids, tissue swelling, and scar tissue formation elicited by the inflammatory stimulus. These two actions of salicylates may be more closely related than might seem to be the case at first sight. Glutamine synthesis is coupled to the availability of ATP, which in turn is dependent upon oxidative phosphorylation.

SUMMARY

Studies *in vitro* and *in vivo* have shown that salicylates depress the biosynthesis of mucopolysaccharide sulphates in representative connective tissues, cartilage, heart valves, and cornea. The oxidation of several ^{14}C-labelled substrates is not affected by salicylates at concentrations that depress the incorporation of *ortho* phosphate into organic phosphates within these tissues. It is concluded that the prime action of salicylates upon these tissues, which would explain their anti-inflammatory properties, is the uncoupling of oxidative phosphorylation. Some other effects of salicylate are discussed, which might consequently inhibit mucopolysaccharide biosynthesis.

Several compounds related to salicylates are more active than salicylic acid in their effects *in vitro* upon the metabolism of connective tissues and upon oxidative phosphorylation by liver mitochondria. The phenolic group and lipid solubility primarily determine these *in vitro* effects.

REFERENCES

A[rcadi], J. A. (1952). *Bull. Johns Hopk. Hosp.*, **90**, 334.
Bollet, A. J. (1961). *Arthr. and Rheum.*, **4**, 624.
Boström, H., Moretti, A., & Whitehouse, M. W. (1963). *Biochim. biophys. Acta (Amst.)*, in press.
Brody, T. M. (1956). *J. Pharmacol. exp. Ther.*, **117**, 39.
Bryant, C., & Smith, M. J. H. (1962). *J. Pharm. Pharmacol.*, **14**, 182.
Charnock, J. S., & Opit, L. A. (1962). *Biochem. J.*, **83**, 596.
Charnock, J. S., Opit, L. A., & Hetzel, B. S. (1962). *Biochem. J.*, **83**, 602.
Lash, J. W., Holtzer, H., & Whitehouse, M. W. (1960). *Develop. Biol.*, **2**, 76.
Meyer, K., & Ragan, C. (1948). *Science*, **108**, 281.
Needleman, P. (1961). *Amer. J. Pharm.*, **133**, 219.
Rodén, L. (1956). *Ark. Kemi*, **10**, 333.
Rosenberg, E. F., Krevsky, D. A., & Kagan, B. M. (1952). *Ann. intern. Med.*, **36**, 1513.
Scott, J. E. (1960). *Meth. biochem. Anal.*, **8**, 145.
Whitehouse, M. W. (1962). *Nature (Lond.)*, **194**, 984.
Whitehouse, M. W., & Boström, H. (1961). *Biochem. Pharmacol.*, **7**, 135.
Whitehouse, M. W., & Boström, H. (1962). *Biochem. Pharmacol.*, **11**, 1175.
Whitehouse, M. W., & Lash, J. W. (1961). *Nature (Lond.)*, **189**, 37.

DISCUSSION

FRANK DICKENS (*Courtauld Institute of Biochemistry, Middlesex Hospital Medical School, London*):

These two papers, which are of very great importance, might almost have been expressly designed to bring out the conflict in interpretation in terms of the possible relation between therapeutic action and the metabolic findings. Perhaps this is some excuse for a non-salicylate biochemist to make some comment on the rather complex situation as it appears to outside observers. Certain interactions of salicylate in metabolic reactions we can accept as being common ground, particularly the uncoupling of oxidative phosphorylation processes, the inhibition of various biosynthetic mechanisms, especially of mucopolysaccharide sulphate synthesis, and the inhibition of glutamic–pyruvic transaminase activity that SMITH has demonstrated, as well as the inhibition of pyridine nucleotide dehydrogenases. There are also a number of miscellaneous effects not so easy to specify, some of which will be dealt with later.

In considering the relationship of these metabolic actions to the anti-inflammatory and other effects of any given drug, we ought to have certain requirements fulfilled. It may be impossible to do this, but they should be borne in mind. In the first place the effect should be produced by therapeutic rather than by toxic doses of the drug, and all the work reported today complies with that, dealing with about 2 mM concentrations of salicylate, which correspond roughly with 25 mg. per 100 ml. in the blood.

Secondly, other anti-inflammatory drugs, even perhaps those of different chemical types, ought also to be found to reproduce the metabolic effect. This is a more difficult criterion to fulfil. For example, in the case of oxidative phosphorylation, while salicylate and the 2:6-dihydroxybenzoic acid both have been reported to have anti-inflammatory properties, the latter acid does not uncouple phosphorylation. It would be interesting to test these borderline substances in WHITEHOUSE's system to see whether correlation with the uncoupling mechanism applies to this chemically closely similar substance which does not uncouple. SMITH and his group found in extensive studies that in general they were unable to bring forward a common type of metabolic reaction, as judged by the distribution of metabolites in tissues treated with a group of chemically unrelated anti-inflammatory drugs. Nevertheless, this is always subject to further studies which eventually may reveal a common point of attack.

The third criterion is that drugs that produce similar metabolic effects to those that are claimed to be basic to the action should also be anti-inflammatory. I realize that there may be conditions where the drug does not in fact reach the inflamed tissues, but by and large, for instance in the case of uncoupling as a basis of the mechanism, one may reasonably enquire why a powerful uncoupling agent like dinitrophenol has been reported to have no effect on inflammatory reactions. There may be some reason, but it is a question that we should legitimately ask.

ANDERSON: In a recent paper WHITEHOUSE suggested that the chelating properties of salicylate derivatives with iron might be more important than their uncoupling effects. To which view does he subscribe, the one he put forward today or that postulated in *Nature*?

WHITEHOUSE: I did not actually make the claim, I merely said that this was a property with which you could correlate biological activity. Nobody has yet explained why salicylate is an uncoupler, whether it is due to the metal ion binding or not.

VAN CAUWENBERGE: Sodium salicylate affects connective tissues *in vivo* by decreasing the formation of insoluble collagen. This effect of salicylate is much greater than that of either ACTH or cortisone (Lapière, C. M., & van Cauwenberge, H. [1960]. *J. belge Méd. phys. Rhum.*, **15**, 62).

CALABRO: The administration of 4·5 g. of aspirin daily produced a 46–64 per cent decrease in the excretion of urinary hydroxyproline in three patients with Paget's disease (Dull, T. A., & Henneman, P. H. [1962]. *Arthr. and Rheum.*, **5**, 294). This finding suggests that salicylates may affect collagen metabolism in Paget's disease.

J. E. SCOTT: The observations of Brown, Consden and Glynn ([1958]. *Ann. rheum. Dis.*, **17**, 196) suggest that salicylate has a moderately specific and quite marked effect on collagen whereby the stability and resistance to proteolytic digestion is much reduced.

Has WHITEHOUSE any information on the possible products that might be obtained when the antirheumatic compounds he mentioned are incubated in the way he described? I believe that many representatives of the classes of compounds he described are sulphated, glucuronidated, and acetylated by enzyme systems distributed throughout the body, particularly in the liver. If this were so, in these experiments the effect would be to divert the building blocks of polysaccharide synthesis into an unproductive side channel.

HUGGINS: Has WHITEHOUSE any information about the effects of 2:6-dihydroxybenzoic acid on adenosine triphosphatase activity? There does appear to be some uniformity amongst salicylate congeners with respect to their inhibitory activity against transaminases and dehydrogenases.

WHITEHOUSE: I have no data on the latter point.

I think SCOTT's criticism is very valid, but I doubt whether it could affect phosphate metabolism.

G. CUMMING: Has SMITH done any chromatographic studies on serum obtained from salicylate-intoxicated patients to see if there are increased amounts of organic acids present?

M. J. H. Smith: No. We are doing some experiments on rats poisoned with various doses of salicylates to see if the tissue levels of organic and amino acids are altered in the presence of the drugs, and also to measure the effects of salicylate administration on the activities of the tissue transaminases and dehydrogenases.

The relation between uncoupling and clinical activity

Anderson: Is there any evidence that salicylate derivatives that do not uncouple oxidative phosphorylation processes have any effect on rheumatoid conditions?

M. J. H. Smith (*Chairman*): This is a point of very considerable importance to all those experimental workers who attempt to correlate the biochemical, physiological, or pharmacological properties of drugs with their clinical actions. It is exceedingly difficult to find any reliable written information about the clinical status of salicylate derivatives. One hears plenty of verbal opinions but not much is committed to paper and early workers such as Stockman ([1913]. *Brit. med. J.*, **i**, 597) have to be consulted. There is a definite need for a series of small but carefully controlled clinical trials on a number of salicylate derivatives, particularly those that have pronounced effects on biochemical parameters.

Bywaters: I am sure that some more clinical testing of these drugs should be done. Useful therapeutic effects have been claimed for gentisic acid, which we have found to be quite useless; we also studied γ-resorcylic acid and found that it had little effect. This sort of thing happens very often, and if you find that drugs have little or no effect you do not trouble to publish anything about it.

Duthie: We were involved in the same trials as Bywaters and confirmed that γ-resorcylic acid is not an active drug in rheumatism.

Consden: There may be a reason why drugs such as gentisic acid are claimed to be effective clinically. Many samples contain salicylate, possibly as much as 10 per cent; thus a patient receiving 10–20 g. of this impure gentisic acid would also be getting a therapeutic dose of salicylate.

Whitehouse: Biochemical mechanisms are known whereby dihydroxyphenols may be dehydroxylated *in vitro*. Is it possible that in the whole animal the dihydroxybenzoates may be converted to salicylate?

Austen: An important consideration is that the salicylate congeners are not necessarily handled in the same way. It is difficult to obtain adequate blood levels with gentisic and γ-resorcylic acids. For example, the administration of 20–30 g. of gentisic acid will not produce blood levels comparable with those achieved with 6–7 g. of salicylate.

SALICYLATES AND CLINICAL DIABETES, AND REMARKS ON OTHER ENDOCRINE EFFECTS

J. M. STOWERS

Department of Materia Medica and Therapeutics
University of Aberdeen

SALICYLATES were among the earliest chemical compounds to be used to lower the blood sugar of diabetics, and were fairly widely employed in Germany towards the end of the nineteenth century (Ebstein, 1876; Bartels, 1878), and to a small extent in Britain at the turn of the century (Williamson, 1901). The doses of sodium salicylate given were as large as 10–12 g. daily, and it is therefore not surprising that many side effects were produced, including vomiting, which sometimes precipitated diabetic ketosis. Ketosis before the advent of insulin could seldom be reversed, so that such fatalities naturally discouraged the use of salicylates for the treatment of all but the milder degrees of diabetes. Yet in 1957 Reid and his colleagues showed that aspirin, in a dose of about 6 g. daily, could gradually but significantly reduce moderate ketonuria in diabetic patients.

The effects of salicylate on the blood sugar

The actions of salicylate on carbohydrate metabolism are complex because several sites of action appear to be involved, some tending to lower the blood sugar and others to raise it, the net result depending mainly on the blood salicylate level and the height of the initial blood sugar. Diabetic blood sugar levels, although not normal ones (Morris & Graham, 1931), tend to fall with serum salicylate levels up to about 40 mg. per 100 ml. This fall is probably due to an increased uptake of glucose in peripheral tissues, mainly muscle, for there is some evidence that the capillary-venous blood sugar differences can be increased in human diabetics (Fig.; Stowers, Constable & Hunter, 1959), and Manchester, Randle and Smith (1958) have demonstrated an increased glucose uptake by normal rat diaphragm *in vitro* in the presence of concentrations of sodium salicylate about double those attained in human therapy. This hypoglycaemic effect does not appear to depend on insulin since it is slower in onset, is seen in severely diabetic animals and men rather than in non-diabetics (Gilgore & Rupp, 1961), and is not associated with any measurable change in insulin sensitivity (Hecht & Goldner, 1959). Furthermore, salicylate-induced hypoglycaemia differs strikingly from that induced by insulin in its association with protein catabolism and loss of intracellular potassium (Manchester, Randle & Smith, 1958).

Several mechanisms tend to raise the blood sugar. Smith (1954), for instance, showed in rats that salicylate appeared to increase the speed of absorption of glucose from the gut, although Hecht and Goldner (1959) did not confirm this in man, nor was I able to in my own studies. Toxic levels of salicylate seem to reduce the aerobic metabolism of glucose by inhibition of at least two steps in the tricarboxylic acid cycle, namely the conversion of α-ketoglutarate to succinate and of succinate to fumarate

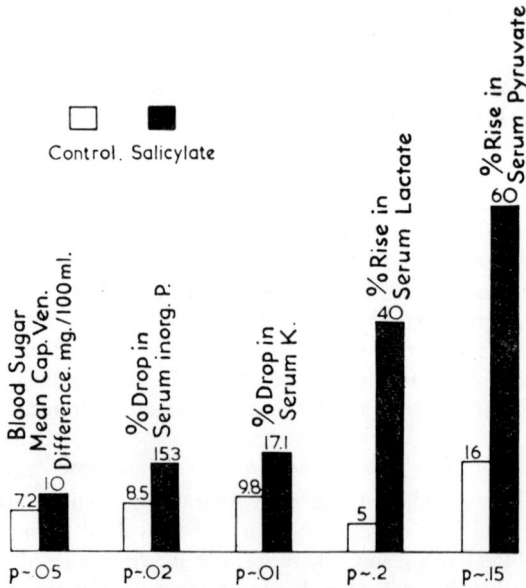

EFFECT OF SALICYLATE ON CERTAIN BIOCHEMICAL PARAMETERS IN THE BLOOD DURING ORAL GLUCOSE TOLERANCE TESTS

Mean values from eleven patients with mild diabetes after 50 g. of glucose orally (control), and on another occasion when 3 g. of calcium aspirin was given orally three hours before the glucose (salicylate).

Reproduced by permission of the Editor in Chief, *Annals of the New York Academy of Sciences.*

(Kaplan, Kennedy & Davis, 1954). A factor contributing to the hyperglycaemia induced by toxic doses of salicylate in normal animals (Barbour & Herrmann, 1921; Sproull, 1954; Smith, 1955) and man (Charters, 1944) may be the increased glucose-6-phosphatase activity demonstrable in the liver (Andrews, 1961), such as occurs in untreated alloxan-diabetic rats. This mechanism would help to explain the glycogenolytic effect of salicylate in normal (Lutwak-Mann, 1942) but not in diabetic animals (Smith, Meade & Bornstein, 1952), but the glycogenolysis may occur without a rise in the blood sugar. Another factor contributing to the hyperglycaemia induced by toxic doses of salicylate in normal subjects is the increased adrenal cortical activity shown in such conditions (Done, Ely & Kelley, 1954).

Diagnostic problems associated with salicylate administration

In acute salicylism there are reasons other than the hyperglycaemia for simulating a diagnosis of diabetic ketosis. In both there tends to be air-hunger, vomiting, dehydration and polyuria, a low serum bicarbonate level, and a strongly positive ferric chloride reaction by the urine. In salicylism, too, reducing substances may be found in the urine (Leas, 1926). These are mainly salicyl glucuronide and small amounts of gentisic acid and ascorbic acid; the excretion of the latter is increased by salicylates (Daniels & Everson, 1936). There may be sufficient hyperglycaemia to produce true glycosuria as well. The differential diagnosis between salicylism and diabetic ketosis may be made on a clinical level by the frequency of tinnitus, muscular irritability, and petechiae in salicylism, and the greater degree of dehydration that occurs in diabetic ketosis (Cohen, 1956). Simple tests will settle the diagnosis, for in salicylism the ferric chloride reaction of the urine is unaffected by boiling, Rothera's nitroprusside test is at most only weakly positive and, of course, the serum salicylate level is high.

More chronic salicylism may induce a Cushingoid appearance in certain patients (Cochran, Watson & Reid, 1950), but with none of the typical biochemical features of Cushing's syndrome, although in both there may be some fluid retention, abnormal glucose tolerance, and a negative nitrogen balance. In salicylism there may be a respiratory alkalosis and in Cushing's syndrome a metabolic alkalosis. Cochran's case was a 13-year-old boy with rheumatic fever receiving up to 5 g. daily of sodium salicylate. The urinary 17-ketosteroid excretion was normal. With the development of better methods of assessing adrenal cortical function it was shown that therapeutic levels of salicylate did not increase the plasma level of cortisol or the urinary excretion of corticoids (Peterson, Black and Bunim, 1958). Furthermore, the anti-inflammatory response to salicylate has been shown to be independent of the adrenals. Toxic doses of salicylate, on the other hand, are associated with evidence of increased adrenal cortical activity (Done, Ely & Kelley, 1954). When a more detailed comparison is made between the effects of cortisone and salicylate more differences emerge. Thus salicylate tends to reduce liver glycogen (Lutwak-Mann, 1942), and cortisone raises it. Salicylate, too, can reduce hyperglycaemia induced by cortisone (Smith, 1952).

The mechanism of salicylate-induced hypoglycaemia

Salicylate may reduce the raised blood sugar of some, but apparently not all, human diabetics, both of the maturity-onset and juvenile types.

The fasting blood sugar is more affected than the postprandial ones. From this two conclusions can be drawn. Firstly, that salicylate must depress gluconeogenesis or glycogenolysis, which are the sources of the fasting blood sugar; secondly, in the human at least, that there is no significant depression of the rate of glucose absorption from the intestine. Plasma levels of salicylate as low as 6–10 mg. per 100 ml. may effectively reduce hyperglycaemia.

Uncertainty remains concerning the mechanism of the hypoglycaemic action of salicylate in human diabetics, and various mechanisms have to be considered. One such suggested mechanism is the well-known metabolic stimulant action of salicylate, which appears to be correlated with its ability to uncouple oxidative phosphorylation (Brody, 1956). If the basal metabolic rate (BMR) is raised, it might be expected that the hyperglycaemia would tend to fall in proportion. If this is so then 2:4-dinitrophenol, which is also a metabolic stimulant and an uncoupler of oxidative phosphorylation, should lower the raised blood sugar in a manner parallel to that of salicylate. In fact Reid (1958) found that 2:4-dinitrophenol in equivalent dosage had significantly less hypoglycaemic action than salicylate when given to human diabetics; the BMR-raising effect was also less. I have found also that the hypoglycaemic effect and the metabolic stimulant effect of salicylate can be dissociated. In one diabetic patient, for instance, salicylate produced a hypoglycaemic effect and nearly a doubling of the BMR; when the BMR was measured again after two weeks continuous salicylate treatment, it had returned almost to its control level, although the hypoglycaemic effect was more marked than ever. A similar dissociation between these two effects of salicylate has been reported by Gilgore (1960).

It might be possible to explain some lowering of the blood sugar by haemodilution, for it has long been known that salicylate tends to expand the plasma volume (Barbour, 1926). In one diabetic patient we measured an expansion of plasma volume of about 15 per cent during, as compared with before, salicylate therapy. Such a mechanism, however, is quantitatively inadequate to account for the fall in blood sugar that salicylate may induce.

It is not possible to explain the hypoglycaemic effect on the basis of reduced dietary intake because salicylate treatment does not usually produce weight reduction and, in any event, it is the fasting blood sugar that tends to fall most. If the work of Smith, Meade & Bornstein (1952) on diabetic rats can be applied to the human diabetic, salicylate-induced hypoglycaemia cannot be accounted for by changes in liver glycogen, for in the diabetic rat no such changes occurred, and in any case a long-term hypoglycaemic effect could not be explained by a change in distribution of carbohydrate that could have only a transient effect on blood sugar. Evidence at present available suggests that the main hypoglycaemic action of salicylate is to increase glucose uptake in the periphery independent of insulin, although some insulin appears to be necessary to prevent diabetic ketosis.

The hypoglycaemic action of salicylate is quite different from that of the sulphonylureas, which depend mainly on stimulation of the secretion of endogenous insulin. It is therefore theoretically plausible that the hypoglycaemic action of these two drugs should be additive. This has been shown to be so. Such a synergism may be explained in part in two different ways. Firstly, it can be shown that salicylate reduces the renal clearance of chlorpropamide, and *vice versa*; thus the administration of one drug increases the plasma level of the other one given concurrently (Stowers, Constable & Hunter, 1959). It may be supposed that these two drugs compete for the same tubular secretion mechanism in the kidney. Secondly, Wishinsky, Glasser and Perkal (1962) have shown that salicylates reduce the protein binding of the sulphonylurea drugs in the plasma, thus releasing a greater proportion of the active drug in the blood stream. In many respects the hypoglycaemic action of the salicylates simulates that of the biguanides. For instance, both raise the serum lactate level (Fig.). It would appear from the few cases studied that their individual hypoglycaemic effects are not additive, and there is no justification for the use of these two oral hypoglycaemic agents together.

SUMMARY

Salicylates were among the earliest oral hypoglycaemic drugs to be used. They may lower or raise the blood sugar, depending on the dose and the height of the initial blood sugar, and they affect the metabolism of carbohydrate in a number of different ways. The hypoglycaemic action is independent of insulin, and differs from that of insulin. The differential diagnosis between diabetic ketosis and acute salicylism is considered. Chronic salicylism may occasionally induce a Cushingoid appearance, but there is evidence that this is not due to adrenal cortical overactivity; however, the latter may be present in acute salicylism.

Salicylates may reduce the blood sugar of both maturity-onset and juvenile type diabetics, the fasting blood sugar being more affected than postprandial levels. The hypoglycaemic action of salicylate is apparently independent of its metabolic stimulant effect and cannot satisfactorily be explained by haemodilution or changes in liver glycogen. The main action appears to depend on an increased uptake of glucose in the peripheral tissues, especially muscle. There is a synergism between the hypoglycaemic actions of salicylate and the sulphonylureas, the mechanism of which is considered. There is apparently no such synergism between the hypoglycaemic action of salicylate and the biguanides.

Some of the work mentioned in this paper was done during the tenure of a grant from the Scottish Hospital Endowments Research Trust.

REFERENCES

Andrews, M. M. (1961). *Metabolism*, **10**, 678.
Barbour, H. G. (1926). *J. Pharmacol. exp. Ther.*, **29**, 427.
Barbour, H. G., & Herrmann, J. B. (1921). *J. Pharmacol. exp. Ther.*, **18**, 165.
Bartels, K. (1878). *Dtsch. med. Wschr.*, **4**, 423.
Brody, T. M. (1956). *J. Pharmacol. exp. Ther.*, **117**, 39.
Charters, A. D. (1944). *Brit. med. J.*, **i**, 10.
Cochran, J. B., Watson, R. D., & Reid, J. (1950). *Brit. med. J.*, **ii**, 1411.
Cohen, A. S. (1956). *New Engl. J. Med.*, **254**, 457.
Daniels, A. L., & Everson, G. J. (1936). *Proc. Soc. exp. Biol. (N.Y.)*, **35**, 20.
Done, A. K., Ely, R. S., & Kelley, V. C. (1954). *J. Pediat.*, **44**, 153.
Ebstein, W. (1876). *Berl. klin. Wschr.*, **13**, 337.
Gilgore, S. G. (1960). *Diabetes*, **9**, 392.
Gilgore, S. G., & Rupp, J. J. (1961). *Metabolism*, **10**, 419.
Hecht, A., & Goldner, M. G. (1959). *Metabolism*, **8**, 418.
Kaplan, E. H., Kennedy, J., & Davis, J. (1954). *Arch. Biochem.*, **51**, 47.
Leas, R. D. (1926). *J. Lab. clin. Med.*, **12**, 15.
Lutwak-Mann, C. (1942). *Biochem. J.*, **36**, 706.
Manchester, K. L., Randle, P. J., & Smith, G. H. (1958). *Brit. med. J.*, **i**, 1028.
Morris, N., & Graham, S. (1931). *Arch. Dis. Childh.*, **6**, 273.
Peterson, R. E., Black, R. L., & Bunim, J. J. (1958). *Arthr. and Rheum.*, **1**, 29.
Reid, J. (1958). *Brit. med. J.*, **ii**, 724.
Reid, J., Macdougall, A. I., & Andrews, M. M. (1957). *Brit. med. J.*, **ii**, 1071.
Smith, M. J. H. (1952). *Biochem. J.*, **52**, 649.
Smith, M. J. H. (1954). *Biochem. J.*, **57**, 349.
Smith, M. J. H. (1955). *Brit. J. Pharmacol.*, **10**, 110.
Smith, M. J. H., Meade, B. W., & Bornstein, J. (1952). *Biochem. J.*, **51**, 18.
Sproull, D. H. (1954). *Brit. J. Pharmacol.*, **9**, 121.
Stowers, J. M., Constable, L. W., & Hunter, R. B. (1959). *Ann. N.Y. Acad. Sci.*, **74**, 689.
Williamson, R. T. (1901). *Brit. med. J.*, **i**, 760.
Wishinsky, H. S., Glasser, E. J., & Perkal, S. (1962). *Diabetes*, **11**, Suppl., p. 18.

DISCUSSION

STANTON SEGAL (*Clinical Endocrinology Branch, National Institute of Arthritis and Metabolic Diseases, Bethesda, Md., U.S.A.*):

I do not think there is any doubt that salicylates may be useful in the treatment of diabetes. One of the critical points to consider is the difference between the diabetic and the normal with respect to the effect of salicylates on the blood sugar. The administration of 5 g. of salicylate caused a 28 per cent fall in the blood sugar of diabetic patients but no reduction in the blood sugar of normal subjects (Gilgore & Rupp, 1961). Austen (K.F., personal communication) also found no effect of 8 g. of salicylate on the blood sugar of normal individuals, and Frawley (T.F., personal communication) has observed similar results in the normal dog.

Salicylates and the regulation of blood sugar

With respect to the possible site or sites of action of salicylates on the mechanism responsible for the regulation of blood sugar, it seems clear that salicylates do not increase pancreatic venous blood insulin and do not act like the sulphonylureas (Seltzer, 1962). The other two important factors in maintaining a steady state of glucose are the peripheral metabolism of the sugar and the release and formation of glucose in the liver. Manchester, Randle and Smith (1958a, b) reported that they had achieved an increased uptake of glucose in the isolated rat diaphragm in the presence of salicylate. In our own studies (1960) we were never able to repeat this, although Seltzer obtained results similar to those of Randle and his colleagues. However, Huggins and Smith (1962) have also found no effect of salicylate on glucose uptake in the isolated diaphragm under similar experimental conditions, and I do not consider that an increased peripheral uptake of the sugar explains the hypoglycaemic effect of salicylates. One has to remember that in Randle's experiments diaphragms from normal rats were used, yet in the normal individual and in the normal animal salicylates do not reduce the blood sugar. It does not seem logical to explain the hypoglycaemic effect of salicylate in the diabetic in terms of results found in a normal diaphragm when salicylates do not lower the blood sugar in a normal person.

We have observed (1959) that salicylates inhibit phosphorylase activity in the rat diaphragm muscle, and this effect may have some relevance to other tissues, including the liver. I wonder if liver phosphorylase activity may not be decreased in diabetics receiving salicylates. Many of the studies on liver glycogen levels in animals given salicylate show that these are decreased, but Fonnesu and Severi (1955) reported some interesting results in that 2:4-dinitrophenol caused a delayed accumulation of liver glycogen in rats trained to feed once a day. Perhaps this finding may also apply to salicylates and there may be a decreased rate of glycogen breakdown and hence a decreased hepatic production of glucose during salicylate therapy. Hecht and Goldner (1959) gave glucagon in the presence of salicylates and obtained a normal response in the blood sugar, which is against this suggestion. However, glucagon resembles epinephrine in being a very potent stimulus to glycogen breakdown, and in our experiments (1960) we found that epinephrine reduced the glycogen content of diaphragm even when the phosphorylase activity was only 15 per cent of normal.

In recent years it has become accepted that insulin may have a direct action on the liver and that this is one of the mechanisms concerned in the regulation of blood glucose. I wonder whether the site of salicylate action may also be in the liver; the most direct way of obtaining evidence about this would be the hepatic vein catheterization type of experiment. There also appear to be differences between various types of diabetic patients. One particular example is the maturity-onset patient who seems to have an adequate amount of endogenous insulin; however, this insulin is bound in some form and is not easily available. It is possible that salicylates, which certainly bind with proteins, may exert an effect in this area by interfering with insulin-binding and thus releasing more free insulin.

With respect to STOWERS's results on the synergism between the hypoglycaemic actions of salicylate and the sulphonylureas, could one show this synergism in a patient in whom no further increase in the chlorpropamide dose would be effective?

REFERENCES

Fonnesu, A., & Severi, C. (1955). *Brit. J. exp. Path.*, **36**, 35.
Gilgore, S. G., & Rupp, J. J. (1961). *Metabolism*, **10**, 419.
Hecht, A., & Goldner, M. G. (1959). *Metabolism*, **8**, 418.
Manchester, K. L., Randle, P. J., & Smith, G. H. (1958a). *Brit. med. J.*, **i**, 1028.
Randle, P. J., & Smith, G. H. (1958b). *Biochem. J.*, **70**, 490.
Segal, S., & Blair, A. (1959). *Nature (Lond.)*, **183**, 1609.
Segal, S., Blair, A., & Weinberg, A. (1960). *Metabolism*, **9**, 1033.
Seltzer, H. S. (1962). *J. clin. Invest.*, **41**, 289.
Huggins, A. K., & Smith, M. J. H. (1962). *Biochem. J.*, **85**, 394.

STOWERS: I have not done that. It might be dangerous to give a very high dose of chlorpropamide. I have not altered the dose of chlorpropamide, but the experiment has been tried on different patients.

G. H. SMITH: I do not think the paradox of the rat diaphragm posed by SEGAL is quite as important as it may seem. In the experiments that Randle and I did diaphragms from normal rats were used, but they were incubated in a medium containing 2·5 mg. per ml. glucose, i.e. a diabetic level. If you take it down to 1 mg. per ml. or less, then the effect of salicylate on glucose uptake may well disappear, but then you are in the range of normal blood sugar levels on which salicylate does not seem to act *in vivo* anyway.

SEGAL: We studied both diabetic and normal rats and we found no difference in the parameters of glycogen deposition and glucose oxidation, no difference whatever between the normal and the diabetic diaphragm in salicylate responsiveness.

STOWERS: With regard to glucose production, it is difficult to see why a diabetic, if he is producing less glucose and having a marked rise in BMR, does not become ketotic—and yet we know that salicylates may reduce ketosis.

SEGAL: The reduction of ketonuria is an argument for the use of the drug in diabetes. It can reduce ketonuria. This is the peripheral action of salicylate on muscle. Salicylate markedly increases fatty acid oxidation in the diaphragm, and I think this was brought out today by WHITEHOUSE. I wonder whether, in a diabetic who has mild ketosis, salicylate might not increase the oxidation of ketone bodies by muscle.

VAN CAUWENBERGE: Our experiments have led us to conclude that the estimation of liver glycogen is not a reliable test of adrenal activity in the rat, and that salicylates exert their own direct pharmacodynamic action on carbohydrate metabolism (Roskam, J., & van Cauwenberge, H. [1960]. *Bull. Acad. roy. Méd. Belg.*, **25**, 462).

PROTEIN BINDING OF SALICYLATES

W. L. STAFFORD

Department of Experimental Medicine
Guy's Hospital, London

DRUGS exist in the plasma partly in the free state and partly bound by protein. It is generally thought that it is the free form and not the total concentration of the drug that determines its therapeutic activity. In addition, the portion bound to plasma can be regarded as a reservoir, keeping the free drug continuously available by release over a longer time.

We may represent drug-protein interaction in a general way as:

$$\text{Drug} + \text{Protein} \rightleftharpoons \text{Drug-Protein Complex.}$$

As this is a reversible reaction we may apply the Law of Mass Action. The association constant is then defined as:

$$K_A = \frac{(\text{Complex})}{(\text{Drug})\,(\text{Protein})}.$$

The higher the value of the constant the stronger is the association, because more of the drug exists in the bound form. A series of equilibria are presumed to exist when tissue is in contact with drug-carrying plasma (Fig. 1). The positions of the equilibria, the K_A values, are of fundamental importance. Only the free molecules can pass through the cell wall. The human erythrocyte membrane seems to be permeable to free salicylate and does not itself bind the compound.

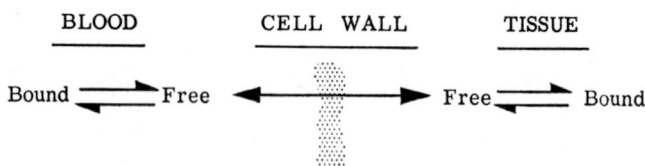

FIG. 1   SERIES OF EQUILIBRIA PRESUMED TO EXIST WHEN TISSUE IS IN
CONTACT WITH DRUG-CARRYING PLASMA

Unless otherwise stated, all the data in this paper have been obtained using the equilibrium dialysis technique (Goldstein, 1949). This involves placing the drug-carrying protein solution in contact with a buffer solution, but separated from it by a membrane impermeable to protein. The unbound salicylate from the protein solution will pass through until equilibrium is reached, when the free salicylate concentration is the same in either compartment. The additional quantity remaining inside the membrane is that bound to protein. Thus the salicylate level of the dialysate, the free fraction, and that within the membrane, free + bound, allow calculation of the percentage of the drug bound under the particular conditions of the experiment.

I have found that there is virtually no binding of salicylate or 3-methylsalicylate by rat liver or kidney homogenates. This is in accordance with the findings of Charnock, Opit and Hetzel (1962) that salicylate is readily washed out of liver mitochondria from salicylate-intoxicated rats. However, plasma protein behaves differently. It is bound equally *in vitro* and *in vivo*. This is fortunate; besides allowing the figures obtained *in vitro* to be used with more confidence, one need not consider a metabolic factor in the formation of the salicylate-plasma link. A typical salicylate binding curve for normal plasma was derived by Smith and his co-workers (1946) using the ultrafiltration technique. This method of representation enables the level of free salicylate to be read directly off the graph; saturation is not reached even at levels in the toxic range.

Reynolds and Cluff (1960), using separated plasma fractions, have shown that albumin is the only plasma protein to bind salicylate to any extent. Since at pH 7·3 this protein carries a net negative charge, its value as a complexing agent for a negative ion such as salicylate might appear to be limited. Nevertheless it has been calculated to carry 80 positive centres per molecule, at the end group of the chain and on each of the arginine and lysine residues. The predominant role of lysine was shown by Davison, Spitzer and Smith (1959), who found that the salicylate binding capacity of bovine albumin was completely eliminated by blocking the free amino group using formaldehyde and acetamide or by acetylation. Experimental data reveal that altogether about 28 molecules of salicylate can be bound per albumin molecule. The strong affinity of salicylate for albumin depends to some extent on the structure. The importance of the proximity of the hydroxyl to the carboxyl group of benzoic acid was demonstrated by Lindenbaum and Schubert (1956). This permits ring formation, which is thought to decrease the hydration around the hydroxyl group and therefore to allow closer interaction with the protein molecule.

I have examined the binding of salicylate and some of its 3-alkyl analogues by Armour's bovine serum albumin at physiological concentration and pH (Stafford, 1962a). The extent of binding at a particular molar concentration increases as the side chain is lengthened from 0 to 4 carbon atoms (Klotz, 1946; Klotz & Walker, 1947). This is a fact worth remembering when considering relative potencies. The curves obtained using fresh heparinized bovine plasma with the same albumin content were qualitatively the same, but differed quantitatively.

Comparison of the binding curves for each drug by plasma and by albumin revealed a considerably reduced binding capacity by plasma, especially for the isopropyl compound. Salicylate was exceptional because the two curves coincided. Could this decrease in the plasma be due to the presence of the other proteins masking some of the albumin binding sites through protein-protein interactions? In fact, addition of a mixture of globulins raised the binding of 3-methylsalicylate. It is noteworthy that the globulins alone bind 3-methylsalicylate, but do not bind unsubstituted salicylate.

Another possibility was the effect of the heparin present in the plasma.

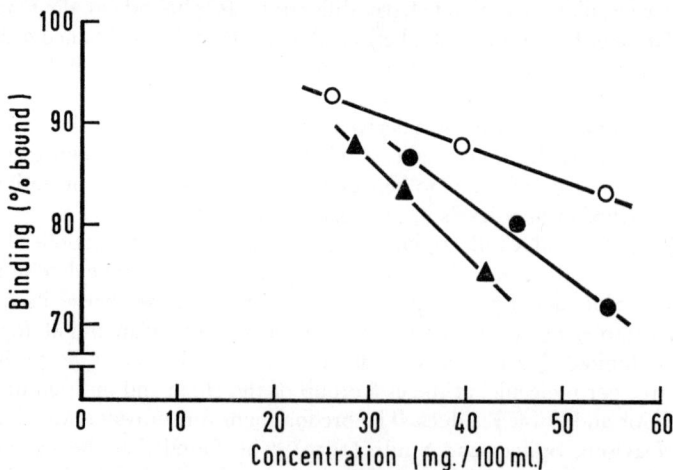

FIG. 2 THE BINDING OF 3-METHYLSALICYLATE BY HUMAN SERUM AND PLASMA

Studies were carried out at physiological concentration and pH by the equilibrium dialysis technique. The binding of serum (open circles) is compared with that of heparinized serum (closed circles) and of heparinized plasma (closed triangles).

I have determined the binding capacities of heparinized plasma, and of serum derived from the same blood in the presence or absence of heparin, 24 mg. per 100 ml. The resulting curves are shown in Fig. 2. It is apparent that addition of heparin to the serum reduced its ability to bind the drug towards that of plasma. As this was not true for human albumin this inhibition probably involves serum globulins. The fibrinogen in plasma lowers the capacity still further, as it did when added to Armour's bovine serum albumin. It seems probable that some interaction takes place between a globulin–heparin complex and albumin, resulting in a reduction in the number of the available sites on the albumin. This observation has a bearing on the results obtained with plasma and suggests that more nearly physiological values obtain *in vitro* if serum is used.

The importance of free drug levels to therapy suggests a study of possible changes that may occur in pathological states where the plasma proteins are quantitatively and perhaps qualitatively altered. Lester, Lolli and Greenberg (1946) reported a decreased binding capacity for salicylate in the serum of patients with rheumatic fever. This study was extended by Reynolds and Cluff (1960), who repeated the investigation in patients suffering from a variety of acute infections. Their results, calculated in terms of binding per gram of albumin, led to the conclusion that there was no change in the binding capacity; there was more free salicylate in the blood only because of the lower albumin concentration.

However, a different property does appear in the serum of certain diabetic patients. The protein from insulin-treated individuals binds less salicylate than the normal (Stafford, 1962b). I determined the binding curves as before, after addition of salicylate *in vitro*, and the fraction bound was read off for a serum level of 40 mg. per 100 ml. Conversion to molar concentration and division by the molarity of the serum albumin enabled the calculation of the bound salicylate ratio; that is, the average number of molecules of salicylate bound to each albumin molecule. Values were obtained for normal serum with or without the addition of glucose or palmitic acid. Doubling the free fatty acid content to the fasting diabetic level did not result in a decreased binding capacity. The mean value for the bound salicylate ratio was 2·96 (s.d. 0·19). Sera from four groups of diabetic patients were examined, those controlled by diet, by chlorpropamide, by insulin, and newly-diagnosed untreated patients. Only in the third group, those that took insulin, was the ratio significantly and consistently lower. The value for the diet-controlled patients was normal, but it was elevated in those taking chlorpropamide, probably significantly. This is in accordance with the finding of Stowers, Constable and Hunter (1959) that higher blood levels of salicylate are achieved in diabetics taking chlorpropamide and salicylate together than in those on salicylate therapy alone. The values of the untreated cases extended over a wide range, with the one non-ketotic patient exhibiting the lowest and most abnormal ratio. I failed to find a consistent inverse relation between the binding capacity and the protein-bound hexose level in the sera from chlorpropamide-treated or from untreated patients. This contrasts with the data of Larsen (1958), who has studied this in relation to Congo Red binding in rheumatoid arthritis and in diabetic nephropathy.

SUMMARY

There is a considerable difference in the extent to which salicylate and its structurally related compounds are bound to blood proteins. This is relevant in comparing the potency of a new compound, since the amount free in the blood may be only a fraction of the total blood level. For this determination commercially available crystalline albumin or heparinized plasma do not appear to be reliable models of the situation *in vivo*. This technique may provide a tool for studying the proteins of pathological sera.

The sera of the newly-diagnosed untreated diabetic patients was obtained from the Diabetic Clinic of King's College Hospital through the courtesy of Dr. W. G. Oakley.

REFERENCES

Charnock, J. S., Opit, L. J., & Hetzel, B. S. (1962). *Biochem. J.*, **83**, 602.
Davison, C., Spitzer, L. E., & Smith, P. K. (1959). *Fed. Proc.*, **18**, 381.
Goldstein, A. (1949). *Pharm. Rev.*, **1**, 102.
Klotz, I. M. (1946). *J. Amer. chem. Soc.*, **68**, 2299.
Klotz, I. M., & Walker, F. M. (1947). *J. Amer. chem. Soc.*, **69**, 1609.
Larsen, B. (1958). *Ann. rheum. Dis.*, **17**, 240.
Lester, D., Lolli, G., & Greenberg, L. A. (1946). *J. Pharmacol. exp. Ther.*, **87**, 329.
Lindenbaum, A., & Schubert, J. (1956). *J. phys. Chem.*, **60**, 1663.
Reynolds, R. C., & Cluff, L. E. (1960). *Bull. Johns Hopk. Hosp.*, **107**, 278.
Smith, P. K., Gleason, H. L., Stoll, C. G., & Ogorzalek, S. (1946). *J. Pharmacol. exp. Ther.*, **87**, 237.
Stafford, W. L. (1962a). *Biochem. Pharmacol.*, **11**, 685.
Stafford, W. L. (1962b). *Lancet*, **i**, 243.
Stowers, J. M., Constable, L. W., & Hunter, R. B. (1959). *Ann. N.Y. Acad. Sci.*, **74**, 689.

DISCUSSION

K. FREMONT-SMITH (*Robert Breck Brigham Hospital, Boston, Mass., U.S.A.*):

Godfrey, working in our laboratory, compared the ability of sera from 18 patients with active rheumatoid arthritis to bind salicylate *in vitro* to that of sera from eight control subjects. At a concentration of 1,000 μmole per litre rheumatoid sera bound, on the average, 475 μmole of salicylate. This is 28 per cent less than the average of 615 μmole bound by the control sera. However, the rheumatoid sera were hypoalbuminaemic, the average serum albumin concentration being 32 per cent less than that of the control group. Thus when one calculates the moles of bound salicylate per mole of albumin it would appear that each mole of rheumatoid albumin binds salicylate at least as well as normal, assuming negligible binding by globulin; because of the decreased albumin concentration in the plasma, the total salicylate bound per unit of plasma is significantly reduced.

BAYLES has already reported to you our observation that patients with active rheumatoid arthritis have lower salicylate concentrations following a single intravenous injection of sodium salicylate than do control subjects. When the individual plasma salicylate concentrations following the intravenous injection were compared with the corresponding serum albumin concentrations, using data from both rheumatoid patients and control subjects, a positive correlation that is statistically significant became apparent. This correlation supports the possibility that the hypoalbuminaemia characteristic of severe active rheumatoid arthritis results in decreased salicylate binding in the plasma, and is thus responsible for the lower plasma concentrations of salicylate that we have found in such patients.

M. J. H. SMITH (*Chairman*): The results on the binding of salicylates to plasma proteins raise a very important general point about the significance of such binding. If the amount of free drug determines its biological and other activities, then is the effectiveness of salicylate reduced by the extent of its protein binding and should drugs that are almost completely bound to circulating proteins be considered of little potential value as chemotherapeutic agents? Of course this is debatable, since protein binding may well be a desirable property in ensuring and maintaining a circulating reservoir of such a drug.

WEST: In their *in vitro* experiments SMITH and WHITEHOUSE used concentrations that were thought to be almost physiological. Was this a free level or was 75 per cent protein bound? This would make all the difference between a dose that was toxic and one that was in the therapeutic range.

M. J. H. SMITH: Essentially these were free levels. These concentrations were chosen originally because this was the blood concentration in diabetic rats having a marked hypoglycaemic phase. Nevertheless one can get effects *in vitro* in concentrations down to 0·5 mM, which is equivalent to 7 mg. per 100 ml. Even allowing for protein binding, therapeutic doses must be achieving at least that concentration within the cells.

WHITEHOUSE: My experiments were done in the presence of various plasma proteins; in the presence of these the salicylate level was 5 mM or less.

COLLIER: Perhaps the binding of drugs to protein has a deeper therapeutic meaning. Receptors are presumably proteins, and salicylates and other anti-inflammatory agents might block receptors for either pharmacological or physiological responses by being bound to such proteins. Is there any correlation between anti-inflammatory activity and the intensities with which non-steroidal anti-inflammatory drugs are bound to protein?

OSORIO: 2:4-Dinitrophenol is also bound by albumin, perhaps more so than salicylate, but as far as I know it has no anti-inflammatory action. It may be, therefore, that there is no relation between binding and anti-inflammatory action.

In reply to the question whether the biological effect depends on the concentration of the non-protein-bound molecule, I can quote the position only with respect to thyroxine. Values for free thyroxine correlate better with the thyroid status of the individual than do values for the total concentration of thyroxine, which suggests that only free thyroxine reaches the cells. On the other hand, the binding of unesterified fatty acids to albumin has a very high association constant, but the turnover of fatty acids in blood is very fast. There you have an example where the binding does not seem to affect the ability of a small molecule to get from the blood into the cells. It is not possible to generalize.

BYWATERS: Protein binding applies to drugs in the blood; in the tissues, where there is little protein, presumably the greater part of the drug is in the free state, except in areas of inflammation where the protein concentration may approximate to that in the plasma.

BROWN: Has anyone done experiments on salicylate concentrations in inflammatory fluids, as distinct from plasma levels?

FREMONT-SMITH: The results from a number of fluids showed that the unbound salicylate was identical within the limits of our analytical method, whereas the bound salicylate varied with the protein concentration.

WILHELMI: We produced an exudative peritonitis in the rat by injecting formalin intraperitoneally and we found that the concentration of salicylic acid was practically the same in the blood plasma as in the inflammatory exudate (Wilhelmi, G., Herrmann, B., & Tedeschi, G. [1959]. *Drug. Res.*, **9**, 241).

DIXON: We need to distinguish between equilibrium binding and the rate at which equilibrium binding is achieved after a dose of salicylate. The equilibrium binding of salicylate may be 70 to 80 per cent at normal therapeutic levels, but we are concerned with the concentration of unbound salicylate before the equilibrium is achieved.

DAVISON: One interesting aspect is the effect of competing compounds upon the binding of salicylate, determining its distribution within the tissues. A wide variety of compounds will compete with salicylate for binding to albumin. This effect ranges from compounds such as methylated and alkylated salicylates to substances like sulphinpyrazone, and particularly to the high molecular weight dyes such as Evans Blue. These compounds will be very strong competitors for the binding of salicylate with albumin. In rather preliminary experiments we have found that co-administration of certain of these compounds increases the salicylate in the tissues up to several-fold, notably in liver and brain, with a considerable decrease in the rate of excretion. This is potentially an important clinical aspect; at any time when you are giving two drugs together, you may be altering the distribution and excretion rate of one or both of them.

WHITEHOUSE: Many drugs will induce enzymes that metabolize them. I wonder whether salicylate has such an action that would mean that as a result of prolonged therapy the drugs would be rendered less effective in the body.

BACHMAN: In *Neurospora crassa* there is an induction or adaptation of an enzyme by salicylate. The enzyme appears to be a salicylate reductase, and this finding suggests the possibility that the drugs may induce or adapt enzymes in mammalian tissues (Bachman, D. M., Dragoon, B., & John, S. [1960]. *Arch. Biochem.*, **91**, 326).

M. J. H. SMITH: Over a short period of time salicylates will probably militate against their own metabolism quite effectively by virtue of their uncoupling action.

4

EFFECT OF SALICYLATE ON THE BINDING OF THYROID HORMONE

C. Osorio

*Medical Research Council Experimental Radiopathology Research Unit
Hammersmith Hospital, London*

THE administration of salicylate to rats or humans for a period of 7–10 days produces a fall in the concentration of protein-bound iodine in blood (Austen et al., 1958) and thyroid function is reduced, but no signs of hypothyroidism appear and the secretion of thyroid-stimulating hormone (TSH) is not increased (Wolff & Austen, 1958).

A possible explanation for these effects is that salicylate interferes with the binding of thyroid hormones by the serum proteins, thereby increasing the proportion of thyroid hormone that is free and biologically active, so that a lower concentration of total thyroid hormone in blood is needed to maintain a euthyroid status. In support of this hypothesis, Christensen (1959) has shown that salicylate increases the dialysis rate of thyroxine (T4) from human plasma. Electrophoretic studies using barbiturate buffer at pH 8·6 did not support this concept. If electrophoresis is done in tris (2-amino-2-hydroxymethylpropane-1:3-diol) and maleic acid (tris-maleate) buffer at pH 8·6, salicylate added to the buffer inhibits the binding of thyroxine by thyroxine-binding pre-albumin (TBPA) (Wolff, Standaert & Rall, 1961). Nevertheless, it is difficult to explain the increase in the dialysis rate of T4 from human plasma and the *in vivo* effect of salicylate on T4 metabolism on the basis of an interference with the binding of T4 by TBPA, since it is unlikely that TBPA binds T4 in physiological conditions (Myant & Osorio, 1960b; Christensen & Litonjua, 1961; Osorio et al., 1961).

The alternative hypothesis is that salicylate interferes with the normal relationship between the thyroid gland and the hypophysis (Wolff & Austen, 1958). The binding of thyroid hormones by plasma proteins is affected by the hydrogen ion concentration of the medium (Myant & Osorio, 1960b). Effects obtained *in vitro* are more likely to reflect biological actions if the *in vitro* experiments are carried out at the pH of the blood rather than at pH 8·6.

Experimental studies

In the present work an attempt has been made to determine the effect of sodium salicylate on the binding of thyroxine by the electrophoretic fractions of human and rat serum proteins at pH 7·4 and to relate it to the effect of sodium salicylate on T4 metabolism *in vivo*. Tracer amounts of radioactive thyroxine were added to human serum and submitted to paper electrophoresis in tris-maleate buffer at pH 7·4. After electrophoresis, 85 per cent of the radioactivity appeared mainly in the inter-alpha region, the region of thyroxine-binding globulin (TBG), 12 per cent in the albumin, and about 3 per cent in the pre-albumin region. When the concentration of T4 in the serum is increased, the proportion of radio-activity bound to albumin increases at the expense of that bound to TBG.

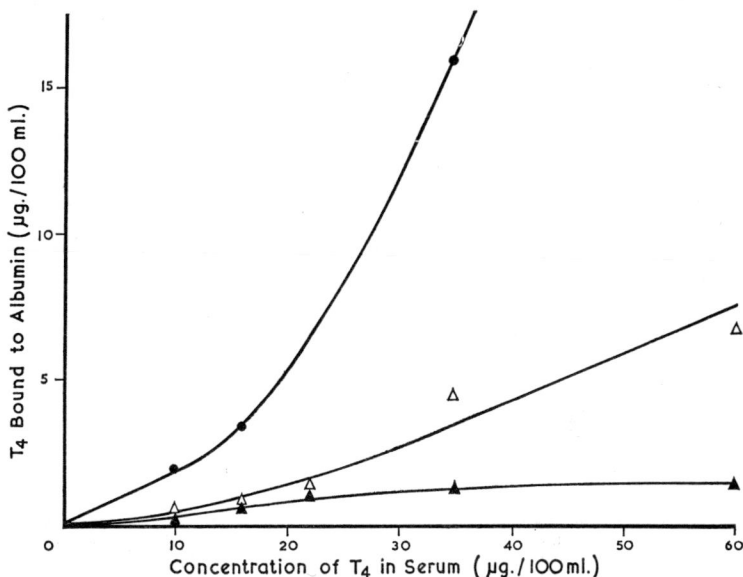

FIG. 1. RELATION BETWEEN THE CONCENTRATION OF THYROXINE IN SERUM AND THE AMOUNT OF THYROXINE CARRIED BY ALBUMIN

Determined by electrophoresis in tris-maleate buffer at pH 7·4 (closed circles), and with the addition of sodium salicylate in concentrations of 13·8 mg. (open triangles) and 41·4 mg. (closed triangles) per 100 ml. of buffer.

At high concentrations of T4 in serum, over 20 μg. per 100 ml., an increasing proportion of radioactivity appears in the α_2- and β-globulin regions. From these observations it may be concluded that in human serum at pH 7·4 the strongest binding sites for T4 are in the TBG region. When these binding sites approach saturation a larger proportion of T4 is bound by albumin, and when the T4 concentration is very high it is also bound by the weaker binding sites of the α_2- and β-globulins. It is possible that unbound T4 also migrates in this region (Myant & Osorio, 1960a; Farer, Robbins & Blumberg, 1962). From the total concentration of T4 in the serum and the percentage of the total radioactivity in the albumin or in TBG, it is possible to calculate the total amount of thyroxine bound to either of these protein bands. By adding salicylate to the buffer used for electrophoresis it is possible to test whether this drug interferes with the binding of T4 by these proteins (Ingbar, 1960).

In Fig. 1 the amount of thyroxine bound to albumin has been plotted against the total concentration of thyroxine in serum. It can be seen that the addition of sodium salicylate to the buffer, 13·8 or 41·4 mg. per 100

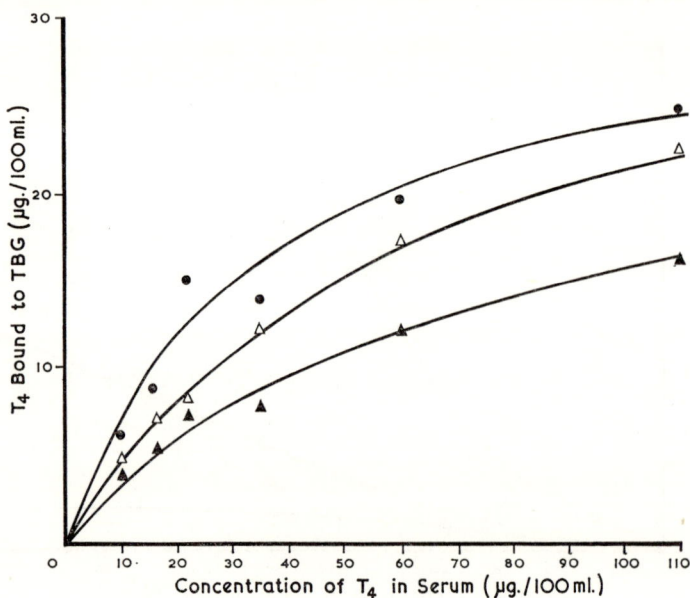

FIG. 2   RELATION BETWEEN THE CONCENTRATION OF THYROXINE IN SERUM
AND THE AMOUNT OF THYROXINE CARRIED BY TBG
Determined in the manner described in Fig. 1. TBG corresponds to the inter-alpha zone.

ml., has a very marked effect on the ability of human albumin to bind T4 at all the T4 concentrations studied. The results in Fig. 2 show that sodium salicylate also decreases the binding power of TBG for T4. Therefore sodium salicylate interferes with the two main binding sites for thyroxine in human serum. The higher the concentration of the drug in the buffer, the greater is the effect. This effect is probably due to competition of the salicylate ion and thyroxine for the same binding sites in these two groups of proteins. Unfortunately with this technique it is not possible to make a quantitative assessment of this competition (Osorio, 1962).

Salicylate has a similar effect on the thyroxine-binding protein of rat serum. Figure 3 shows that at pH 7·4 thyroxine is bound to a protein which moves in paper electrophoresis to a position just behind the albumin band (Dubowitz, Myant & Osorio, 1962). The addition of salicylate to the buffer displaces the radioactivity to the slower moving globulin regions. This suggests that salicylate *in vivo* will have an immediate action on the disappearance rate of T4 from the blood. This possibility was tested in rats. Tracer amounts of radioactive T4 were injected into the femoral vein of a rat, and samples of blood taken from

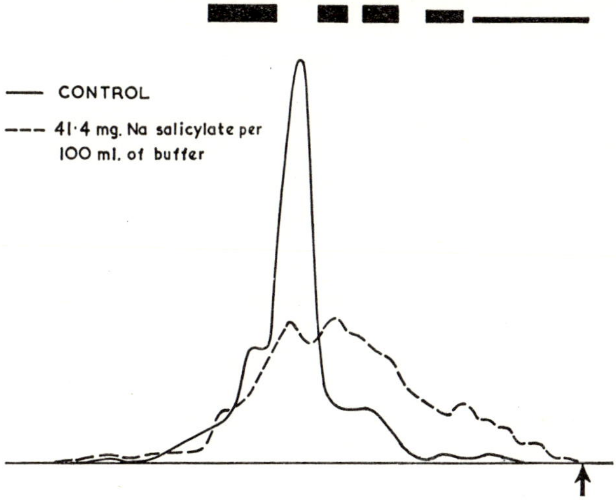

FIG. 3 DISTRIBUTION OF RADIOACTIVITY ALONG THE ELECTRO-
PHORETIC PAPER STRIP

Rat serum, to which less than 0·1 μg. per 100 ml. of radioactive thyroxine had been added. Electrophoresis in tris-maleate
buffer at pH 7·4 (continuous line), and with the addition of
sodium salicylate, 41·4 mg. per 100 ml. of buffer (interrupted
line). The blocks at the top of the figure represent the protein
bands, and the arrow shows the line of application of the
samples.

the femoral artery at varying intervals. Total radioactivity, protein-bound radioactivity, and trichloroacetic-acid-soluble radioactivity were measured before and after the intravenous injection of 20 mg. sodium salicylate in 0·3 ml. of saline. The injection of salicylate produced an immediate fall in the total concentration of radioactivity in blood. The concentration of trichloroacetic-acid-soluble radioactivity, which repre-sents inorganic ^{131}I, started to increase 20 minutes after the injection, which suggests that the rate of catabolism of thyroxine in the tissues has increased, perhaps as a consequence of the increased availability of T4. Injection of saline alone does not produce these effects (Osorio & Myant, 1963).

To test whether the catabolism of thyroxine was increased after the injection of salicylate, the liver was chosen as an organ that in the normal rat has an active role in the excretion of thyroid hormone; the catabolites appear in the bile, where it is possible to identify at least seven ^{131}I-containing substances by means of paper chromatography (Cuarón, Myant & Osorio, 1962). The bile duct of a rat was cannulated four hours after the injection of [^{131}I]T4, and samples of bile collected every 20 minutes. The total concentration of radioactivity in bile and the concentration of four ^{131}I-containing compounds was estimated before and after the intravenous injection of 20 mg. of sodium salicylate in 0·3 ml. of saline. The injection of salicylate produced an increase in the total amount of radioactivity in bile; the four main components increased at the same rate, although there was a delay of about 20 minutes in the rise of the T4 catabolites in relation to the rise of unchanged T4. These results indicated that the only effect of salicylate was to increase the amount of radioactive T4 available to the liver cell.

Implications

These experiments suggest that salicylate, by interfering with the binding of thyroxine by the plasma proteins, increases the proportion of the total T4 that is free, thereby accelerating the rate of disappearance of thyroxine from blood. This probably raises the concentration of T4 in the tissues, including the hypophysis, which will result in an increase in the rate of catabolism of thyroxine and a diminution in the rate of secretion of TSH, with a consequent depression of thyroid activity. Eventually a new equilibrium is achieved at a lower concentration of protein-bound iodine, but at a normal concentration of free thyroxine. There is evidence suggesting that free thyroxine determines the thyroid status of an individual (Robbins & Rall, 1960; Osorio et al., 1962). However, since salicylate has known effects on body temperature and basal metabolic rate, these biological effects could in turn affect the hypothalamus–hypophysis–thyroid axis independently of the action of the drug on thyroid-hormone binding by the plasma proteins.

SUMMARY

The effect of sodium salicylate on the binding of thyroxine by human and rat serum proteins has been studied by means of paper electrophoresis in tris-maleate buffer at pH 7·4. Salicylate interferes with the binding of thyroxine by human albumin, human thyroxine-binding globulin, and rat thyroxine-binding protein.

As a biological consequence of the interference by salicylate with the binding of thyroxine by serum proteins, it was shown that the intravenous injection of salicylate into a rat produced an immediate fall in the concentration of ^{131}I-labelled thyroxine in the blood. The concentration of trichloroacetic-acid-soluble ^{131}I in the blood and the concentration of thyroxine catabolites in bile increased after the administration of salicylate.

The present address of the author is Rheumatism Research Wing, Queen Elizabeth Hospital, Birmingham.

REFERENCES

Austen, F. K., Rubini, M. E., Meroney, W. H., & Wolff, J. (1958). *J. clin. Invest.*, **37**, 1131.
Christensen, L. K. (1959). *Nature (Lond.)*, **183**, 1189.
Christensen, L. K., & Litonjua, A. D. (1961). *J. clin. Endocr.*, **21**, 104.
Cuarón, A., Myant, N. B., & Osorio, C. (1962). *J. Physiol. (Lond.)*, **163**, 160.
Dubowitz, L. M. S., Myant, N. B., & Osorio, C. (1962). *J. Physiol. (Lond.)*, **162**, 358.
Farer, L. S., Robbins, J., & Blumberg, B. S. (1962). *Endocrinology*, **70**, 679.
Ingbar, S. H. (1960). *Ann. N.Y. Acad. Sci.*, **86**, 440.
Myant, N. B., & Osorio, C. (1960a). *J. Physiol. (Lond.)*, **152**, 391.
Myant, N. B., & Osorio, C. (1960b). *J. Physiol. (Lond.)*, **152**, 601.
Osorio, C. (1962). *J. Physiol. (Lond.)*, **163**, 151.
Osorio, C., Jackson, D. J., Gartside, J. M., & Goolden, A. W. G. (1961). *Clin. Sci.*, **21**, 355.
Osorio, C., Jackson, D. J., Gartside, J. M., & Goolden, A. W. G. (1962). *Clin. Sci.*, **23**, 525.
Osorio, C., & Myant, N. B. (1963). *Endocrinology*, **72**, 253.
Robbins, J., & Rall, J. E. (1960). *Physiol. Rev.*, **40**, 415.
Wolff, J., & Austen, F. K. (1958). *J. clin. Invest.*, **37**, 1144.
Wolff, J., Standaert, M. E., & Rall, J. E. (1961). *J. clin. Invest.*, **40**, 1373.

EFFECT OF SALICYLATE THERAPY ON THYROID FUNCTION TESTS

A. W. G. GOOLDEN

Department of Radiotherapy
Hammersmith Hospital, London

SALICYLATE is known to have certain effects on iodine metabolism and thyroid function. The administration of salicylate produces a striking fall in the protein-bound iodine (PBI) level in euthyroid people (Austen et al., 1958), and in thyrotoxic patients (Hetzel et al., 1962). In euthyroid people salicylate depresses thyroid function, as judged by the ability of the thyroid to accummulate [131]I (Austen et al., 1958). It has been suggested that salicylate may bring about these changes by modifying the binding of thyroid hormone by plasma proteins or by a direct effect on the secretion of thyrotrophic hormone (TSH); alternatively, both mechanisms may be implicated. Salicylate also increases oxygen consumption. There is a marked increase in the basal metabolic rate when salicylate is given to euthyroid people (Alexander et al., 1959) and a similar effect is obtained when salicylate is given to myxoedematous patients (Alexander & Johnson, 1956). From a practical standpoint it is manifestly difficult to interpret the results of thyroid function tests in patients being treated with salicylate.

The T3 [RBC] test

The uptake *in vitro* of ^{131}I-labelled tri-iodothyronine by the red cells (T3 [RBC]), introduced as a diagnostic test of thyroid function by Hamolsky, Stein and Freedberg (1957), has provided another approach to the problem of evaluating thyroid function in salicylate-treated patients. Tri-iodothyronine is bound by a protein with an inter-alpha mobility known as thyroxine-binding protein (TBP) or thyroxine-binding globulin (TBG). It is also bound to a minor extent by the α_2- and β-globulins. Under the conditions of the test ^{131}I]tri-iodothyronine is distributed between the red cells, the α_2- and β-globulins, and the binding sites on thyroxine-binding protein not occupied by thyroxine (free TBP), according to the relative binding powers of these substances. Since the binding power of the α_2- and β-globulins appears to be relatively constant the test is an indirect measurement of free TBP capacity (Osorio et al., 1961).

Values for T3 [RBC] have been determined in a series of 40 patients being treated with salicylates for rheumatoid arthritis. The normal range with the method used is between 15 and 20 per cent (Goolden et al., 1962). Values above the normal range were found in more than half the patients tested (Goolden & Osorio, 1962). None of these patients had any clinical evidence of thyroid disorder. A significant increase in T3 [RBC] values has also been demonstrated in normal people after a single oral dose of salicylate. T3 [RBC] values above the normal range have been observed for several hours after a single dose of 1·3 g. of aspirin. It is clearly important to exclude the recent administration of salicylate when this test is being used to assess thyroid function. The action of salicylate was investigated further by adding increasing concentrations of salicylate to samples of blood *in vitro* and determining the T3 [RBC] value for each sample. T3 [RBC] values were found to increase as the concentration of salicylate in blood was increased (Goolden & Osorio, 1962).

The results of the *in vitro* experiments indicated that salicylate modified the partition of [^{131}I]tri-iodothyronine between the red cells and the plasma proteins. In order to find out whether salicylate interfered with the binding of tri-iodothyronine by the α_2- and β-globulins or with binding by TBP, experiments were devised based on the fact that T3 [RBC] values are inversely proportional to free TBP capacity. Increasing amounts of thyroxine were added to samples of blood to which a constant amount of salicylate, 40 mg. per 100 ml. of plasma, had been added. A series of values for free TBP capacity was thus obtained. T3 [RBC] values for each sample of blood were determined and compared with a control series to which no salicylate had been added, and regression lines representing the relation between free TBP capacity and the reciprocal of T3 [RBC] were plotted. It was found that the regression line of a substance that affects the binding power of TBP had a different slope from the control curve, but cut the X axis at the same point. On the other hand, when the effect is on the binding power of the α_2- and β-globulins the regression line has the same slope, but cuts the X axis at a different point (Osorio et al., 1962). The results of the experiments with salicylate showed that both the slope of the regression line and the point at which it cut the X axis were different from the control curve (Fig.). From this it may be deduced that salicylate affects the binding power both of TBP and of the α_2- and β-globulins.

It has been shown that salicylate increases the dialysis rate of thyroxine from human plasma (Christensen, 1959), probably by interfering with the binding of thyroxine by TBP (Osorio, 1962). The thyroid status of an individual probably is determined by the concentration of free thyroxine in plasma, which may be derived from T3 [RBC] and PBI values (Osorio et al., 1962). It may be possible to estimate free thyroxine in salicylate-treated patients, and this is perhaps the only way in which their thyroid status may be satisfactorily assessed; in order to do so it will

4*

first be necessary to devise correction factors to allow for the effect of salicylate on the mechanism of the T_3 [RBC] test.

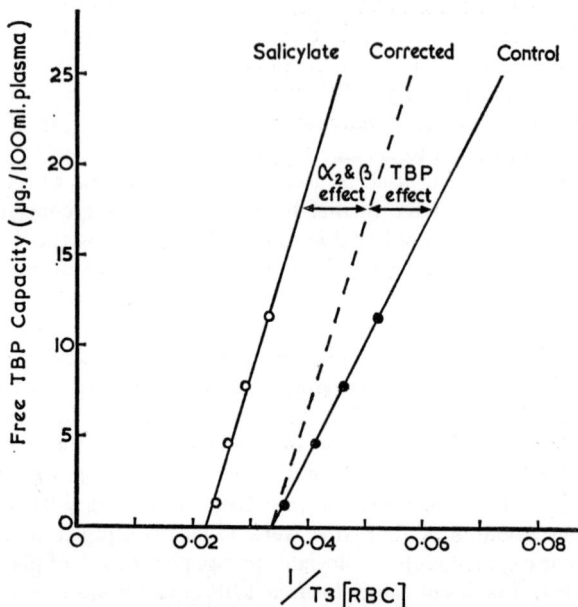

RELATION BETWEEN FREE TBP CAPACITY AND THE RECIPROCAL
OF T_3 [RBC]

Comparison of regression lines for control blood (closed circles) and blood to which sodium salicylate in a concentration of 40 mg. per 100 ml. plasma had been added (open circles). The interrupted line has been drawn after making a correction for the effect of salicylate on the binding of tri-iodothyronine by the α_2- and β-globulins.

SUMMARY

In a series of 40 patients being treated with salicylate for rheumatoid arthritis, values for the uptake of [^{131}I]tri-iodothyronine by the red cells (T_3 [RBC]) were found to be above the normal range in more than half the patients tested. None of the patients had any clinical evidence of thyroid dysfunction. A significant increase in T_3 [RBC] values has also been shown to occur in normal people after a single oral dose of salicylate. Salicylate added to blood *in vitro* has a similar effect, T_3 [RBC] values increasing as the concentration of salicylate in blood is increased. Further experiments have shown that salicylate modifies the partition of tri-iodothyronine between the red cells and the plasma proteins by affecting the binding power of both thyroxine-binding protein and the α_2- and β-globulins.

REFERENCES

Alexander, W. D., & Johnson, K. W. M. (1956). *Clin. Sci.*, **15**, 593.

Alexander, W. D., Macdougall, A. I., Oliver, M. F., & Boyd, G. S. (1959). *Clin. Sci.*, **18**, 195.

Austen, F. K., Rubini, M. E., Meroney, W. H., & Wolff, J. (1958). *J. clin. Invest.*, **37**, 1131.

Christensen, L. K. (1959). *Nature (Lond.)*, **183**, 1189.

Goolden, A. W. G., Gartside, J. M., Jackson, D. J., & Osorio, C. (1962). *Lancet*, **ii**, 218.

Goolden, A. W. G., & Osorio, C. (1962). *Lancet*, **ii**, 936.

Hamolsky, M. W., Stein, M., & Freedberg, A. S. (1957). *J. clin. Endocr.*, **17**, 33.

Hetzel, B. S., Good, B. F., Wellby, M. L., & Begg, M. W. (1962). *Aust. Ann. Med.*, **11**, 34.

Osorio, C. (1962). *J. Physiol. (Lond.)*, **163**, 151.

Osorio, C., Jackson, D. J., Gartside, J. M., & Goolden, A. W. G. (1961). *Clin. Sci.*, **21**, 355.

Osorio, C., Jackson, D. J., Gartside, J. M., & Goolden, A. W. G. (1962). *Nature (Lond.)*, **196**, 275.

Osorio, C., Jackson, D. J., Gartside, J. M., & Goolden, A. W. G. (1962). *Clin. Sci.*, **23**, 525.

EFFECTS OF SALICYLATES ON CHOLESTEROL METABOLISM

A. I. Macdougall and W. D. Alexander

Medical Research Council Clinical Chemotherapeutic Research Unit
Western Infirmary, Glasgow

It has previously been reported that large doses of aspirin lower the serum cholesterol concentration in myxoedematous patients (Alexander & Johnson, 1956) and in subjects with coronary artery disease associated with hypercholesterolaemia (Alexander et al., 1959). These observations have now been extended to include a study of changes in the serum cholesterol in more than 70 patients who received aspirin orally for at least two weeks, usually in a daily dosage of 5 g. or more. Each of these patients had at least one of a variety of disorders that can be associated with elevation of the serum cholesterol level: diabetes mellitus, coronary artery disease, hypothyroidism, obesity, xanthomatosis, and the nephrotic syndrome.

The patients remained in hospital during a control period of a week, which was extended to about two weeks in the diabetic and obese groups, and for the first two to four weeks of the treatment period. Five equal doses of aspirin were given daily, the tablets being crushed and suspended in milk. In the control period three or more serum cholesterol determinations were made at intervals of a few days by a modification of Bloor's method (Sackett, 1925), and in the treatment period both serum cholesterol and serum salicylate (Trinder, 1954) were estimated twice weekly for the first three weeks and weekly thereafter.

Effect of aspirin

Observations on a few patients from other diagnostic categories confirmed that, as for those with coronary disease (Alexander et al., 1959), daily doses of 4 g. of aspirin were insufficient to alter serum cholesterol levels. The subsequent results therefore refer to patients given 5–8 g. daily, dosage being adjusted to maintain the serum salicylate as near as possible to 40 mg. per 100 ml. It was thought desirable to divide the patients into two groups for the analysis of the results, according to whether the serum cholesterol in the initial control period was normal or high; for this purpose the upper limit of normality was taken to be 280 mg. per 100 ml. This limit has purposely been set rather high so that all those allocated to the hypercholesterolaemic group were likely to have had clearly abnormal serum cholesterol concentrations, although a few in the 'normal' group may have had a pathological hypercholesterolaemia of mild degree.

The results for the group with a high initial serum cholesterol showed that for each diagnostic category the mean serum cholesterol after two weeks of aspirin treatment was considerably lower than that in the control period. The decreases for the patients with diabetes and with coronary disease, and for the entire group, were all very highly significant ($P < 0.001$). In the patients with an initially normal serum cholesterol no significant change in cholesterol concentrations was observed.

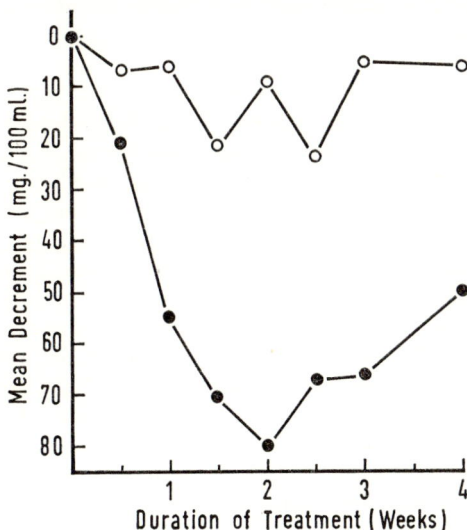

CHANGES IN SERUM CHOLESTEROL CONCENTRATIONS DURING ASPIRIN THERAPY

Mean values from 35 patients who had a high serum cholesterol initially (closed circles), and from 31 patients in whom the initial serum cholesterol was normal (open circles).

The figure shows the mean changes in serum cholesterol in the two groups at intervals during the period of treatment. The slight decrements seen in the group whose serum cholesterol in the control period was considered to be normal may be attributable to the rather high limit of normality that we employed. The tendency to a rise in serum cholesterol level during the third and especially the fourth weeks in the hypercholesterolaemic group is also of interest; it may be due partly to less accurate control of aspirin dosage at this time, when some of the subjects were attending as out-patients, but it is probable that there is also a trend towards escape from the effect of salicylate similar to that which sometimes occurs during administration of thyroid hormones to patients with hypercholesterolaemia. Inspection of the records during long-term administration of aspirin, for up to 44 months, suggests that such a secondary rise in serum cholesterol occurs in some, but not in all, cases.

Those patients whose original serum cholesterol was highest showed the greatest decrease during salicylate treatment, as exemplified by a 43 year-old woman with xanthomatosis and coronary insufficiency, whose serum cholesterol fell from 546 to 300 mg. per 100 ml. after two weeks of aspirin. This case also illustrated the tendency to escape from the cholesterol-lowering action after four weeks despite maintenance of active serum salicylate levels.

Effect of salicylate congeners

The dosage of salicylate necessary to reduce a pathologically high serum cholesterol often produced troublesome side-effects – deafness, tinnitus, and sometimes nausea and vomiting. Studies were therefore undertaken, in collaboration with Lightbody and Reid (cf. Reid, 1961), of compounds chemically related to salicylate, to ascertain whether the metabolic effects could be dissociated from such side-effects. The provisional conclusions suggest that both γ-resorcylate and o-cresotinate can reduce a high serum cholesterol, though quantitatively this effect may be less than that of salicylate. The side-effects occurring with salicylate have not been noted with γ-resorcylate, but this compound is more difficult to synthesize. With o-cresotinate aural side-effects were not found; gastro-intestinal symptoms can occur, and tachycardia and cardiac conduction defects have also been observed.

These studies have dealt only with effects on the serum cholesterol concentration, which do not necessarily reflect changes in tissue cholesterol distribution (Boyd & Oliver, 1958), and which can be altered by various mechanisms (Chiu, 1961). At present we do not wish to speculate on the mode of action of salicylate on cholesterol metabolism, but in conclusion it might be useful to assemble the facts that should be explained by any valid hypothesis on this subject:

(i) Despite the preliminary report to the contrary by Eidlitz (1960), we believe that high dosage of aspirin is necessary for significant lowering of the serum cholesterol.

(ii) The changes in serum cholesterol concentration are not explained by the haemodilution that is produced by large doses of salicylate.

(iii) It seems significant that only when the serum cholesterol is pathologically high is it reduced by aspirin; this is similar to the effect of salicylate on the blood sugar.

(iv) The effect on cholesterol appears not to be directly dependent on the increase in metabolic rate induced by salicylate, as the two changes are not associated in time nor in occurrence in individual cases; moreover, the chemically related γ-resorcylate and p-aminosalicylate (Tygstrup, Winkler & Warburg, 1959), which are not metabolic stimulants, can lower the serum cholesterol.

(v) Other serum lipids are affected as well as cholesterol; there is a comparable change in serum phospholipid, and the proportion of α- to β-lipoprotein is unaltered (Alexander et al., 1959). In the case of p-aminosalicylic acid (Tygstrup, Winkler & Warburg, 1959) the reduction in serum lipids affected both esterified and non-esterified cholesterol fractions, and there was a less sustained fall in phospholipids and triglycerides. It is of interest that the effect of aspirin on the α/β-lipoprotein ratio is similar to that of L-thyroxine, whereas oestrogens increase the α/β-lipoprotein ratio and lower the cholesterol/phospholipid ratio (Oliver & Boyd, 1956).

(vi) The alterations in serum cholesterol were not secondary to changes in thyroid activity, since in four of our patients the 4-hour and 48-hour ^{131}I-uptakes by the thyroid after three weeks and eight weeks of salicylate therapy were unaltered despite significant reduction of the serum cholesterol at these times (Alexander & Johnson, 1958); we did not confirm the diminished thyroid function reported by Austen and his co-workers (1958).

(vii) Although our studies were concerned with the effects of aspirin on serum lipids during a period of weeks, other workers have noted a reduction in the serum cholesterol within an hour or two in acute experiments using single large doses of salicylate (Laborie & Laborie, 1959; Hetzel, Charnock & Lander, 1959); the former authors also noted an increase in serum lipase activity. A fall in plasma free fatty acids was observed in acute experiments by Carlson and Östman (1961).

It appears that the reduction of high serum cholesterol concentrations during aspirin treatment must be incorporated in the increasingly complex pattern of effects on tissue metabolism known to be induced by salicylates.

SUMMARY

Aspirin, in a dosage of 5 g. or more daily for at least two weeks, produced a significant fall in the serum cholesterol concentration in patients with hypercholesterolaemia associated with diabetes mellitus, coronary artery disease, hypothyroidism, obesity, xanthomatosis, and the nephrotic syndrome, but not in patients whose serum cholesterol initially was normal. Similar decreases in other serum lipid fractions have been described. Some other compounds structurally related to salicylate have a comparable effect. The mechanism of this action of aspirin is uncertain, but it is apparently not directly dependent on the increase in metabolic rate induced by salicylate, nor can it be explained on the basis of haemodilution or altered thyroid function.

REFERENCES

Alexander, W. D., & Johnson, K. W. M. (1956). *Clin. Sci.*, **15**, 593.
Alexander, W. D., & Johnson, K. W. M. (1958). *Clin. Sci.*, **17**, 377.
Alexander, W. D., Macdougall, A. I., Oliver, M. F., & Boyd, G. S. (1959). *Clin. Sci.*, **18**, 195.
Austen, F. K., Rubini, M. E., Meroney, W. H., & Wolff, J. (1958). *J. clin. Invest.*, **37**, 1131.
Boyd, G. S., & Oliver, M. F. (1958). *Brit. med. Bull.*, **14**, 239.
Carlson, L. A., & Östman, J. (1961). *Metabolism*, **10**, 781.
Chiu, G. C. (1961). *Arch. intern. Med.*, **108**, 717.
Eidlitz, M. (1960). *Lancet*, **ii**, 1123.
Hetzel, B. S., Charnock, J. S., & Lander, H. (1959). *Metabolism*, **8**, 205.
Laborie, F., & Laborie, R. (1959). *J. Méd. Bordeaux*, **136**, 1127.
Oliver, M. F., & Boyd, G. S. (1956). *Lancet*, **ii**, 1273.
Reid, J. (1961). *In* 'Drugs Affecting Lipid Metabolism', p. 423, ed. Garattini, S., & Paoletti, R. Amsterdam: Elsevier.
Sackett, G. E. (1925). *J. biol. Chem.*, **64**, 203.
Trinder, P. (1954). *Biochem. J.*, **57**, 301.
Tygstrup, N., Winkler, K., & Warburg, E. (1959). *Lancet*, **i**, 503.

DISCUSSION

A. G. MACGREGOR (*Department of Materia Medica and Therapeutics, University of Aberdeen*):

We have all accepted for some time that salicylates affect thyroid function tests. If you belong to the unfortunately increasing body of doctors who prefer to look at test results sitting at a desk and who forget to look at the patient lying in bed, you can readily convince yourself that the many potentialities of aspirin include the effective treatment of myxoedema and of thyrotoxicosis. There is a rise in BMR and a fall in blood cholesterol in myxoedema, and a fall in thyroid clearance rate and in the protein-bound iodine level in hyperthyroid patients. There is some difference of opinion about the radio-iodine effects and whether salicylates do or do not affect thyroid radio-iodine concentration. Austen says that they do, and he has measured it, but we cannot demonstrate this. MACDOUGALL said that it did not happen in Glasgow and we could not get it to happen in Edinburgh, although we were using a different technique from Austen's. Austen also said that the level of oxygen consumption relative to a given plasma concentration of salicylate falls with time after the start of salicylate therapy. In other words, there is a relatively higher increase in consumption at the beginning of treatment, and this falls with time. MACDOUGALL showed a comparable change in cholesterol levels, there being a fall and later an escape, with a rise in the serum cholesterol level in certain patients.

What is interesting is a consideration of the mechanisms involved in these changes. We do not honestly know what happens to cholesterol metabolism. The increase in oxygen consumption is certainly due to the metabolic stimulant effect by virtue of the uncoupling action upon oxidative phosphorylation, a characteristic common to dinitrophenol. It was shown a few years ago by Christensen that both salicylate and dinitrophenol were able to displace bound thyroxine and to increase the amount of free thyroxine *in vitro*, and this has been shown again this afternoon. This is the major but not necessarily the only factor responsible for the fall in PBI that has been widely reported at all levels of thyroid function; probably there is also a central effect. Austen has shown that salicylates are capable of inhibiting the goitrogenic response in goitrogen-treated rats. It looks as though there may be some effect of salicylate in inhibiting TSH output centrally, and it is conceivable that any increase in this effect after the start of treatment may be responsible for some of the changes that have been shown to occur with salicylates. The hypothalamic suppression may result in the changes in thyroid iodine-uptake that Austen has demonstrated. It has also been shown that if you produce specific hypothalamic lesions you can inhibit the dinitrophenol-induced changes in thyroid function. If the same sort of thing happens with salicylates you may have further evidence that this is the mechanism involved. The Australian group, Hetzel and co-workers, have suggested that this TSH inhibition effect, if it is such, can be induced in thyrotoxic individuals as well, but to a much lesser extent than in normal people. This is a fundamentally interesting suggestion for there is some evidence that a TSH-like component may be concerned in hyperthyroidism, and it is intriguing that it should be affected.

One point that deserves emphasis is that these changes in thyroid function are not mediated at all by any interruption in thyroid hormone synthesis, such as occurs with *p*-aminosalicylate. The effect on thyroid function, if it is real, is probably a central effect upon TSH. The demonstrable effect upon PBI is probably an alteration in the distribution of thyroid hormones peripherally, with a reduction of the bound component.

AUSTEN: The discrepancy as to the ^{131}I-uptake is a real discrepancy and we each have to stand on our own findings. Our conclusion that ^{131}I-uptake was depressed was based on serial studies in more than a dozen patients. After the agent was discontinued the uptake returned to about the pre-salicylate level. We also did ^{131}I-clearance studies in three patients. The clearance of ^{131}I was definitely depressed during salicylate therapy, and when salicylates were discontinued it returned to the pretreatment level. For the same salicylate level in man there seems to be an increased metabolic rate during the first week, as compared to later periods. In studying the rat we found that if we gave a salicylate dose sufficient to achieve the desired blood level immediately, the rats became quite ill and unable to eat. If we took four weeks to achieve the same dose level there was no difficulty. With time there seems to develop a tolerance to a given salicylate level.

As to the mechanism whereby chronic salicylate administration produces a fall in PBI and reduction in ^{131}I-uptake, I am not completely satisfied that interference with thyroxine binding is a sufficient explanation. The PBI falls during the first week of salicylate treatment and then falls no further, regardless of an increase in dose or prolonged administration. I do not understand why increasing the dose fails to reduce the PBI further. If all the effects of salicylate on thyroid function are mediated by an effect on binding and an increase in free thyroxine, which suppresses TSH release, it seems that we might expect some clinical evidence of an increase in free thyroxine. This is easy to suggest but hard to prove. We carried out studies in which patients were given infusions of adrenaline or noradrenaline before, during, and after salicylate treatment. Infusions were carried out 24 hours after starting salicylates, at which time the BMR was rising and an increased thyroxine turnover was apparent, seven days after starting salicylates, and again at two months. The response to the catecholamines was unchanged from control values. Thus salicylate treatment does not resemble thyroid administration in increasing the responsiveness to the catecholamines. This failure to find evidence of free thyroxine represents only a gross attempt. Nevertheless I would still feel that salicylate depresses TSH release by a central action as well as by interference with thyroxine binding.

Osorio: I would like to congratulate Austen on the ingenuity of the experiments designed to show an increase in free thyroxine after the administration of salicylate. However, I think it is very difficult to interpret the implications of a negative result in this type of experiment, since we know very little of the way in which thyroxine potentiates the effect of adrenaline on the heart, and salicylate on the other hand has an action of its own on the cardiovascular system. The other point, that in his experiments salicylate failed to depress the PBI below a certain level despite its prolonged administration, fits perfectly well with the theory that the fall in PBI is a compensatory mechanism to bring free thyroxine down to the pre-salicylate level. When the level of free thyroxine reaches a normal value and a new equilibrium is established the PBI will not fall any further. The fact that increasing the concentration of salicylate in blood does not produce any further reduction in the PBI may be explained by supposing that there are two kinds of binding sites for thyroxine, one of which is affected by salicylate and one of which is not. When the salicylate-labile binding sites are completely blocked, any further increase in the salicylate concentration will not affect the PBI. A similar situation occurs in experiments with electrophoresis. The effect of salicylate on the binding of thyroxine increases with the salicylate concentration, but a plateau is reached at a salicylate concentration of about 50 mg. per 100 ml.

The crucial point in the discussion whether salicylate affects thyroid function only by its effect on the binding of thyroxine by the plasma proteins depends on a fact about which there is conflicting evidence, does thyroid function remain depressed after the PBI has achieved a constant value? If salicylate causes an initial depression of thyroid function that returns to the original level when the PBI value is stabilized, this will prove that salicylate acts only by affecting the binding of thyroxine by the plasma proteins. If thyroid activity remains depressed, some other explanation in addition to the protein-binding effect must be sought.

ALEXANDER: Our evidence (1958) was that at three weeks and eight weeks there was no influence on thyroid function. I am not sure that there is a conflict between AUSTEN's data on thyroid uptake and ours. In AUSTEN's study enteric-coated salicylate was used and, as has been shown, much more constant levels are achieved with this than with the aspirin that we employed. In order to resolve this problem we must have serial studies of thyroid function. Until we have them we shall not know whether the evidence so far collected is conflicting or not.

MACGREGOR: One of the explanations for the high thyroid clearance that occurs in simple goitre is that there may be a high renal clearance and loss of iodine. If measurements are made of the absolute iodine uptake in non-toxic goitre, one finds that the apparent high clearance with radio-iodine is merely a compensatory mechanism for coping with a much lower plasma inorganic iodide. You are clearing a bigger volume to get the same absolute amount of iodine into the gland. Could MILNE say whether salicylates decrease the renal clearance of iodide? It would be possible then to say that any decrease in thyroid clearance was merely compensatory for a lowered renal clearance. You thereby raise the plasma inorganic iodine level and then do not need to clear such a large volume to get the same absolute thyroid iodine-uptake. What does salicylate do to renal clearance of iodine?

MILNE: On first principles I think that it is unlikely because my conception of free iodine clearance is that of diffusion. Free iodine clearance is about one-third of the filtration rate and does not vary greatly at different plasma levels. The usual conception is that it is filtered at the glomerulus and that a certain amount diffuses back. I personally have never seen any proof that inorganic anions behave like the organic anions we discussed in relation to salicylate secretion. It may be so, but I am not prepared to admit it.

AUSTEN: MILNE is quite correct. Although salicylates depress ^{131}I-clearance, they have no effect on renal clearance.

WHITEHOUSE: If one compares the activity of o-cresotinate and of γ-resorcylate with that of salicylate, there is an interesting correlation between capacity to lower ATP levels in the liver, by uncoupling, and the effect in lowering serum cholesterol levels, which suggests that cholesterol biosynthesis is inhibited. Cholesterol biosynthesis is a highly energy-consuming process.

M. J. H. SMITH: There is some work in support of this general thesis (Wright, L. D., & Loeb, M. [1960]. *Proc. Soc. exp. Biol. (N.Y.)*, **103**, 183). Nevertheless if it were a fact that general uncoupling agents interfere in this way, why does it not happen in the normal subject?

ADAMS: Are we convinced that γ-resorcylate is effective in lowering cholesterol levels?

MACDOUGALL: We were aware of the studies of Goldstein ([1955]: Thesis, McGill University; quoted by Kritchevsky, D. [1958]. 'Cholesterol', p. 213. New York: John Wiley) suggesting that cholesterol biosynthesis from acetate *in vitro* was inhibited by salicylate. We did not think that this was a likely explanation of our results, partly because there is some evidence that the abnormality of the serum cholesterol in hyper-cholesterolaemic subjects is not due to excessive biosynthesis but to a reduction in the rate of removal from the blood (Symposium—Lipid Metabolism [1962]. *Metabolism*, **11**, 741–934).

Our results with γ-resorcylate certainly were not conclusive. The effect of resorcylate is important in relation to whether the cholesterol-lowering effect is related to uncoupling, because it is the one apparent exception.

I agree with AUSTEN about the escape in the metabolic stimulant effect over a period of time. BMR estimations were done on most patients we studied, and when we were analysing the results we noticed the escape.

SALICYLATES AND MEMBRANE PERMEABILITY

J. A. HICKLIN

The Medical Unit
The London Hospital, London

THE energy derived from oxidation is made available in many tissues as high-energy phosphate bonds. Salicylates uncouple oxidation from phosphorylation (Brody, 1955) and many of the actions of salicylates may be due to this uncoupling (Smith, 1959). The maintenance of ionic gradients across membranes involves the expenditure of energy (Keynes & Maisel, 1954), and it is possible that in some tissues the energy is derived from oxidative phosphorylation (Glynn, 1958). Where such gradients exist it has been assumed that energy is expended in moving ions up the concentration gradient, and that movement down the concentration gradient is passive. In the case of potassium energy would be required to move the ion into the cell, and efflux would be passive.

In rat diaphragms Manchester, Randle and Smith (1958) have shown that 5 mM sodium salicylate causes loss of intracellular potassium; they assumed that this was due to deprivation of energy from active mechanisms maintaining the intracellular concentration of potassium. The importance of oxidative phosphorylation in rat tissues has been shown clearly (Brody, 1955; Penniall, 1958; Jeffrey & Smith, 1959), and 2:4-dinitrophenol, another uncoupler, has been shown to deplete the intracellular potassium of rat diaphragm (Barnes, Duff & Threlfall, 1955).

Bianchi (1953) has claimed that salicylates increase synovial permeability by a direct action on the membrane, and Waltner, Csernovszky and Kelemen (1959) found that human red cells *in vitro* and *in vivo* lost intracellular potassium under the influence of 3 mM sodium salicylate. However, there is reason to believe that phosphorylation is coupled to glycolysis in synovium (Thomas & Dingle, 1958), and this is also true of red cells (Ponder, 1952). The present work is an attempt to examine the connexion between the type of metabolism and the effects of salicylate on potassium movement in the three tissues discussed, and to determine the phases of potassium movement affected.

Experimental studies

Fluxes in human red cells were estimated by the methods described by Joyce and Weatherall (1958). Cells were suspended in a phosphate-buffered saline containing some of its potassium as ^{42}K. Samples of 1 ml.

were taken at intervals and centrifuged. The cell volume, total potassium, and radioactive potassium contents were measured and the influx calculated. Attempts to follow efflux were made by re-suspending cells containing ^{42}K in inactive saline and sampling as before.

Fluxes in rat diaphragms were estimated as described by Creese (1954). Influx was measured in hemidiaphragms, one member of a pair from each animal being treated with drug, and one being kept as the control. The tissues were soaked in bicarbonate-buffered saline containing ^{42}K for 25 minutes. The wet weight, dry weight, and total and radioactive potassium contents of the tissues were measured. Efflux was measured by soaking hemidiaphragms in [^{42}K]saline and then mounting the tissue over the end window of a Geiger counter in a stream of inactive saline.

TABLE I. EFFECT OF 10 mM SODIUM SALICYLATE ON THE POTASSIUM CONTENT
AND INFLUX IN HUMAN RED BLOOD CELLS

The cells were suspended in phosphate saline: phase 1 of higher specific activity than that of the cells; phase 2 with specific activity of supernatant lower than that of the cells.

Subject	Suspension	Phase	Mean intracellular potassium concentration (mM)	Mean flux ($\mu\mu mole/cm.^2/sec.$)
Healthy	Control	1	$102 \pm 1 \cdot 1$	0·147
		2	$98 \pm 4 \cdot 3$	
	Salicylate	1	$107 \pm 1 \cdot 9$	0·146
		2	$99 \pm 3 \cdot 2$	
Active rheumatoid arthritis	Control	1	$109 \pm 1 \cdot 6$	0·112
	Salicylate	1	$113 \pm 3 \cdot 14$	0·097

Movement of potassium through human synovial membrane was measured in an apparatus similar to that of Ussing (1958) but designed to measure movements in two pieces of tissue at once (Hicklin, 1962). A central chamber contained bicarbonate-saline with ^{42}K of high specific activity. Two lateral chambers contained inactive saline. A piece of synovial membrane 2 cm. × 1 cm., obtained at arthrotomy of the knee, was cut in half and each half sandwiched between a lateral compartment and the central compartment, so that ^{42}K passed through the membrane into the lateral compartments. Each lateral compartment was emptied and refilled at 15 minute intervals, and the number of counts accumulating was proportional to the amount of ^{42}K passing through.

Red cells. Table 1 shows the results of exposing red cells from a healthy human subject to media of higher and of lower specific activity in the presence and absence of 10 mM sodium salicylate. The salicylate produced no change in the intracellular potassium concentration over the nine-hour period and the rate of influx was not changed. The attempt to measure efflux directly in phase two encountered the phenomenon described by Solomon and Gold (1955), cells appearing to gain ^{42}K from a medium of lower specific activity. However, since neither the potassium

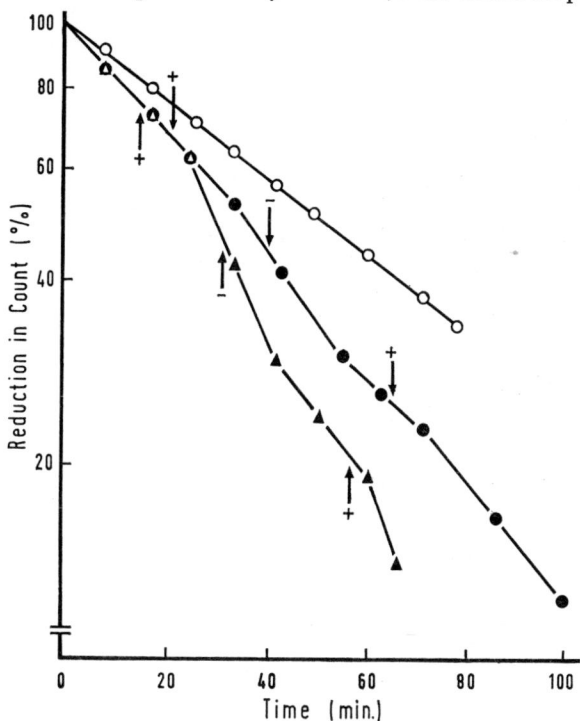

EFFECT OF UNCOUPLING AGENTS ON THE RATE OF LOSS OF ^{42}K
FROM RAT DIAPHRAGM

The reduction in radioactivity is represented on the ordinate as the percentage of the initial count, on a logarithmic scale. Observations were made in saline (open circles), in 5 mM sodium salicylate (closed circles), and in 0·1 mM 2:4-dinitrophenol (closed triangles). + and − denote exposure and end of exposure to the uncoupling agent.

concentration nor influx were affected, effects on efflux must have been small or absent. Table 1 also shows the results of an experiment on the red cells from a patient with active seropositive rheumatoid arthritis. Here, although the intracellular potassium did not fall during the period of observation, there was a small but definite slowing of influx under the influence of 10 mM sodium salicylate. A reduction of this order would not cause a measurable fall in potassium concentration in four hours.

Rat diaphragm. Efflux from rat diaphragm proceeds as a single exponential for long periods, that is, rectilinearly on a log-count/time scale. Exposure to 5 mM sodium salicylate produced an acceleration of efflux that was reversible and repeatable (Fig.). The internal potassium concentration fell, but this fall was entirely accounted for by the increased efflux, the average rate of influx being unaffected (Table 2). Similar experiments with 0·1 mM 2:4-dinitrophenol showed a more marked acceleration of efflux and a marked loss of intracellular potassium. However, there was a significant slowing of influx as well as the acceleration of efflux.

TABLE 2. EFFECTS OF UNCOUPLING REAGENTS ON POTASSIUM FLUX IN PAIRS
OF RAT HEMIDIAPHRAGMS

Parameters—PERC: Potassium efflux rate constant, per sec.;
        IPC: Intracellular potassium concentration, m-mole per litre of cell water;
        PI: Potassium influx rate, $\mu\mu$mole per cm.^{2} per sec.

Uncoupling reagent	Parameter	No. of pairs	Control	Treated	Significance $(P <)$
5 mM sodium salicylate	10^4 PERC	6	3·0	4·0	0·02
	IPC	7	118·0	96·0	0·01
	PI	7	15·5	14·7	0·4
10 mM sodium salicylate	10^4 PERC	4	3·5	8·3	0·02
	IPC	4	129·0	89·0	0·001
	PI	4	16·7	12·3	0·02
0·01 mM 2:4-dinitrophenol	10^4 PERC	4	3·2	5·9	0·001
	IPC	4	136·0	96·0	0·01
	PI	4	20·6	16·0	0·001

Experiments were carried out with 10 mM sodium salicylate to see if the failure of 5 mM salicylate to slow influx represented a difference between the modes of action of salicylate and of dinitrophenol. The acceleration of efflux and the fall of potassium concentration were more marked than with 5 mM sodium salicylate; as with dinitrophenol, the rate of influx was slowed by 10 mM salicylate (Table 2).

Synovium. After the number of counts appearing in 15 minutes had become constant a series of control observations was made and the mean called 100 per cent. Other values were expressed as percentages of this mean. 5 mM sodium salicylate was then added to the saline in one or both lateral chambers and a further group of observations was made. The percentage transformation was valuable because the fibrous tissue in some sheets of synovium varied in thickness from end to end and the absolute values of the equilibria reached differed in the two halves. In the first experiment normal synovium obtained at meniscectomy was placed so that the joint surfaces were away from the source of ^{42}K, so that movement of ^{42}K was as if it were into the joint space. 5 mM sodium salicylate was admitted to one side chamber only, the other being kept as a control. The rate of movement of ^{42}K was not significantly changed $(P > 0.3)$.

In the second experiment normal synovium was again used, but after a group of control observations salicylate was admitted to both side chambers. The tissues were placed so that collections in one side chamber represented movement into the joint space, and into the other chamber represented movement out of the joint space. Again there was no significant change in the rate of movement of ^{42}K in either direction $(P > 0.3)$.

The third experiment was of similar design but the synovial tissue was acutely inflamed. The patient seemed to be suffering from rheumatoid arthritis clinically, but diagnostic arthrotomy was undertaken because she was seronegative. Exposure to salicylate produced a statistically significant increase in movement of ^{42}K in both directions across the membrane (Mean values—control 100 per cent; in the presence of salicylate: into the joint space 111 per cent $(P < 0.01)$; out of the joint space 108 per cent $(P < 0.02.)$. Moreover, while salicylate passed into the central chamber in the first two experiments, as judged by the colour change on adding ferric chloride, in this experiment it failed to penetrate despite an exposure of four and a quarter hours and a coincident increase in the permeability to potassium.

Implications

The depletion by salicylate of intracellular potassium in rat diaphragm, where phosphorylation is coupled to oxidation, and the failure of salicylate to change the movement of potassium in normal red cells and in synovium, where phosphorylation is coupled to glycolysis, suggests that the depletion is due to uncoupling of oxidative phosphorylation. However, this deprivation of energy did not produce the predicted slowing of influx but a totally unexpected acceleration of efflux. Slowing of influx appeared with more concentrated salicylate and with dinitrophenol, and suggests the important conclusion that both influx and efflux of potassium were energy-dependent, and that efflux was the more sensitive to energy deprivation. The similarity of the effects of dinitrophenol and 10 mM sodium salicylate suggests that the two drugs were acting in the same way; nevertheless, in man therapeutic concentrations rarely rise above 2 mM (Smith, 1959).

The results on red cells and on synovium are in contrast to those of Waltner, Csernovszky and Kelemen (1959) and of Bianchi (1953). This might be due to differences in technique. However, on theoretical grounds and from the work of Maizels (1951) the results on red cells were as expected. In the experiments of Bianchi on synovium *in vivo* the subsynovial plexus of vessels was intact (Bauer, Ropes & Waine, 1940), and the widely-described effects of salicylates on vessels may have been responsible for their findings. In my experiments only the permeability of the membrane and of its fibrous tissue support were involved.

The difference between the influence of salicylate on tissues from healthy people and on those from people with inflammatory joint disease is strongly suggestive, although the number of experiments is small. • Were this difference general, explanations of the actions of salicylates in rheumatic diseases would be subject to a potent source of error if they were based only on experiments in healthy tissues. The failure of salicylate to penetrate inflamed synovium despite the increased permeability to potassium emphasizes the main conclusion of this work: the permeability of a membrane may not be a passive, non-selective, sieve-like property, but a series of substance-specific and possibly energy-consuming reactions.

SUMMARY

Salicylate depletes intracellular potassium in the rat diaphragm by accelerating efflux, but the drug has no effect on potassium movement in normal red cells and in synovium. It is suggested that potassium depletion is due to uncoupling of oxidative phosphorylation, and also that both influx and efflux of potassium are energy-dependent.

In contrast to its effect on healthy synovial tissue, salicylate does not penetrate inflamed synovium although the latter has an increased permeability to potassium. Thus the permeability of a membrane appears to be substance-specific and possibly energy-consuming.

REFERENCES

Barnes, J. M., Duff, J. I., & Threlfall, C. J. (1955). *J. Physiol. (Lond.)*, **130**, 585.
Bauer, W., Ropes, M. W., & Waine, H. (1940). *Physiol. Rev.*, **20**, 272.
Bianchi, C. (1953). *Brit. J. Pharmacol.*, **8**, 130.
Brody, T. M. (1955). *Pharmacol. Rev.*, **7**, 335.
Creese, R. (1954). *Proc. roy. Soc. B*, **142**, 497.
Glynn, I. M. (1958). *In* 'The Method of Isotopic Tracers applied to the Study of Active Ion Transport', p. 46, ed. Coursaget, J. London: Pergamon Press.
Hicklin, J. A. (1962). The effects of salicylate and other drugs on the movement of potassium through some biological membranes. Ph.D. Thesis, University of London.
Jeffrey, S. W., & Smith, M. J. H. (1959). *Biochem. J.*, **72**, 462.
Keynes, R. D., & Maisel, G. W. (1954). *Proc. roy. Soc. B*, **142**, 383.
Joyce, C. R. B., & Weatherall, M. (1958). *J. Physiol. (Lond.)*, **142**, 453.
Maizels, M. (1951). *J. Physiol. (Lond.)*, **112**, 59.

Manchester, K. L., Randle, P. J., & Smith, G. H. (1958). *Brit. med. J.*, i, 1028.

Penniall, R. (1958). *Biochim. biophys. Acta (Amst.)*, 30, 247.

Ponder, E. (1952). 'Haemolysis and Related Phenomena', p. 364. London: Churchill.

Smith, M. J. H. (1959). *J. Pharm. Pharmacol.*, 11, 705.

Solomon, A. K., & Gold, G. L. (1955). *J. gen. Physiol.*, 38, 371.

Thomas, D. P. P., & Dingle, J. T. (1958). *Biochem. J.*, 68, 231.

Ussing, H. U. (1958). *In* 'The Method of Isotopic Tracers applied to the Study of Active Ion Transport', p. 139, ed. Coursaget, J. London: Pergamon Press.

Waltner, K. Jr., Csernovszky, M., & Kelemen, E. (1959). *Biochem. Pharmacol.*, 2, 50.

CIRCULATORY EFFECTS OF SALICYLATES

W. Donald Alexander

University Department of Medicine, Gardiner Institute
Western Infirmary, Glasgow

It is frequently stated that salicylates do not have any deleterious effect on the heart (Goodman & Gilman, 1955; Smith, 1960). The pharmacological studies on which this statement is based have usually been made on healthy animals or their tissues. In patients with damaged hearts, however, it is now clear that salicylates can precipitate pulmonary oedema or congestive heart failure, although this does not happen commonly. The patients with cardiac damage most likely to receive large doses of salicylate are those with rheumatic fever, and the circulatory effects of the drug in this disease therefore deserve particular study. The aim of treatment in rheumatic fever is rapid cure of the acute attack and reduction of cardiac sequelae. The influence of salicylates on the course of acute rheumatic carditis and on the late incidence of chronic valvular disease have therefore been considered separately.

Long-term studies. Table 1 reviews the effect of salicylate therapy during the acute rheumatic attack on the subsequent incidence of carditis. Comparisons between the results reported in one study and in another must not be pressed too far because, as Feinstein (1961) has shown, the incidence of carditis and the criteria for its diagnosis vary markedly from one study to the next. However, comparison of those treated with salicylates and with steroids shows the incidence of carditis at the end of the studies to be about the same in each group. Secondly, in the four studies containing controls the weight of evidence favours the view that salicylates do not give any clear advantage over symptomatic measures in preventing residual carditis. Illingworth and co-workers (1957) make the interesting suggestion that the best results were obtained by using aspirin and cortisone simultaneously, and more evidence is urgently needed on this important point. In contrast to the steroid and salicylate trials, there is ample evidence of the value of long-term prophylactic penicillin in preventing relapses and thus, also, chronic rheumatic heart disease.

Influence of salicylate on acute rheumatic carditis. Although salicylates usually suppress arthritis and fever, there is no acceptable evidence that they shorten the course or reduce the severity of acute rheumatic carditis. On the other hand, several reports of deterioration in cardiac status with the onset of congestive failure or pulmonary oedema during salicylate therapy have appeared, and in some instances (Sutcliffe, 1955; Bywaters & Thomas, 1961) congestive failure or pulmonary oedema was repeatedly precipitated by courses of salicylate.

TABLE 1. EFFECT OF SALICYLATE THERAPY ON THE INCIDENCE OF RHEUMATIC CARDITIS

Study	Salicylate therapy compared with	Minimum duration of follow up (yr.)	Difference in incidence of carditis at end of study
Illingworth et al., 1954	Controls	1 (ave. 3)	none
Illingworth et al., 1957	Controls Steroid Steroid + salicylate	1	best results with cortisone + salicylate
M.R.C. Rheumatic Fever Working Party, 1960	ACTH Cortisone	5	none
Combined Rheumatic Fever Study Group, 1960	Prednisone	1	none
Thomas, 1961	Controls ACTH Cortisone	5	none (recurrences excluded)
Dorfman, Gross and Lorincz, 1961	Controls Hydrocortisone (HC) HC + aspirin	1	Steroid and Steroid + aspirin better than Aspirin + Controls
Bywaters and Thomas, 1962	Cortisone	5	none

Experimental studies

We therefore studied the prevalence of heart failure in all patients admitted and treated with salicylate during a 16-month period (Alexander & Smith, 1962). There were 50 patients in all. None had failure on admission, but nine developed clinical signs of heart failure during the first week of treatment with salicylate. The commonest signs of failure were overfilling of the neck veins and crepitations at the lung bases, but in three patients X-ray evidence of pulmonary vascular congestion also developed, and one had sacral oedema and orthopnoea. In three of the nine patients signs of failure persisted for several days, and one required treatment with mersalyl.

Clinical examination of the nine patients in whom failure developed showed that eight had unequivocal evidence of carditis, diastolic murmurs in six and pericardial friction in two, and seven had an abnormal electrocardiogram, ST-T changes in five, including a pericarditis pattern in four, and first degree heart block in two. Six patients gave a previous history of rheumatic fever. Of the total series of 50 rheumatic patients, 16 showed clinical evidence of carditis by the criteria of the M.R.C. Rheumatic Fever Working Party (1960). Thus half of the patients with rheumatic carditis developed congestive signs during the first week of salicylate therapy, whereas only one of the 34 patients with rheumatic fever but without clinical carditis showed congestive failure.

Previous work (Tenney & Miller, 1955; Alexander & Johnson, 1956) had suggested that the onset of cardiac failure might be related to increased cardiac output and work induced by salicylates, and these parameters have been studied by two groups independently; the findings are set out in Table 2. In both studies salicylate ingestion caused a 45 per

TABLE 2. CIRCULATORY ADAPTATION TO THE INCREASED METABOLISM INDUCED
BY SALICYLATES

	Alexander and Smith, 1962	*Kroetz et al., 1961*
Method of study	cardiac catheterization	dye dilution
Subjects	6 patients, mainly with chronic rheumatic heart disease	7 normal individuals
Preparation and dosage	7·0 g. sodium salicylate in a single dose	7·2–10·2 g. aspirin daily
Time of study	$\frac{1}{2}$–$1\frac{1}{2}$ hours after dose	after 2–4 days
Serum salicylate	36·2 ± 2·0 mg. per 100 ml.	63 mg. per 100 ml.
Oxygen consumption	+45 per cent	+45 per cent
Arteriovenous oxygen difference	+18 per cent	+25 per cent
Cardiac output	+23 per cent	+18 per cent
Left ventricular work	+23 per cent	+21 per cent

The values shown for the last four parameters were the average increments. The values of Alexander and Smith were all at one hour.

cent increase in oxygen consumption. Approximately half this increase in tissue oxygen requirement was met by increased cardiac output, and the remaining half was accounted for by increased peripheral uptake of available oxygen, i.e. a widening of the A-V oxygen difference. The left ventricular work increased by about one-fifth in both studies. In one of our patients, a young adult female admitted because of salicylate poisoning, the cardiac output was twice the normal value calculated from age and surface area; her serum salicylate concentration was 83 mg. per 100 ml.

The mechanism by which salicylate induces cardiac failure in some rheumatic patients has given rise to much speculation. The main possibilities are:

(i) increased sodium intake (York & Fischer, 1947; Phear, 1955);

 (ii) increased plasma volume (Reid, Watson & Sproull, 1950), plus an allergic factor (Sutcliffe, 1955);
(iii) electrolyte changes:
    (*a*) sodium retention (Hetzel, Charnock & Lander, 1959);
    (*b*) potassium loss (Robin, Davis & Rees, 1959);
    (*c*) hypokalaemia (Hetzel, 1962);
 (iv) increase in free circulating thyroxine (Christensen, 1960);
 (v) increased cardiac output (Kroetz et al., 1961; Alexander & Smith, 1962).

Failure cannot be due to the sodium content of salicylate mixtures because several cases have occurred following aspirin therapy. Evidence of allergy is absent in most reported cases. OSORIO has shown that there is no increase in circulating free thyroxine, and so this probably is not responsible. There remain electrolyte changes, particularly sodium retention and hypokalaemia, and increased cardiac output due to augmented tissue requirement for oxygen. The latter could explain the onset of congestive failure. Another peripherally-acting metabolic stimulant, thyroid hormone, is well recognized as being responsible for heart failure in thyrotoxic patients, although here, too, failure almost always occurs in those who already have cardiac damage. In a group of thyrotoxic patients the mean increase in cardiac output, compared with values obtained after successful treatment, was 61 per cent (Humerfelt, Müller & Storstein, 1958).

Whatever the mechanism, salicylate rarely precipitates failure unless the heart is already injured by acute carditis, with or without chronic rheumatic endocarditis. Our experience, therefore, supports the conclusion of Bywaters and Thomas (1961) that in those rheumatic patients with active disease and clear evidence of carditis salicylates are potentially dangerous because they may precipitate failure.

SUMMARY

With very few exceptions the circulatory effects of salicylates are of clinical importance only in patients with rheumatic fever. Salicylates may influence either the course of the acute illness or the late incidence of valve disease. Long-term studies show no convincing evidence that salicylates or steroids have any advantage over symptomatic treatment.

Salicylates can induce cardiac failure or pulmonary oedema in a proportion of patients with rheumatic carditis. The increased cardiac output and work induced by salicylates are reviewed. In two studies salicylate ingestion caused a 45 per cent increase in oxygen consumption. Approximately half the increase in oxygen requirement was met by increased cardiac output; the remaining half was accounted for by increased peripheral uptake of available oxygen. Doses of salicylate sufficient to cause increased cardiac output and work are best avoided when there is clear evidence of carditis.

REFERENCES

Alexander, W. D., & Johnson, K. W. M. (1956). *Clin. Sci.*, **15**, 593.
Alexander, W. D., & Smith, G. (1962). *Lancet*, **i**, 768.
Bywaters, E. G. L., & Thomas, G. T. (1961). *Brit. med. J.*, **i**, 1628.
Bywaters, E. G. L., & Thomas, G. T. (1962). *Brit. med. J.*, **ii**, 221.
Christensen, L. K. (1960). *Acta med. scand.*, **166**, 133.
Combined Rheumatic Fever Study Group (1960). *New Engl. J. Med.*, **262**, 895.
Dorfman, A., Gross, J. I., & Lorincz, A. E. (1961). *Pediatrics*, **27**, 692.
Feinstein, A. R. (1961). *Pediatrics*, **27**, 819.
Goodman, L. S., & Gilman, A. (1955). 'The Pharmacological Basis of Therapeutics', 2nd Ed., p. 285. New York: Macmillan.
Hetzel, B. S. (1962). *Lancet*, **i**, 1409.
Hetzel, B. S., Charnock, J. S., & Lander, H. (1959). *Metabolism*, **8**, 205.
Humerfelt, S., Müller, O., & Storstein, O. (1958). *Amer. Heart J.*, **56**, 87.
Illingworth, R. S., Burke, J., Doxiadis, S. A., Lorber, J., Philpott, M. G., & Stone, D. G. H. (1954). *Quart. J. Med.*, N.S. **23**, 177.
Illingworth, R. S., Lorber, J., Holt, K. S., & Short, J. R. (1957). *Lancet*, **ii**, 653.
Kroetz, F. W., deGroot, W. J., Leonard, J. J., & Warren, J. V. (1961). *Circulation*, **24**, 975.
M.R.C. Rheumatic Fever Working Party, joint report (1960). *Brit. med. J.*, **ii**, 1033.
Phear, D. N. (1955). *Arch. Middx Hosp.*, **5**, 172.
Reid, J., Watson, R. D., & Sproull, D. H. (1950). *Quart. J. Med.*, N.S. **19**, 1.
Robin, E. D., Davis, R. P., & Rees, S. B. (1959). *Amer. J. Med.*, **26**, 869.
Smith, P. K. (1960). *Ann. N.Y. Acad. Sci.*, **86**, 38.
Sutcliffe, J. (1955). *Brit. J. Radiol.*, **28**, 314.
Tenney, S. M., & Miller, R. M. (1955). *Amer. J. Med.*, **19**, 498.
Thomas, G. T. (1961). *Brit. med. J.*, **i**, 1635.
York, C. L., & Fischer, W. J. H. (1947). *New. Engl. J. Med.*, **237**, 477.

EFFECTS OF ACETYLSALICYLIC ACID UPON BODY WATER DISTRIBUTION IN MAN

DANIEL M. BACHMAN, EVAN CALKINS, AND WALTER BAUER

Department of Medicine, Massachusetts General Hospital
Boston, Mass., U.S.A.

SINCE the early reports of Hanzlik (1917) and of Swift (1922) pertaining to salicyl oedema, controversy has waged concerning the question of whether the salicylates increase or decrease the several body water compartments. Increased plasma volume has been reported to result from salicylate therapy (Jager & Alway, 1946; York & Fischer, 1947); increased water content of erythrocytes exposed to therapeutic concentrations of salicylates has been observed both *in vitro* and *in vivo* (Waltner, Csernovszky & Kelemen, 1958; 1959); positive water balance and increased body weight have been reported to occur in dogs fed aspirin (Gaebler et al., 1957); and diuresis has been reported to follow the discontinuance of aspirin therapy (Reid, Macdougall & Andrews, 1957). In contrast, Reid, Watson and Sproull (1950) inferred from balance studies that sodium salicylate had effected a net decrease in total body water in their patients with acute rheumatic fever; reduction in radiosodium space in two patients with rheumatic fever treated with aspirin has been reported (Aikawa, 1952); and oedema produced in the hind paw of the rat by hyaluronidase has been observed to subside more rapidly in animals treated with salicylates (Kelemen, 1955).

Experimental studies

In an attempt to resolve some aspects of this problem, direct measurements of body water compartments have been made in three normal male medical students (Table, subjects 1–3) and in four male and four female patients with arthritis; five patients suffered from rheumatoid arthritis (subjects 4–7 & 11), two had rheumatoid spondylitis (subjects 8 & 10), and subject 9 had infective arthritis. Subject 9 suffered from diabetes mellitus and chronic pyelonephritis, but all the other subjects were without cardiac, hepatic, or renal disease. Six patients were studied in hospital, and in three of them (subjects 4–6) diet and fluid intake were controlled during balance studies; the remaining subjects were confined to the overnight ward only for the period of several hours required for each set of fluid space measurements.

Measurements of body water compartments were made off treatment and during periods of high dosage with aspirin. The sequence of control and aspirin periods was varied, and the mean interval between the two sets of measurements was 8 ± 4 days. Aspirin dosage ranged from $3\cdot6$ to $6\cdot0$ g. daily, and the combined mean salicylate level attained was 21 ± 5 mg. per 100 ml. (Brodie, Udenfriend & Coburn, 1944). All space-measuring substances were administered intravenously by means of

EFFECT OF ASPIRIN ON BODY WATER COMPARTMENTS

| | Body water compartments | | | | | |
| | Total body (antipyrine space[1]) | | Extracellular (bromide space[2]) | | Intracellular (antipyrine − bromide spaces) | |
Subject	Control (l.)	Net change on aspirin (l.)	Control (l.)	Net change on aspirin (l.)	Control (l.)	Net change on aspirin (l.)
1	40·8	+7·0	20·7	+1·8	20·1	+5·2
2	44·9	+2·9	21·8	+2·3	23·1	+0·6
3	45·2	+1·7	21·1	+1·8	24·1	−0·1
4	24·7	+2·1	14·9	−0·3	9·8	+2·4
5	32·7	+5·9	18·0	+3·7	14·7	+2·2
6	27·0	+4·6	18·2	+1·4	8·8	+3·2
7	22·9	+4·5	14·1	+3·2	8·8	+1·3
8	24·1	−0·7	14·7	−1·1	9·4	+0·4
9	24·7	+2·6	15·7	−0·3	9·0	+2·9
10	32·5	+2·0	18·2	+0·4	14·3	+1·6
11[3]	25·1	+2·5	12·4	−0·1	12·7	+2·6
Mean change	+3·2		+1·2		+2·0	
Significance*	$P < 0\cdot001$		$P < 0\cdot05$		$P < 0\cdot001$	

[1] Soberman et al., 1949. Antipyrine zero-time concentrations were calculated by regression analysis (Hoel, 1954); F analysis of regression was applied as a test of linearity, and data not meeting the criterion $P < 0\cdot1$ were eliminated from the study.

[2] Brodie, Brand & Leshin, 1939. Bromide chemical analyses (Brodie & Friedman, 1938) were carried out in triplicate, and the four- and five-hour bromide spaces averaged.

[3] Total body water measured by deuterium oxide space (Schloerb et al., 1950). Deuterium atom per cent excess was determined by means of the mass spectrometer (Solomon, Edelman & Soloway, 1950).

* t test for correlated means (Dixon & Massey, 1957).

calibrated apparatus, and space measurements were corrected for plasma water content, assumed to be $0\cdot93$. Total body water was estimated by deuterium oxide space in one subject, and by antipyrine space in the remainder. Extracellular water was estimated by bromide space, and intracellular water calculated from the differences between these two space measurements. Plasma volume was estimated by means of Evans

Blue (Gregersen, 1944). The precision of the techniques was evaluated by repeated measurements on the same subjects under conditions assumed to be identical. The combined standard deviations were: deuterium oxide space $\pm 1\cdot4$ litres, antipyrine space $\pm 1\cdot6$ litres, bromide space $\pm 0\cdot7$ litres, and Evans Blue space $\pm 0\cdot3$ litres.

There was a definite trend towards increased antipyrine and bromide spaces, and in the difference between these two spaces, during aspirin therapy (Table). The most likely interpretation of these data would seem to be that aspirin therapy tends to increase total body water, intracellular water, and, to a lesser extent, extracellular water. Nevertheless, despite these significant increases in body water spaces no changes in body weight were observed. The three patients who received a constant diet while undergoing balance studies did not lose weight, despite the known stimulatory effect of therapeutic doses of salicylates upon oxidative metabolism; maintenance of a constant weight might be explained by retained body water replacing an equal weight of body solid lost by oxidation. Plasma volume was estimated in five patients; in two it increased during aspirin therapy, in two it decreased, and it was unchanged in the fifth patient. Of the three patients studied by balance techniques, two showed urinary water and sodium retention and an increased bromide space during aspirin therapy, whereas none of these changes were seen in the third patient (subject 4).

Implications

A fundamental objection might be raised to the effect that the administration of therapeutic doses of aspirin in some way negates the usual meaning of the spaces measured; that the changes observed in the present study do not actually reflect changes in body water but rather an increased permeability to antipyrine, bromide, and deuterium oxide of some unknown body compartment. The absence of changes in body weight might be cited in favour of this point of view. It is difficult to conceive what this hypothetical body compartment or compartments might be that would become more permeable to substances chemically and physically so diverse as antipyrine, bromide ion, and deuterium oxide. Nevertheless it must be admitted that this objection cannot be answered by the data of this study, and indeed cannot be answered by dilutional techniques of measurement alone. Preliminary *in vitro* studies in our laboratory have shown that salicylates do not increase the permeability to antipyrine of ox fat. Measurements of total body water by the specific gravity technique of Rathbun and Pace (1945) might afford a means of answering this objection definitively.

If it be assumed that the data presented in this study actually represent increases in body water compartments, failure to find changes in body weight requires explanation. Increase in total body water exactly balanced by loss of an equal weight of body solid would result in no change in body weight. One example of this type of exchange is the maintenance of a constant body weight during the early stages of a weight reduction diet when, despite diminished intake of food, body weight is maintained or even increased, due to retention of water (Newburgh, 1944). The increase in oxidative metabolism that results from aspirin therapy could be expected to result in losses of body weight in patients receiving a constant diet, yet in balance studies no changes in body weight have been observed with therapeutic (non-toxic) doses of aspirin (Bachman, Calkins & Bauer, 1956). Failure to find weight loss during aspirin therapy in the case of patients receiving a constant diet, despite significant increase in oxidative metabolism resulting from aspirin administration, could best be explained by retention of body water. Bansi and Olsen (1959) have reported that the administration of tri-iodothyronine to obese subjects resulted in increased total body water and intracellular water, findings that are similar to our results with aspirin. When the effects of therapeutic doses of aspirin upon oxidative metabolism are taken into account, the finding of no change in body weight in the patients in this study tends to support, rather than detract from, the point of view that the space measurements presented represent real changes in body water compartments.

SUMMARY

Therapeutic doses of aspirin were found to increase antipyrine space, bromide space, and the difference between these two spaces, in normal individuals and in patients with arthritis.

Therapeutic doses of aspirin were found to increase the deuterium oxide space in one patient with arthritis.

The present address of Dr. Bachman is University of Oregon Medical School, Portland, Ore., U.S.A., and of Dr. Calkins is State University of New York at Buffalo Medical School, Buffalo, N.Y., U.S.A.

REFERENCES

Aikawa, J. K. (1952). *Amer. J. Med.*, **13**, 640.
Bachman, D. M., Calkins, E., & Bauer, W. (1956). *Ann. rheum. Dis.*, **15**, 385.
Bansi, H. W., & Olsen, J. M. (1959). *Acta endocr. (Kbh.)*, **32**, 113.
Brodie, B. B., Brand, E., & Leshin, S. (1939). *J. biol. Chem.*, **130**, 555.
Brodie, B. B., & Friedman, M. M. (1938). *J. biol. Chem.*, **124**, 511.
Brodie, B. B., Udenfriend, S., & Coburn, A. F. (1944). *J. Pharmacol. exp. Ther.*, **80**, 114.
Dixon, W. J., & Massey, F. J. Jr. (1957). 'Introduction to Statistical Analysis', 2nd Ed., p. 124. New York: McGraw Hill.
Gaebler, O. H., Glovinsky, R., Lees, H., & Vitti, T. (1957). *Canad. J. Biochem. Physiol.*, **35**, 1183.
Gregersen, M. I. (1944). *J. Lab. clin. Med.*, **29**, 1266.

Hanzlik, P. J., Scott, R. W., & Reycraft, J. L. (1917). *Arch. intern. Med.*, 20, 329.
Hoel, P. J. (1954). 'Introduction to Mathematical Statistics', 2nd Ed., p. 125. New York: John Wiley.
Jager, B. V., & Alway, R. (1946). *Amer. J. med. Sci.*, 211, 273.
Kelemen, E. (1955). *Acta med. Acad. Sci. hung.*, 9, 125.
Newburgh, L. H. (1944). *Physiol. Rev.*, 24, 18.
Rathbun, E. N., & Pace, N. (1945). *J. biol. Chem.*, 158, 667.
Reid, J., Macdougall, A. I., & Andrews, M. M. (1957). *Brit. med. J.*, ii, 1071.
Reid, J., Watson, R. D., & Sproull, D. H. (1950). *Quart. J. Med.*, N.S. 19, 1.
Schloerb, P. R., Friis-Hansen, B. J., Edelman, I. S., Solomon, A. K., & Moore, F. D. (1950). *J. clin. Invest.*, 29, 1296.
Soberman, R., Brodie, B. B., Levy, B. B., Axelrod, J., Hollander, V., & Steele, J. M. (1949). *J. biol. Chem.*, 179, 31.
Solomon, A. K., Edelman, I. S., & Soloway, S. (1950). *J. clin. Invest.*, 29, 1311.
Swift, H. F. (1922). *Boston med. surg. J.*, 187, 331.
Waltner, K. Jr., Csernovszky, M., & Kelemen, E. (1958). *Experientia (Basel)*, 14, 277.
Waltner, K. Jr., Csernovszky, M., & Kelemen, E. (1959). *Biochem. Pharmacol.*, 2, 50.
York, C. L., & Fischer, W. J. H. Jr. (1947). *New. Engl. J. Med.*, 237, 477.

DISCUSSION

H. VAN CAUWENBERGE (*Institut de Clinique et de Pathologie médicale, University of Liège, Belgium*):

I was not aware of the effect of aspirin on body water distribution in man, described by BACHMAN. In relation to the circulatory effects of salicylates, it would be interesting to study water distribution to compare in the same patient the effects of therapeutic doses of salicylate and cortisone.

ALEXANDER said that it is occasionally dangerous to give salicylate to patients with rheumatic fever because the drug may precipitate heart failure. I wonder whether it is much less dangerous to give cortisone to these patients. I have seen some patients who were treated with digitaline for heart failure, apparently without any effect, but treatment with salicylate then produced a satisfactory response, with improvement in the heart failure. However, I agree that now the best results in these cases are obtained with salicylates and cortisone.

HICKLIN's paper is of especial interest because we have also studied the modifications of permeability induced by various substances and the effects of salicylates on these modifications (Roskam, J., van Cauwenberge, H., Lecomte, J., & Hugues, J. [1959]. VI Congr. int. Ther., p. 81. Strassburg). I wonder whether potassium is a rather particular case to study in this connexion, because its movements may be affected by other substances that influence the permeability.

In general we have observed good inhibitory effects by salicylates on the increased permeability induced by such agents as histamine (van Cauwenberge, H., Lapière, C., Halkin, F., & Lecomte, J. [1959]. *C.R. Soc. Biol. (Paris)*, **153**, 514) and 5-hydroxytryptamine in the whole animal (Franchimont, P., Lecomte, J., & van Cauwenberge, H. [1961]. *C.R. Soc. Biol. (Paris)*, **155**, 180), or by application of chloroform to the skin, but correspondingly little effect of ACTH and cortisone (van Cauwenberge, H., Franchimont, P., Lapière, C. M., & Lecomte, J. [1962]. *J. belge Méd. phys. Rhum.*, **17**, 53, 69). On the basis of many experiments, including those using adrenalectomized animals (van Cauwenberge, H., Lapière, C. M., & Lecomte, J. [1960]. *Ann. ital. Derm. Sif.*, **15**, 3; Halkin, F. [1960]. *C.R. Soc. Biol. (Paris)*, **154**, 1668), we have concluded that the effect of salicylates on impaired permeability is not mediated through the pituitary-adrenal system.

HICKLIN: I agree with VAN CAUWENBERGE that perhaps potassium is a rather particular case, but any substance that is being investigated must fall into this category. Permeability is particular to the tissue, the substance studied, and the drug applied. For instance, it has been shown that dinitrophenol blocks sodium transport in frog skin but not in the muscle of the same animal. The term permeability should not therefore be used to represent a 'blanket' effect, and more subtle definitions expressed in terms of ions and substances, handled separately by membranes, might be employed.

Movement of sodium and potassium

WINTERS: It is known that in some tissues potassium movements are linked with those of sodium. What happens to sodium in the rat diaphragm experiments? Is the water content of the tissue altered, since the potassium data is expressed as millimoles per litre of tissue water?

HICKLIN: With respect to the liaison between sodium and potassium, this certainly appears to be true in most tissues studied, so that work done on potassium may be done via work done on sodium. The actual thing moved may be sodium, but the steps in the argument are identical whether one regards it as a first or as a second-order phenomenon. However, one must remember the argument that the membrane potential is not equal to the equilibrium potassium potential. That is to say, if you calculate what the potential would be if potassium were entirely passive, the observed effect is smaller. Therefore, we can infer that some work is done on the potassium directly. In the diaphragm experiments it was found that when the potassium concentration fell, the sodium concentration was increased. However, it is not on a one-to-one basis, and in some cases they both fell (Hicklin, unpublished data). This may be due to the fact that one measures the sodium space by the extracellular potassium space.

All my reported values were corrected for changes in cell volume, i.e. in some cases there was a change of volume. However, what I did was to obtain a wet–dry weight ratio for the control half of the diaphragm and make the wet–dry weight ratio of the other half of the diaphragm equal to this mathematically; I corrected the cell volume to this value to allow for these changes. There were slight changes in volume in the red cells, but the changes were not sufficient to account for the results.

WINTERS: If an appreciable part of the potassium gradient in normal tissues represents work done on sodium, is it so surprising that if metabolism is interrupted then sodium leaks in and potassium leaks out?

HICKLIN: Yes, because the paths by which sodium moves in and out of the cell are different (Keynes, R. D. & Swan, R. C. [1959] *J. Physiol. (Lond.)*, **147**, 626), and the connecting links between efflux and potassium–sodium exchanges are specific carriers that move in both directions. Moreover, if outward movement of potassium were purely passive then it would be proportional to the intracellular concentration. Stopping inward movement does not increase the intracellular concentration and thus the observed accelerated efflux of potassium would not be an expected result. Sodium has been the ion most intensively studied and is often considered as the prime mover, but there is nothing in the experimental evidence to prove this logically. Indeed the reported effects on sodium movement could have been secondary to potassium movement, as well as *vice versa*. Perhaps the best comment is that of a much earlier scientific meeting, 'It still moves'.

EFFECTS OF SALICYLATES ON INFLAMMATION

Chairman L. E. GLYNN

ANTAGONISM BY ASPIRIN AND LIKE-ACTING DRUGS OF KININS AND SRS-A IN GUINEA-PIG LUNG

H. O. J. COLLIER

Department of Pharmacological Research, Parke, Davis and Company
Hounslow, Middlesex

THESE studies concern aspirin antagonism of the kinins, bradykinin, kallidin, and related peptides, in guinea-pig lung (Collier et al., 1959, 1960). They also concern its antagonism of Slow Reacting Substance in Anaphylaxis (SRS-A), an endogenous substance differing from kinins both chemically and pharmacologically (Berry, Collier & Holgate, 1963). The studies extend to drugs acting like aspirin, among which is mefenamic acid, recently reported by Winder and co-workers (1962), which potently antagonizes kinins in guinea-pig lung (Collier & Shorley, 1963).

Antagonism of kinins by aspirin

Our experiments started from the double hypothesis that some inflammatory reactions, including pain, are caused by release of endogenous substances and that non-steroidal anti-inflammatory agents are pharmacological antagonists of one or more such substances. Assuming that bradykinin was one of the substances released, we tested the second part of this hypothesis on the Konzett-Rössler preparation of guinea-pig lungs *in vivo* because it was found that partially purified bradykinin was a potent bronchoconstrictor. When tested, aspirin antagonized bradykinin bronchoconstriction at doses comparable with small clinical doses in man. This effect comes on quickly and can outlast the normal life of the Konzett-Rössler preparation. It is of interest to know whether this effect was, in the terms used by Gaddum (1957), surmountable and specific (Table 1).

After a dose of aspirin that suppresses the response to a normally effective dose of bradykinin, a higher dose of kinin restores it. For example, after 4 mg. per kg. of aspirin intravenously, about 40 μg. of bradykinin produces the same response as 1 μg. before aspirin. Even very high doses of aspirin, 128 mg. per kg. intravenously, can be surmounted by a sufficient dose of bradykinin (Collier & Shorley, 1963); in fact, high doses of aspirin are relatively more easily overcome than are low doses.

TABLE I. TYPES OF PHARMACOLOGICAL ANTAGONISM
(Gaddum, 1957)

Type of antagonism	Relationship of agonist to antagonist	Pharmacological features	Example
NOT AT RECEPTORS			
Independent	opposite and independent effects	non-specific	of histamine, acetylcholine, or 5-hydroxy-tryptamine by adrenaline on bronchioles
Neutralizing	chemical combination to form inactive products	specific surmountable	of arsenic or mercury by dimercaprol
AT RECEPTORS			
Non-competitive	combination with different parts of receptor mechanism so that antagonist renders agonist ineffective	non-surmountable dose response curve flattened	of acetylcholine by cinchonidine on guinea-pig ileum[1] (imperfect–perfect case unknown)
Competitive	competition for same part of receptor	specific surmountable parallel shift of dose response curve along dose axis	of acetylcholine by atropine on guinea-pig ileum

[1] Arunlakshana & Schild, 1959.

Aspirin antagonizes synthetic bradykinin and the decapeptide kallidin as easily as it does impure natural bradykinin (Shorley & Collier, 1961; Bhoola et al., 1962). Wasp kinin (Collier et al., 1960) and several synthetic close analogues of kinins (Collier, 1963) are also susceptible to the antagonism. In contrast, even high doses of aspirin are ineffective against histamine, acetylcholine, 5-hydroxytryptamine (Collier & Shorley, 1960), and Substance P (Bhoola et al., 1962). Therefore the antagonism is selective for certain bronchoconstrictors or is, in Gaddum's term,

5*

specific, differing from the non-specific antagonism of all broncho-constrictor agents by adrenaline, which he calls independent.

Judged by minimal effective dose (MED) aspirin, given intravenously as the calcium or sodium salt, was about the most potent known drug tested. After it, in descending order of potency by this route, were sodium phenylbutazone, amidopyrine, phenazone, paracetamol, sodium cincho-phen, and sodium salicylate. Several other chemical relatives of salicylate, including salicylamide, gentisic, γ-resorcylic, 4-hydroxyisophthalic, 3:4-dihydroxybenzoic, and 3:4-dihydroxycinnamic acids, were inactive at the largest doses given. The high potency of intravenous soluble aspirin, MED 2 mg. per kg., compared with that of salicylate, MED

TABLE 2. POTENCY OF SOME NON-STEROIDAL ANTI-INFLAMMATORY AGENTS
IN THE GUINEA-PIG

Potencies, *in vivo*, are expressed relative to phenylbutazone

Drug	Anti-erythema[1]	Anti-bradykinin[2]		Anti-SRS-A[3]
	(*oral*)	(*i.v.*)	(*intraduodenal*)	(*i.v.*)
Phenylbutazone	1·0	1·0	1·0	1·0
Mefenamic acid*	0·5	4·0	0·5	0·5
Amidopyrine	0·13	0·5	1·0	0·25
Aspirin	0·10	2·0	0·25	0·5

* The structural formula of mefenamic acid is

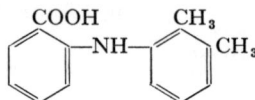

[1] Winder et al., 1962.
[2] Collier & Shorley, 1960; 1963.
[3] Berry, Collier & Holgate, 1963.

64 mg. per kg., suggests that acetylsalicylate has its own activity. When they are given intraduodenally, the potency difference is less, perhaps because most of the acetylsalicylate is converted to salicylate before reaching the target.

In general, the pattern of activity and inactivity of drugs corresponds with that for delaying skin erythema after exposure of guinea-pigs to ultraviolet irradiation (Winder et al., 1958; Adams, 1960). This corres-pondence extends to mefenamic acid (Table 2), which is active in the anti-erythema test (Winder et al., 1962). The antagonism of bradykinin by mefenamic acid resembles that by aspirin in all respects except that it is brief enough to allow the Konzett-Rössler preparation to recover completely from a single dose (Collier & Shorley, 1963).

The antagonism between non-steroidal anti-inflammatory agents and bradykinin can be demonstrated also in the isolated trachea (Bhoola et al., 1962) or the heart-lung preparation (Carpi, Klupp & Konzett, 1962) of the guinea-pig. In all other preparations tried this effect cannot be demonstrated unequivocally (Collier & Shorley, 1960; Lewis, 1962; Schachter, 1962). Aspirin and phenylbutazone show hardly any action against bradykinin bronchoconstriction in the rabbit, and aspirin does not antagonize the hypotensive action of bradykinin in the guinea-pig, nor the contraction of rat uterus *in situ*. Aspirin and like-acting drugs given systemically also fail to inhibit skin wealing due to the intradermal injection of bradykinin, but in this situation the preponderating local concentration of agonist might make the struggle rather unequal. *In vitro*, specific antagonism failed in isolated rat uterus, guinea-pig ileum, and rat duodenum. The result was the same when kallidin was used instead of bradykinin.

The failure of aspirin and like-acting drugs to antagonize bradykinin in preparations other than those of guinea-pig bronchial tree shows that the antagonism is not caused by chemical inactivation of kinin by the drug. In Gaddum's terminology, the antagonism is not by neutralization.

The features of the drug antagonism show that it probably happens at the receptors for bradykinin in the bronchial muscle and takes the form of attachment of molecules of antagonist to the receptors for the agonist. The relatively long duration of action of aspirin is interesting, but it is not essential to this type of action because related drugs are short acting. Possibly aspirin remains attached to the bradykinin receptors. If so, surmountability can be explained by supposing, with Stephenson (1956), that only a fraction of all receptors for one agonist need be activated to give a maximal response. If some receptors are occupied by antagonist, enough remain free to be activated by higher concentrations of agonist.

The contrast between the effectiveness of non-steroidal anti-inflammatory agents in guinea-pig lung and their ineffectiveness in other sites suggests that more than one type of receptor for bradykinin exists. Those sensitive to aspirin and like-acting drugs may be called A-receptors. These are probably the receptors in guinea-pig lung that are more readily activated by bradykinin, but the relative ease with which high doses of aspirin are surmounted suggests that other receptors for bradykinin, which are not blocked by aspirin, might exist there. In other tissues A-receptors may occur, but if they are in the minority aspirin antagonism will be hard to demonstrate.

Failure to show this specific antagonism elsewhere than in guinea-pig lung does not support the view that non-steroidal anti-inflammatory drugs act by kinin antagonism. It has been suggested (Collier, 1962) that there might be another endogenous substance that these drugs antagonize. SRS-A may be such a substance (Berry, Collier & Holgate, 1963).

Antagonism of SRS-A

The observation that aspirin antagonizes SRS-A arose from an earlier one that SRS-A causes bronchoconstriction in the guinea-pig. This effect was obtained with relatively crude material prepared from Tyrode perfusates of the isolated lungs of sensitized animals shocked with antigen in the perfusion fluid. To make sure that the bronchoconstriction was not due to contamination with histamine, acetylcholine, or 5-hydroxytryptamine, it was shown to occur after prior administration of the specific antagonists of these substances. A first attempt to ensure that the material was not contaminated with kinins failed, because aspirin suppressed the bronchoconstrictor response to SRS-A. However, contamination with kinin was easily excluded in other ways, because the material did not affect rat uterus and resisted chymotrypsin. The possibility that SRS-A acted by liberating bradykinin was also elimi-nated, since the latencies of the two responses were about equal; the bronchoconstriction to SRS-A occurred a little faster than that to bradykinin, and reached its peak earlier. Therefore it was concluded that aspirin also antagonizes SRS-A in guinea-pig lung and that its action is selective.

Like the antagonism of bradykinin by aspirin, that of SRS-A can also be surmounted by higher doses of agonist. For example, after 1 mg. per kg. of aspirin intravenously, the response could be restored by eleven times the previous dose of SRS-A. Aspirin shifts the dose-response line to SRS-A horizontally along the dose axis without flattening it. This suggests a competitive type of antagonism.

Potencies of drugs against SRS-A are much like those against brady-kinin except that phenylbutazone appears to be a little stronger and mefenamic acid a little weaker. This brings their rank order closer to that against guinea-pig skin erythema (Table 2). Hydrocortisone and 4-hydroxyisophthalic acid are inactive against SRS-A.

Because SRS-A also contracts isolated preparations of bronchial tree, it may be concluded that it acts locally on bronchial muscle. How then are the receptor mechanisms for bradykinin, SRS-A, and aspirin related? Bradykinin and SRS-A show slightly different patterns of response to antagonists. In some preparations they seem to reinforce one another. They do not show obvious cross-tachyphylaxis, as bradykinin and kallidin do. These facts suggest that bradykinin and SRS-A do not act on the same receptors. Since the shape of the bronchoconstrictor response to SRS-A differs from that to kinin, although their latencies are alike, aspirin seems unlikely to act by blocking a common pathway between the receptors for each agonist and the muscle. In short, aspirin and like-acting drugs seem to block two types of receptor in guinea-pig lung.

Clinical implications

Brocklehurst (1956) showed that human lung produces SRS-A when subjected to anaphylactic shock and that SRS-A contracts isolated human bronchus. These facts led him to suggest that 'SRS-A is of particular importance in human asthma'. However, Brocklehurst failed to show that SRS-A contracts isolated guinea-pig trachea. The fact that SRS-A does this and causes bronchoconstriction *in vivo* in this species supports his view and suggests that the guinea-pig provides a better model for asthma than he supposed. The finding that aspirin and like-acting drugs antagonize SRS-A bronchoconstriction may help to explain the observations that amidopyrine, phenazone, aspirin (Herxheimer & Stresemann, 1961), and phenylbutazone (von Rechenberg, 1962) relieve asthma.

Brocklehurst (1960) found that antigen releases SRS-A from blood vessels and from some other tissues of the guinea-pig and from the lungs of several species. A number of authors (see Brocklehurst, 1962; Mongar & Schild, 1962) have described the release of the same or allied substances from cells or tissues by antigens or poisons. These findings enable the general hypothesis with which this work started to be restated in these particular terms: some reactions to injury are caused by release of SRS-A, and non-steroidal anti-inflammatory agents act as its pharmacological antagonists. It does not exclude the possibility that release of kinins and other agents plays a part also.

SUMMARY

In guinea-pig lung, but not in other tissues, aspirin exerts a potent and long-lasting but surmountable antagonism against peptides of the kinin group. Aspirin is ineffective against bronchoconstriction due to histamine, acetylcholine, 5-hydroxytryptamine, or Substance P. In descending order of potency intravenously, phenylbutazone, amidopyrine, phenazone, paracetamol, and salicylic acid show a like effect, but salicylamide, several other derivatives of benzoic acid, and corticoids are inactive. Mefenamic acid is also a highly effective, surmountable, and specific antagonist of bradykinin bronchoconstriction in guinea-pigs.

The properties of the antagonism of kinins by non-steroidal anti-inflammatory agents suggest that it occurs at kinin receptors in lung. Only a fraction of the total receptor capacity apparently need be activated to evoke a maximal response, and more than one type of receptor for kinins may exist.

Drugs effective against bradykinin are also antagonists of the bronchoconstrictor action of Slow Reacting Substance in Anaphylaxis (SRS-A), which apparently acts on different receptors in bronchial muscle. Among drugs studied, the patterns of antagonism of SRS-A and of kinins correspond fairly closely with that against UV skin erythema. Some reactions to injury may be caused by release of SRS-A, and non-steroidal anti-inflammatory agents may act as pharmacological antagonists of SRS-A.

REFERENCES

Adams, S. S. (1960). *J. Pharm. Pharmacol.*, **12**, 251.
Arunlakshana, O., & Schild, H. O. (1959). *Brit. J. Pharmacol.*, **14**, 48.
Berry, P. A., Collier, H. O. J., & Holgate, J. A. (1963). *J. Physiol. (Lond.)*, **165**, 41P.
Bhoola, K. D., Collier, H. O. J., Schachter, M., & Shorley, P. G. (1962). *Brit. J. Pharmacol.*, **19**, 190.
Brocklehurst, W. E. (1953). *J. Physiol. (Lond.)*, **120**, 16P.
Brocklehurst, W. E. (1956). *In* 'Ciba Foundation Symposium on Histamine', p. 175. ed. Wolstenholme, G. E. W., & O'Connor, C. M. London: Churchill.
Brocklehurst, W. E. (1960). *J. Physiol. (Lond.)*, **151**, 416.
Brocklehurst, W. E. (1962). *Progr. Allergy*, **6**, 539.
Carpi, A., Klupp, H., & Konzett, H. (1962). *Naunyn-Schmiedeberg's Arch. exp. Path. Pharmak.*, **243**, 356.
Collier, H. O. J. (1962). *Biochem. Pharmacol.*, **10**, 47.
Collier, H. O. J. (1963). *Ann. N.Y. Acad. Sci.*, **104**, 290.
Collier, H. O. J., Holgate, J. A., Schachter, M., & Shorley, P. G. (1959). *J. Physiol. (Lond.)*, **149**, 54P.
Collier, H. O. J., Holgate, J. A., Schachter, M., & Shorley, P. G. (1960). *Brit. J. Pharmacol.*, **15**, 290.
Collier, H. O. J., & Shorley, P. G. (1960). *Brit. J. Pharmacol.*, **15**, 601.
Collier, H. O. J., & Shorley, P. G. (1963). *Brit. J. Pharmacol.*, **20**, 345.
Gaddum, J. H. (1957). *Pharmacol. Rev.*, **9**, 211.
Herxheimer, H., & Stresemann, E. (1961). *Nature (Lond.)*, **192**, 1089.
Lewis, G. P. (1962). *Biochem. Pharmacol.*, **10**, 57.
Mongar, J. L., & Schild, H. O. (1962). *Physiol. Rev.*, **42**, 226.
von Rechenberg, H. K. (1962). 'Phenylbutazone–Butazolidin', 2nd Ed. p. 78. London: Arnold.
Schachter, M. (1962). *In* 'Recent Advances in Pharmacology', 3rd Ed., p. 159. ed. Robson, J. M., & Stacey, R. S. London: Churchill.
Shorley, P. G., & Collier, H. O. J. (1961). *Nature (Lond.)*, **188**, 999.
Stephenson, R. P. (1956). *Brit. J. Pharmacol.*, **11**, 379.
Winder, C. V., Wax, J., Burr, V., Been, M., & Rosiere, C. E. (1958). *Arch. int. Pharmacodyn.*, **116**, 261.
Winder, C. V., Wax, J., Scotti, L., Scherrer, R., Jones, E. M., & Short, F. W. (1962). *J. Pharmacol. exp. Ther.*, **138**, 405.

THE EFFECT OF SALICYLATES AND RELATED COMPOUNDS ON ERYTHEMA IN THE GUINEA-PIG AND MAN

S. S. Adams and R. Cobb

Research Department, Boots Pure Drug Company Ltd.
Nottingham

In exploring the mechanism of the anti-inflammatory action of salicylates, many types of experimental inflammation have been employed. Since in many investigations the doses of salicylates have greatly exceeded those normally used therapeutically, the resulting data are of doubtful relevance to the problem. Of particular interest, therefore, are those inflammatory phenomena that are modified by small or moderate doses of salicylates. We have studied two such phenomena, the erythema produced by ultraviolet irradiation of the skin in guinea-pigs, and that produced by applying thurfyl nicotinate cream to human skin.

Ultraviolet erythema in the guinea-pig

The technique with the guinea-pig is a modification of that of Wilhelmi (1949), as described previously (Adams & Cobb, 1958). Shaved albino guinea-pigs were dosed orally with aspirin 30 minutes before a 20-second exposure to ultraviolet light from a Kromayer lamp. Two hours later the degree of erythema was estimated visually on a scale 0–4 by an observer who was unaware of the dosage schedules. The two-hour erythema could be completely suppressed by doses of aspirin that gave blood levels in the region of 15 mg. per 100 ml.

It must be emphasized that this effect was not one of inhibition, but merely a delaying of the onset of erythema. This is demonstrated in Table 1, where the degree of erythema of the same exposed area was recorded at different times after exposure. We thought originally that these results indicated that some vasodilator substance was liberated after exposure, but that its effects were suppressed as long as the salicylate blood level was above a certain critical value. However, there was no correlation between salicylate blood levels and the delayed development of erythema. The mean salicylate blood level nine and a half hours after exposure in animals receiving 320 mg. per kg. of aspirin was twice as high as that two hours after exposure in animals receiving 80 mg. per kg., yet the degree of erythema was much greater in the first group. Thus it may well be that other factors less sensitive to salicylate are involved in the later stages of development of the reaction.

127

When similar experiments were repeated with Evans Blue, 12·5 mg. per kg. injected intravenously immediately after exposure, this delaying effect of aspirin could also be demonstrated on capillary permeability. Infiltration of the dye from the outside of the exposed area began more slowly in the aspirin-treated animals than in the controls. Within 24 hours, however, the exposed areas were deep blue in both series and they could not be distinguished from each other. Once the erythema was

TABLE I. EFFECT OF ASPIRIN ON THE DEVELOPMENT OF ULTRAVIOLET ERYTHEMA

Erythema scores at different times after a single exposure to UV light. The scores were estimated visually on a scale 0–4, and the results are the mean values from groups of eleven guinea-pigs. Doses of 10 per cent acacia (control) or of aspirin were given 30 minutes before exposure.

Preparation	Oral dose	Mean erythema scores Hours after exposure to UV radiation				
	(mg./kg.)	2	4½	7	9½	24
Control		4·0	4·0	4·0	4·0	4·0
Aspirin	320	0·1	1·1	2·8	3·1	3·7
	160	0·4	2·6	4·0	4·0	4·0
	80	1·7	4·0	4·0	4·0	4·0
	40	3·8	4·0	4·0	4·0	4·0

established, as at 18 hours after exposure, when oedema was also present, it was impossible to reduce the erythema with oral doses of 320 mg. per kg., or even 640 mg. per kg. As judged by the dye experiments, however, the reaction at two hours after exposure seems to be mainly one of vasodilatation, there being little infiltration of the dye to indicate an increase in capillary permeability.

Relationship between anti-erythemic and antirheumatic activity

Steroids and chloroquine, the latter even after prolonged dosage, do not delay erythema. We must emphasize, therefore, that the term anti-rheumatic in this context refers specifically to that type of activity associated with the analgesic-antipyretic drugs, as exemplified by aspirin or phenylbutazone.

Is there a relationship between the ability of drugs to delay ultraviolet erythema and their clinical antirheumatic activity and, if so, what is the common factor? Winder and co-workers (1958) showed that, at reasonable dose-levels, out of over one hundred pharmacologically active agents, only ten pyrazole, salicylate, and cinchophen derivatives delayed ultraviolet erythema and that there was a good correspondence between anti-erythemic and antirheumatic doses. Our own results, collected over a number of years, are similar. Like Winder, we had concluded that there was a connexion between anti-erythemic and antirheumatic activity (Adams & Cobb, 1958). We suggested that the group of compounds known as analgesic-antipyretics could be differentiated experimentally into those that have anti-erythemic activity and those that have not, pointing out that only the former group also had antirheumatic activity

TABLE 2. ANTI-ERYTHEMIC AND ANTIRHEUMATIC ACTIVITY OF A NUMBER OF COMPOUNDS

Activity against UV erythema is recorded as that dose that reduced the erythema to a mean response of 2 in a group of animals. The dose of inactive compounds is recorded in parentheses.

| Compound | Effective oral dose | | Clinical activity in rheumatoid arthritis | Reference |
	UV erythema (mg./kg.)	Thurfyl nicotinate erythema (mg.)		
Phenylbutazone	10	inactive (600)	active	1
Oxyphenbutazone	inactive (80)	inactive (400)	active	2
Amidopyrine	80	—	active	3
Aspirin	80	225	active	1
Sodium salicylate	120	inactive (650)	—	
Salicylamide	inactive (320)	—	—	
Acetylcresotic acid	inactive (240)	inactive (650)	—	
Acetanilide	inactive (240)	—	—	
Phenacetin	inactive (240)	—	—	
Paracetamol	inactive (240)	—	less active*	1
4-Hydroxyisophthalic acid	inactive (320)	—	less active*	1
Ethyl α-(4-phenyl-phenoxy)propionate	10–25	—	less active*	4

*Less active than aspirin under the conditions of the trials.

[1] Hajnal, Sharp & Popert, 1959.
[2] Cardoe, 1959.
[3] Van der Meer & den Oudsten, 1960.
[4] Truelove & Duthie, unpublished data.

(Adams, 1960). Therefore it appeared that the anti-erythemic and clinical antirheumatic activities were related, and a common mechanism of action seemed likely.

We have recently found, since testing oxyphenbutazone and ethyl α-(4-phenylphenoxy)propionate, that this correlation is less perfect than we at first thought (Table 2). Oxyphenbutazone was not active at 80 mg. per kg. orally, nor at 40 mg. per kg. intravenously, yet its antirheumatic action is beyond dispute. Ethyl α-(4-phenylphenoxy)propionate, on the other hand, was two to eight times more active than aspirin as an anti-erythemic agent and yet proved to be inactive in a dose of 1·8 g. a day when tested in rheumatoid arthritis by Duthie and Truelove (unpublished data).

The failure of oxyphenbutazone might be due to inability of the guinea-pig to metabolize this substance. Nevertheless it is unlikely that the clinical failure of the phenoxy acid can be explained by such a difference in metabolism, since blood levels after identical doses were very similar and the only metabolite, which was inactive in ultraviolet erythema, was the same in both man and the guinea-pig. Moreover, when administered intravenously the parent acid was about twice as active as aspirin in suppressing bradykinin-induced bronchoconstriction in the guinea-pig.

Unless the clinical failure of this substance was due to a failure to reach some specific site in man, the evidence presented here suggests that anti-erythemic activity is not related directly to antirheumatic activity, although there seems little doubt that a strong connexion between the two effects does exist. It may be, however, that the peripheral anti-inflammatory component of salicylate-type antirheumatic compounds is an essential adjunct to analgesic and antipyretic activity; in this respect it is interesting to note that the antipyretic activity of ethyl α-(4-phenyl-phenoxy)propionate in the febrile rat was less than that of aspirin.

Thurfyl nicotinate erythema in man

When Trafuril cream, containing 5 per cent thurfyl nicotinate, is applied to the skin it produces a marked erythema in a few minutes. Nassim and Banner (1952) reported that this typical response did not occur in patients with active rheumatoid arthritis. However, in 1959 Truelove and Duthie demonstrated that the reduction in erythema was not dependent on the disease but was the result of the aspirin the patients were receiving. They suggested that the reaction consisted of two phases: an early phase of erythema, oedema, and surrounding flare, fading in 1½–2½ hours; and a later phase of erythema alone, in which oedema was never a feature. Aspirin appeared to exert its effect on the early phase of the reaction. It was further suggested that the action of aspirin under these conditions might bear some relationship to its therapeutic effect in rheumatic conditions. By modifying the techniques previously used we have been able to make a quantitative investigation of the effects of aspirin and similar compounds on erythema due to thurfyl nicotinate.

We have attempted to produce a submaximal response by restricting the amount of cream applied to a given area. To achieve this a celluloid mask was used, with a hole 1·5 mm. in diameter, A, and a hole 1·5 cm. in diameter, B. The mask was placed on the volar surface of the forearm and a small excess of cream placed on it and wiped across A. When the mask was removed a reasonably constant quantity of cream was retained on the skin. By means of a standardized rubbing procedure this quantity was then spread over the area encompassed by hole B. Assessment of the erythema was carried out by the use of the Lovibond reflecting tintometer (Jolles & Mitchell, 1957). The colour is expressed in terms of red, yellow, and blue units. For example, a typical reading of the basic skin colour was 4·5 red, 5·0 yellow, and 4·1 blue units, written as 4·5/5·0/4·1. Forty minutes after the application of thurfyl nicotinate cream the reading was 5·6/5·2/4·1. The yellow and blue readings always changed to a negligible extent and the degree of erythema was therefore expressed solely in terms of red units.

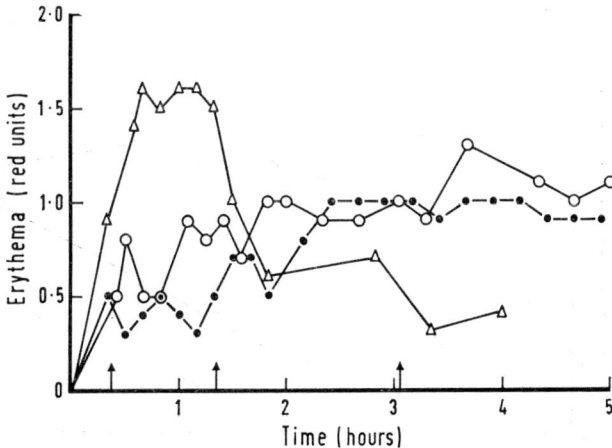

FIG. 1   TIME COURSE OF THURFYL NICOTINATE ERYTHEMA

In a normal subject (open triangles); after the administration of 650 mg. of aspirin two hours before applying thurfyl nicotinate cream (open circles); and after the administration of 650 mg. of aspirin two hours previously, and with 325 mg. administered subsequently at the times shown by the arrows (closed circles).

The course of erythema due to thurfyl nicotinate in a normal subject is shown in Fig. 1. The suppression of erythema in the early stages was very marked. However, it should be noted that after administration of aspirin the erythema still appeared, but was delayed; four hours after the application of thurfyl nicotinate the erythema was more marked than at the same interval in the absence of aspirin. This late appearance of erythema was not due to the fall in aspirin concentration in the blood. Further doses of aspirin given during the development of erythema did not modify the shape of the later part of the erythema curve.

For many purposes it is sufficient to measure the erythema 40 minutes after application of the cream. If R_0 is the red reading for the basic skin-colour and R_{40} is the reading 40 minutes after application of thurfyl nicotinate, the difference, ΔR_{40}, may be taken as a measure of the degree of erythema. The suppressive effect of 325 mg. of aspirin taken two hours before the application of thurfyl nicotinate is indicated by the marked reduction observed in the mean value of ΔR_{40}, from 1·7 to 0·6. The effect of a diminishing range of doses of aspirin indicates that the erythema is modified by doses below the therapeutic range. Moreover, these same doses of aspirin completely inhibited the oedema that occurred in a small proportion of subjects even with the small quantity of thurfyl nicotinate employed.

The most striking aspect of the action of aspirin is the persistence of the effect long after the administration of a relatively small dose. The

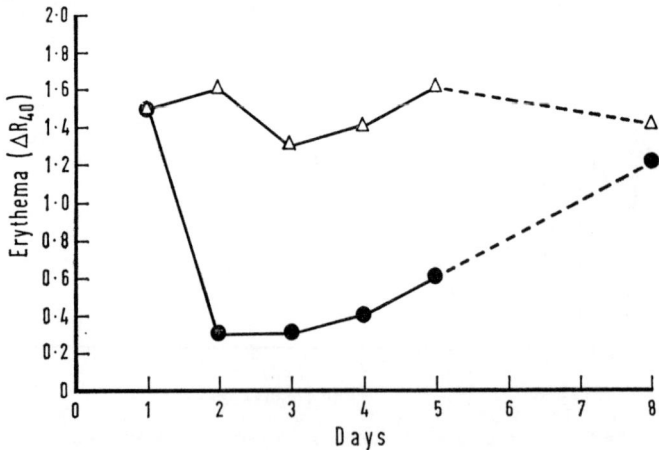

FIG. 2   ERYTHEMA (ΔR_{40}) AFTER THE DAILY APPLICATION OF THURFYL NICOTINATE CREAM
Mean values from five subjects (open triangles), and after a single dose of 650 mg. of aspirin given on Day 2, two hours before the thurfyl nicotinate (closed circles).

reactions to thurfyl nicotinate on successive days were studied in a group of six subjects after a single dose of aspirin. Care was taken that successive applications were made on different sites on the forearm to avoid the possibility of diminished response. The mean ΔR_{40} values are shown in Fig. 2. It is surprising that the effect of a single dose of aspirin was still detectable three days later. The effects of aspirin on the reaction to thurfyl nicotinate, therefore, may be summarized as follows:

(i) the erythema during the first hour after application of thurfyl nicotinate is reduced but not completely abolished;

(ii) erythema develops during the later stages of the reaction despite the continued presence of aspirin in the blood;

(iii) the effect of a single dose of aspirin is still detectable several days after its administration.

Effect of other drugs

No other drug has been found with an effect like that of aspirin (Table 2). It is particularly surprising that sodium salicylate, to which aspirin is rapidly hydrolysed *in vivo*, did not behave like aspirin. Moreover, although *o*-cresotinic acid closely resembles salicylic acid biochemically (Andrews, 1960), acetylcresotinic acid, unlike aspirin, did not affect thurfyl nicotinate erythema. Of the known antirheumatic drugs phenylbutazone, given in a dose of 400 mg. two hours before the test, appeared to inhibit the erythema on some occasions. However, we were unable to demonstrate a statistically significant difference between the response before and after phenylbutazone and therefore must regard this drug as being inactive. This is contrary to the finding in ultraviolet erythema in guinea-pigs. As in ultraviolet erythema, paracetamol and hydrocortisone were inactive. Ethyl α-(4-phenylphenoxy)propionate was inactive, although thurfyl nicotinate erythema was inhibited in an area of skin previously inuncted with this ester. The mechanism of the reaction is unknown. We agree with the findings of Strehler (1949) that histamine is not involved, since we were unable to modify the course of the reaction with various antihistamines.

Judging by the effects of the various drugs on the two types of erythema, it would seem that different basic mechanisms may be involved. Though both systems are aspirin-sensitive, sodium salicylate is effective only against ultraviolet erythema. While there is some correlation between the ability of drugs to delay ultraviolet erythema and their clinical antirheumatic effects, no such parallelism seems to exist for erythema due to thurfyl nicotinate. Nevertheless the fact that aspirin shows this highly specific effect may be of considerable importance, and in this respect it is interesting to note that thurfyl nicotinate erythema is more sensitive to the effects of oral aspirin, approximately 3 mg. per kg., than any other *in vivo* pharmacological system.

SUMMARY

The effects of salicylates and other analgesic-antipyretic drugs on ultraviolet erythema in the guinea-pig and on thurfyl nicotinate erythema in man are described.

In most of the ultraviolet experiments the effects of drugs were measured two hours after exposure, when the reaction is one of vasodilatation; increased capillary permeability is an important feature of the later stages. Although aspirin suppresses the reaction at two hours, the subsequent development of the erythema appears to be unaltered.

Erythema produced by thurfyl nicotinate cream in man consists of an early phase of erythema, oedema, and flare, and a later phase of erythema alone. Aspirin reduced but did not completely abolish the initial erythema, failed to prevent its later development, but completely abolished the oedema. It was effective in a dose as low as 225 mg., 3 mg. per kg. orally, and the effect of 650 mg. could be detected several days after ingestion. Sodium salicylate, phenylbutazone, and oxyphenbutazone were ineffective.

REFERENCES

Adams, S. S. (1960). *J. Pharm. Pharmacol.*, **12**, 251.
Adams, S. S., & Cobb, R. (1958). *Nature (Lond.)*, **181**, 773.
Andrews, M. M. (1960). *Biochem. J.*, **75**, 298.
Cardoe, N. (1959). *Ann. rheum. Dis.*, **18**, 244.
Hajnal, J., Sharp, J., & Popert, A. J. (1959). *Ann. rheum. Dis.*, **18**, 189.
Jolles, B., & Mitchell, R. G. (1957). *Lancet*, **i**, 1333.
Nassim, J. R., & Banner, H. (1952). *Lancet*, **i**, 699.
Strehler, E. (1949). *Schweiz. med. Wschr.*, **79**, 144.
Truelove, L. H., & Duthie, J. J. R. (1959). *Ann. rheum. Dis.*, **18**, 137.
Van der Meer, P., & den Oudsten, S. A. (1960). *Ann. rheum. Dis.*, **19**, 251.
Wilhelmi, G. (1949). *Schweiz. med. Wschr.*, **79**, 577.
Winder, C. V., Wax, J., Burr, V., Been, M., & Rosiere, C. E. (1958). *Arch. int. Pharmacodyn.*, **116**, 261.

DISCUSSION

G. P. Lewis (*Department of Physiology & Pharmacology, National Institute for Medical Research, Mill Hill, London*):

Kinin antagonism and kinin formation

I want to say a few words about antipyretics and kinins. I have been particularly interested in the role that kinins and related peptides play in inflammatory reactions. I ask myself the question, is the antipyretic action of aspirin and related drugs due to the antagonism of bradykinin or to the inhibition of its formation from plasma globulins? I should like to mention a few results which indicate that, with the exception of bradykinin-induced bronchoconstriction in the guinea-pig, aspirin and related antipyretics do not antagonize the actions of bradykinin nor inhibit its formation.

Firstly, let us deal with the actions of bradykinin. It is a potent vasodilator, and Fig. 1 compares the effects of phenylbutazone on the actions of histamine, bradykinin, and acetylcholine on the blood flow through the hind limb of a cat. I could find no specific antagonism of bradykinin, and could only conclude that the reduced response in the case of all three vasodilators was due to the lowering of blood pressure. Another action of bradykinin is the increase of capillary permeability, which can readily be shown by injecting a protein-binding dye intravenously and observing its diffusion into the extravascular space after intradermal injection of bradykinin. Areas of blueing in the skin of guinea-pigs following intradermal injections of 1·0, 0·1, 0·01, and 0·001 μg. of bradykinin were unaffected by the intravenous injection of aspirin, 100 mg. per kg. Bradykinins in concentrations as small as 0·1 μg. per ml. cause pain when applied to the exposed base of a blister in the human forearm. This response was unaltered after oral administration of 1·2 g. of aspirin.

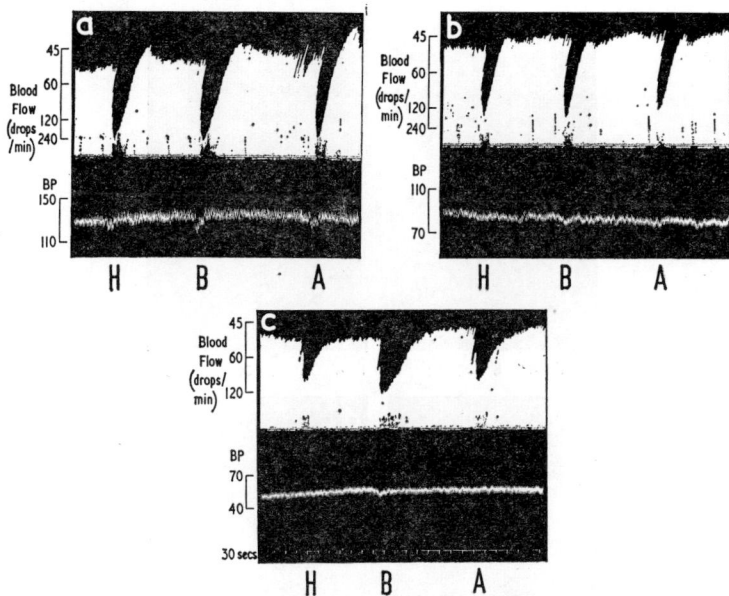

FIG. 1   EFFECT OF PHENYLBUTAZONE ON THE ACTIONS OF VASODILATORS
Cat, anaesthetized with sodium pentobarbitone, 40 mg. per kg. 'a', 'b', and 'c' are all parts of a continuous record, where the upper tracings are a record of venous outflow from the hind limb, recorded with a Gaddum drop counter, and the lower tracings are arterial blood pressure. H, B, and A are responses to close arterial injections of 0·03 μg. of histamine, bradykinin, and acetylcholine respectively, in 'a'; responses to the same injections after intra-arterial injection of 5 mg. of phenylbutazone in 'b'; and after intravenous injection of 100 mg. per kg. of phenylbutazone in 'c'.

However, LIM and his colleagues have found that larger doses of aspirin do inhibit an effect which may be related to pain in dogs. Finally, the actions of bradykinin on various isolated smooth-muscle preparations are not affected by these antipyretics.

Turning to the formation of bradykinin, there are certain enzymes in the body which act upon an α_2-globulin to form bradykinin. Such enzymes, some of which are called kallikrein, are found in glands and glandular secretions, and saliva is a convenient source. If this salivary kallikrein is incubated with plasma globulins, bradykinin is formed and the amount in the mixture can be estimated by comparing its smooth muscle stimulating activity with that of a bradykinin standard. Fig. 2a illustrates this formation. This experiment indicates one of the pitfalls that might have led some investigators to the erroneous conclusion that aspirin inhibits the formation of bradykinin. When the incubation was

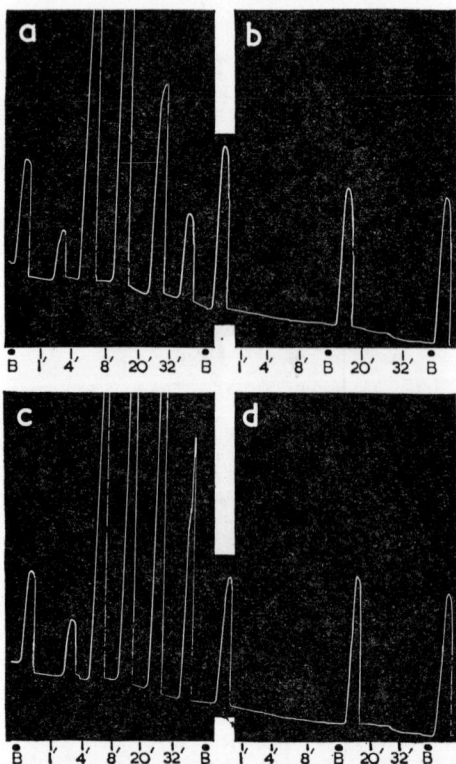

FIG. 2   EFFECT OF pH ON THE FORMATION OF BRADYKININ

Responses of the rat uterus to 0·001 μg. per ml. of bradykinin at B, and to a mixture of salivary kallikrein and plasma globulin incubated at 34°c for 1, 4, 8, 20, and 32 minutes. At pH 7·3 in 'a', and at pH 4·5 in 'd'; and in the presence of calcium acetylsalicylate, 1·5 mg. per ml., at pH 4·5 in 'b' and at pH 7·3 in 'c'

carried out in the presence of soluble aspirin, 1·5 mg. per ml., the formation of bradykinin was completely inhibited (Fig. 2b). However, when I checked the pH of this mixture it was 4·5. On the other hand, when the aspirin was neutralized to pH 7·3 immediately before addition to the mixture, bradykinin formation proceeded normally (Fig. 2c). Finally, when the incubation was carried out at pH 4·5 without aspirin, bradykinin formation was again completely inhibited (Fig. 2d). The inhibition was therefore due to the acid and not to the aspirin.

When injected into the skin of rabbits, salivary kallikrein causes increased capillary permeability because it forms bradykinin. This action was not affected by the injection of aspirin either, 100 mg. per kg. intravenously or 2·5 mg. per ml. intradermally, simultaneously with the salivary kallikrein.

It therefore seems that the antipyretic activity of aspirin and related drugs is not due to antagonism of bradykinin nor to the inhibition of the enzymes which form it. Although there is no doubt that aspirin antagonizes the bronchoconstrictor action of bradykinin in the guinea-pig, neither this substance nor related antipyretics antagonize those actions of bradykinin that it would exert if it were involved in inflammation. I suggest that COLLIER's antipyretic or A-receptors should more appropriately be called GPB-receptors (Guinea-Pig–Bronchoconstrictor receptors)!

Peripheral action of aspirin

LIM: We have obtained evidence that aspirin blocks visceral pain peripherally, using vocalization as an indicator of pain. If bradykinin is injected in small doses, 1–2 μg., into a suitable artery of the dog, vocalization or pain is evoked, which can be blocked by aspirin in doses of 50 mg. per kg. intravenously.

In the first experiment a donor dog perfused the spleen of a recipient that retained its nerve connections with its own central nervous system. The recipient's splenic artery was used to evoke vocalization by the intra-arterial injection of bradykinin, and its vocalization, respiration, and blood pressure were recorded. When morphine was injected into the donor intravenously, it did not block vocalization evoked by intrasplenic bradykinin injected at 5–10 minute intervals; but when the same dose of morphine was injected into the recipient intravenously, vocalization was blocked. As we expected, morphine blocks centrally. In the second experiment, 50 mg. per kg. of aspirin injected intravenously into the donor resulted in almost complete blocking of vocalization, with recovery in about an hour. When the same dose of aspirin was given to the recipient intravenously, no blocking occurred. The blocking effect of aspirin was thus exerted peripherally.

The peripheral blocking action of aspirin can also be shown by recording the action potentials from the splenic or splanchnic nerves after intrasplenic injections of bradykinin. Potentials evoked by bradykinin 20 seconds after injection were recorded on two beams from two electrodes placed 10 mm. apart on the cat's splanchnic nerve. From the time difference between the same potentials in the two records, it was estimated that the fibres stimulated by bradykinin were A-delta fibres, with a conduction velocity of about 18 metres per second and a diameter of approximately 3 μ. The potentials produced by five intrasplenic injections of bradykinin, one before and one at 10, 25, 50, and 80 minutes after an intravenous dose of 50 mg. per kg. of aspirin, were recorded. It was observed that 10 minutes after aspirin the number of spikes was diminished, and at 25 minutes there was no difference between pre- and post-bradykinin records, indicating that the potentials were blocked. Recovery was apparent at 50 minutes and was complete at 80 minutes. The analgesic action of aspirin was thus demonstrated by two methods to be peripheral, at the chemoreceptors being stimulated by bradykinin.

SHAW: Hebborn and I have investigated the effect of sodium salicylate and aspirin on the action of pancreatic, serum, and salivary kallikreins, both pharmacologically and biochemically. Kinin production by all kallikreins was followed by use of the isolated guinea-pig ileum preparation, using bradykinin as a standard in the assay. The esterolytic activity of pancreatic and salivary kallikreins was studied by measuring acid release from the synthetic substrate, p-toluenesulphonyl-L-arginine methyl ester (TAME).

Kinin production by all three enzymes was not inhibited by sodium salicylate concentrations up to 20 mM, or aspirin concentrations up to 5 mM. A 50 per cent inhibition of salivary kallikrein was obtained when a concentration of 50 mM sodium salicylate was employed. No significant inhibition of esterolytic activity was produced by concentrations of either drug up to 5 mM. By contrast the kallikrein inhibitor, Trasylol (Bayer), reduced both kinin production and esterolytic activity. The synthetic ester TAME inhibited kinin production, in agreement with other work using benzoyl-L-arginine ethyl ester (Chapman, L. F., Goodall, H., & Wolff, H. G. [1959]. XXI Int. Congr. Physiol. Sci., Abst. Comm. p. 60. Buenos Aires). These results are at variance with those obtained using sodium salicylate and aspirin in several systems (Northover, B. J., & Subramanian, G. [1961]. *Brit. J. Pharmacol.*, **17**, 107). It is concluded that sodium salicylate and aspirin are poor inhibitors of kallikrein activity *in vitro*.

Correlation of laboratory and clinical findings

WINDER: The high correlation observed in our laboratory and in ADAMS's laboratory between antirheumatic efficacy of drugs on the one hand and their ability to delay the appearance of ultraviolet erythema in guinea-pig skin on the other hand could not, *a priori*, be perfect. The initiating processes as well as the end expressions clearly differ as between the clinical and laboratory situations. Thus any biological process and basis for drug action hypothetically common to both could lie only in some intermediate stage. Just as glucocorticoids affect the clinical rheumatic end-expression, but not the laboratory UV-erythema, so, too, it must be expected that some agents will affect the laboratory erythema but not the clinical rheumatic state. With such obvious deviations at both ends of the two inflammatory phenomena, the surprise is that the correlation of drug influences is so high, rather than that exceptions occur.

AUSTEN: We have to be very careful about ascribing any clinical significance to the observations that COLLIER reported. Although SRS-A is released from guinea-pig lung by *in vitro* anaphylaxis, it has never been detected *in vivo* in the guinea-pig. Even more important, Smith and Humphrey ([1949]. *Brit. J. exp. Path.*, **30**, 560) showed that salicylate at a blood level of 40 mg. per 100 ml. had no effect on anaphylactic shock in the guinea-pig.

Is there any information available on the ability of salicylate to antagonize the activity of SRS-A on a smooth muscle preparation, such as the guinea-pig ileum? Secondly, bradykinin seems to increase pulmonary resistance when injected intravenously, but does the same happen when it is given by inhalation?

COLLIER: Nothing can be concluded from the failure of any one drug to protect the guinea-pig, because several substances are released at the same time in anaphylactic shock and it is necessary to use several antagonists. The effect of histamine is usually overwhelming, and aspirin gives little protection without an antihistamine. Even mepyramine, which antagonizes histamine, does not fully protect against antigen, there is often some bronchospasm left after it. The guinea-pig does not recover from severe bronchospasm spontaneously, and special techniques must be adopted to show the presence of other bronchoconstrictor substances that may be released. I am not particularly impressed with our failure to protect the guinea-pig against anaphylactic bronchospasm with aspirin, nor am I with Smith and Humphrey's similar failure, because a more subtle analysis is needed for this purpose.

I cannot answer about the antagonism of SRS-A on guinea-pig ileum, but aspirin antagonizes SRS-A on isolated trachea. It is more difficult to get satisfactory results with anti-inflammatory agents working with an *in vitro* system; there are the problems of solubility and pH, which LEWIS mentioned. Guinea-pig lung is easier to study because the results are sharp and specific. We shall be studying the antagonism of SRS-A in other tissues, as we did with bradykinin.

Herxheimer and Stresemann have recently confirmed our findings on bradykinin by giving it intracardially and observing bronchoconstriction. They failed to produce bronchoconstriction as a result of bradykinin inhalation in the guinea-pig, but they observed it in human asthmatics. Bradykinin is also highly effective when dropped on the pleural surface of the lung. We know that SRS-A causes contraction of isolated human bronchus, whereas bradykinin does not, although both substances contract isolated guinea-pig trachea, so that the situation is full of paradoxes.

VAN CAUWENBERGE: The results of COLLIER are divergent. They confirm the opinion we had formed that the results depend largely on the technique and the species of animal used.

M. J. H. SMITH: Although LIM's results have revived the possibility that aspirin may block some of the peripheral effects of bradykinin, LEWIS stated that there is little, if any, evidence that this occurs with kinins liberated from globulins. How does LEWIS visualize the combination of kinins with the globulins? Is the kinin an intrinsic part of the protein molecule, or has it been independently synthesized and subsequently attached to the protein? Perhaps aspirin may act by interfering with the synthesis of the kinin peptide, because the drug certainly inhibits transaminase reactions, rather than altering either the release of the kinins from their complexes with globulins or the peripheral actions of the liberated kinins.

LEWIS: There is not much doubt that kinins are formed by the enzymatic breakdown of a protein substrate. At present we have found four kinins, two of which seem to be of a chain length between the substrate and bradykinin. As far as I can see, aspirin can only affect the amino-acid composition of these chains by interfering with the synthesis of plasma proteins.

M. J. H. SMITH: Nevertheless there could be an inhibition of synthesis of the kinin-protein complex by aspirin. The rate of turnover of even large molecules is quite rapid.

ANTI-INFLAMMATORY EFFECTS OF SALICYLATE IN THE RAT

W. G. Spector and D. A. Willoughby

Department of Morbid Anatomy
University College Hospital Medical School, London

To investigate the nature of the anti-inflammatory action of salicylate it is necessary first of all to exclude any specific effects on the production and combination of antibodies. This is best done by using as a test system an inflammatory reaction induced by a fairly simple chemical or physical insult. The second requirement is to establish means for the separate assessment of the various components of the inflammatory response, such as increased vascular permeability to protein and the emigration of leucocytes. Once it is established that a drug suppresses a particular facet of the reaction to injury, there are many ways in which its action can be explored, such as observation of structural changes with the electron microscope or of functional changes such as alteration in blood flow. The present investigation deals with the anti-inflammatory action of salicylate only with regard to the ability of the drug to suppress increased vascular permeability after non-immunological damage. This action is examined solely from the standpoint of the endogenous substances that are potential mediators of increased vascular permeability after injury.

Although standardized thermal injury has many advantages (Spector & Willoughby, 1959b), a good system for the study of the anti-inflammatory effect of salicylate is the pleurisy induced in the rat by the intrapleural injection of turpentine (Spector, 1956; Spector & Willoughby, 1959a). This procedure leads to the rapid formation of a protein-rich exudate, due to the development of increased permeability to plasma protein in the pleural venules and capillaries. This exudate may be collected and measured at any time from 30 minutes to 24 hours after injury, and it has been found that the volume of exudate is a good measure of the permeability of the pleural vessels as a whole. It might be thought that injury induced by turpentine would be too destructive of small blood vessels to be of value in the study of chemical mediators. Some recent unpublished observations of Majno with the electron microscope reveal, however, that venules damaged by turpentine show only those changes observed after injection of histamine, vasoactive polypeptides, and similar potential mediators of the vascular changes of inflammation, and that there is no disintegration of the vessel walls.

There is good evidence that increased vascular permeability in pleurisy induced with turpentine is initiated by locally released histamine (Spector & Willoughby, 1959a). Thus the onset of the pleural exudate is delayed for 1–2 hours if the animals are given small doses of antihistamine drugs or depleted of histamine by repeated injections of compound 48/80 (compound 48/80 is a histamine liberator—see Paton, 1957). However, it is equally clear that the accumulation of exudate subsequent to these times is not dependent upon histamine.

The systemic administration of salicylate in high doses, about 500 mg. per kg., leads to a striking diminution in the volume of exudate after intrapleural injection of turpentine, even up to 24 hours after the injections (Spector & Willoughby, 1959a). The effect of salicylate is considerably more striking if combined with a small dose of an antihistamine drug; this could be interpreted as suggesting that salicylate has little effect on the release or action of histamine, but possesses a strong inhibitory effect on whatever mechanism succeeds histamine release and is responsible for the sustained delayed phase of increased vascular permeability.

With regard to potential chemical mediators, the strongest possibility for this latter mechanism is some form of protease–esterase–vasoactive-polypeptide (kinin) system. Models for such a system include kallikrein-kallidin–bradykininogen–bradykinin or serum globulin permeability factor (globulin PF)–PF/dil (Lewis, 1960; Miles, 1961). Systemic sodium salicylate, 500 mg. per kg., suppresses the effects of all these factors on vascular permeability, but has a similar inhibitory effect on histamine, 5-hydroxytryptamine (5-HT or serotonin), and other compounds (Spector & Willoughby, 1959a). Because of this non-specificity, it was decided to investigate the similar action of salicylate when given locally by intradermal injection in the same inoculum as the permeability factor under test.

Effect of local salicylate

The Table shows that, in sharp distinction to the results of systemic administration, the effects of local salicylate were highly specific. The increased vascular permeability induced by histamine, 5-HT, bradykinin, and peptides from fibrin, was unaffected. However, there was total suppression of the corresponding effect of kallikrein (see also Northover & Subramanian, 1961) or rat serum globulin PF. The vascular permeability effect of diluted rat serum, PF/dil, was unaffected by local salicylate. Kallikrein and globulin PF are widely regarded as enzymes that lead to the formation of vasoactive polypeptides, kinins, and that owe their effect on vascular permeability to this property. The inhibitory action of salicylate on increased vascular permeability in turpentine pleurisy and thermal injury in the rat could therefore be interpreted as interference with the ability of kallikrein or globulin PF to form their active products (Fig.); the effect of the active products themselves would appear to be unaffected by salicylate.

Samples of exudate from turpentine-induced pleurisy withdrawn at the height of permeability changes contain activated globulin PF and also a slow contracting substance with some similarities to the kinins (Spector,

THE EFFECT OF LOCAL SALICYLATE ON VASCULAR PERMEABILITY

Increased vascular permeability was measured by leakage of circulating protein-bound Trypan Blue. Sodium salicylate, 2·5 mg. per ml., was given by intradermal injection in the same inoculum as the permeability factor under test.

Vascular permeability factor	*Inhibition by salicylate*
Histamine	none
5-Hydroxytryptamine	PARTIAL
Bradykinin	none
Peptides from Fibrin ('leucotaxine')	none
Kallikrein	TOTAL
Globulin PF	TOTAL
PF/dil	none
Pleural Exudate	PARTIAL

1956; Spector & Willoughby, 1962). Such exudates increase vascular permeability and it is of interest that this effect is diminished by local salicylate to the extent of about 50 per cent. This result is consistent with the view that the action of the exudate on vascular permeability is due

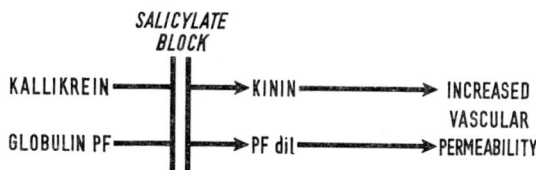

SCHEMATIC REPRESENTATION OF A POSSIBLE MODE OF ACTION OF SALICYLATE IN SUPPRESSING INCREASED VASCULAR PERMEABILITY AFTER INJURY

partly to the existence of preformed kinins, and partly to the formation of such kinins *in vivo* by the action of globulin PF or kininogens. It is also consistent with the interpretation given above of the action of systemic salicylate in suppressing exudate formation.

However, it is impossible to ignore the non-specificity of the effects of systemic salicylate as compared with the selective action of the drug when injected locally. It may be that there are two components to the anti-inflammatory action of salicylate; a specific inhibition of certain enzyme reactions and a general suppression of vascular reactivity. It is possible that this latter effect is really the result of severe diminution of blood flow through the injured vessels.

It is impossible at the moment to estimate the relative importance of these two components in the anti-inflammatory action of salicylate, if indeed two components exist. However, the question might be partially solved by electron microscopy; if salicylate suppresses the characteristic ultrastructural changes in venules in a state of increased permeability it would be a strong point against more diminution of blood flow as a major factor in the action of the drug.

SUMMARY

Systemic sodium salicylate has an inhibitory effect on the volume of exudate in turpentine-induced pleurisy in the rat and causes a non-specific suppression of the action of many substances that increase vascular permeability. When salicylate is administered locally, however, highly specific inhibition of increased vascular permeability due to kallikrein or rat serum globulin permeability factor (globulin PF) is observed. Thus the anti-inflammatory action of salicylate may be due partly to a specific inhibition of certain enzyme reactions and partly to a general suppression of vascular reactivity.

The present address of both authors is: Department of Pathology, St. Bartholomew's Hospital Medical College, London.

REFERENCES

Lewis, G. P. (1960). *Physiol. Rev.*, **40**, 647.
Miles, A. A. (1961). *Fed. Proc.*, Suppl. 9, 141.
Northover, B. J., & Subramanian, G. (1961). *Brit. J. Pharmacol.*, **17**, 107.
Paton, W. D. M. (1957). *Pharmacol. Rev.*, **9**, 269.
Spector, W. G. (1956). *J. Path. Bact.*, **72**, 367.
Spector, W. G., & Willoughby, D. A. (1959a). *J. Path. Bact.*, **77**, 1.
Spector, W. G., & Willoughby, D. A. (1959b). *J. Path. Bact.*, **78**, 121.
Spector, W. G., & Willoughby, D. A. (1962). *J. Path. Bact.*, **84**, 391.

DISCUSSION

A. A. MILES (*Lister Institute of Preventive Medicine, London*):

Speakers have rightly stressed the dangers of arguing from one kind of phenomenon to another. As we have seen, one cannot really argue from one animal to another. In its response to inflammatory agents the guinea-pig differs from the rat, and man is very different from either of them. There are dangers, too, in arguments about the significance of dosage. COLLIER, ADAMS, and LEWIS all implied that since they were using small doses of aspirin and thereby avoiding non-specific effects, the effects upon which the salicylates were acting specifically were significant in salicylate therapy. But their small doses of aspirin were effective on what, considered in the larger context, were really rather minor manifestations. The argument from erythema to what is happening in a chronic arthritic joint seems to me to be remote. This view is not just an exhibition of what LEWIS sometimes calls my doctrinaire nihilism about these things; there are facts pointing to important differences.

For example, if you take an animal with chronic 3–4 day-old inflammation, the blood vessels are quite insusceptible to adrenaline. Even after minor events like erythema or the induction of mildly increased vascular permeability, there are long periods when the vessels are refractory. The chronically inflamed vessel is probably a very different thing from those undergoing the minor acute responses that are suppressed by small doses of salicylates. The doses SPECTOR used were at least paralleling the sort of concentrations that occur in clinical exhibitions of the drug for chronic disease. He thought that there were two effects of systemic salicylate in these doses, and perhaps a more specific one when he injected it intracutaneously.

Here I would mention differences between animals. Heavy doses of salicylates given to guinea-pigs have only a mild suppressing action, equally effective on a wide range of permeability factors, both artificial and of endogenous origin. It seems probable that the manifestations of increased permeability are prevented by change in the circulation. The local suppression in rat skin, in SPECTOR's hands at any rate, poses a problem. It did not occur with any of the small-molecule permeability factors. But though the rat permeability globulin was inhibited, there was no inhibition of the permeability factor, which I have always regarded as the same thing and which is activated by exposure of dilute plasma to glass.

Permeability factors

I have experimental facts that may explain the discrepancy. It is generally assumed that the globulin permeability factors and the plasma kallikreins, the enzymes that release kinins from certain globulins, are the

6

same. In the guinea-pig, and perhaps this may apply also to the rat, we have found the following relation. The globulin permeability factor can be prepared so as to contain no kallikrein, that is, no kininogenase, at all. But using a dilute solution of fresh plasma, which has its own kininogenases and kinin-producing system, as a substrate in the gut-bath or the uterus-bath, there is good evidence that the permeability factor itself activates kininogenases, which then go through the usual process of producing a kinin.

In the guinea-pig, plasma kininogenase and the permeability factor are different. If you take a specimen of plasma and activate it by exposure

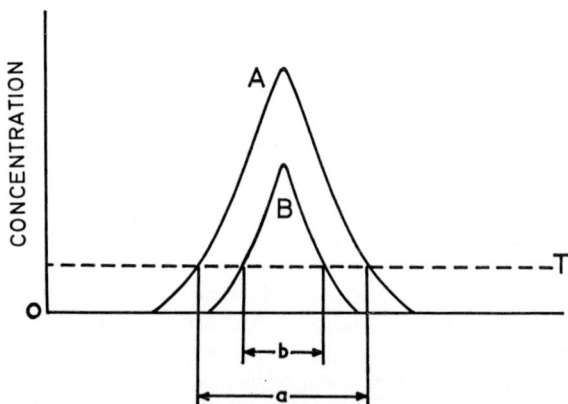

CONCENTRATION PROFILES OF INTRACUTANEOUSLY INJECTED PERMEABILITY FACTORS THROUGH THE CENTRE OF THE INJECTION SITE

A and B represent the concentration profiles of two injections, and 'a' and 'b' the diameters of the respective lesions induced. The dotted line, T, represents the threshold concentration of injected substance inducing a response, in this case increased vascular permeability detectable by exudation of circulating dye.

to glass beads, the curve of the kinin production rises rapidly. There is a parallel activation of permeability factor, but whereas the kininogenase disappears after 40 minutes of glass activation, the permeability factor persists for up to 6 hours and, moreover, it can then activate kininogenase in fresh plasma. The point is that early in the activation the plasma contains both kinins and permeability factor.

If rat plasma behaves like guinea-pig plasma, it is possible that SPECTOR's glass-activated permeability factor, PF/Dil, also contained maximum amounts of kinins. If this were so, the true PF/Dil, like isolated globulin permeability factor, might have been suppressed by the salicylate, the effect being undetectable, however, because of the active kinin present, and the kinin, by analogy with his direct tests on the peptides, would be insusceptible to salicylate. I make the point because SPECTOR declared he was going to add to the confusion in the field; this might clear up just one facet of his alleged confusion.

One point about the view that the action of salicylate is non-specific. We have found that when local salicylates inhibit the action of certain permeability factors, including the human globulin factor in the guinea-pig, the effect is quite unlike that of most other antagonists. On intra-cutaneous injection substances are distributed through the skin to form 'concentration profiles' across the injection site, like A and B in the figure, the peak concentrations corresponding to the point of needle entry. B is the profile for a dose smaller than A, and the relation of measures like 'a' and 'b' for most permeability factors is proportionately of lesion-diameter to log concentration of factor in the injected liquid, so that the response curve to graded doses is linear. Most antagonists, for example triprolidine acting on histamine or 48/80, shift the dose-response line to regions of higher concentrations of permeability factor, corresponding to a reduction from A to B for a given concentration of both factor and antagonist.

The peculiar effect of local salicylates is that the size of the lesion, until extremely high concentrations of salicylates are used, remains exactly the same. The deep blue (+ + +) of the untreated lesion, however, gradually fades with increasing concentration until the lesion is a pale delicate blue (±), as though the threshold sensitivity of the vessels was unaltered but the manifestation of increased permeability was impaired in some way. There is clearly something about salicylate inhibition that suggests that it acts in a way quite different from the usual antagonists of permeability factors.

AN EXPERIMENTAL STUDY OF INFLAMMATORY PERMEABILITY AND SALICYLATE ACTION IN THE RAT

E. KELEMEN

*Postgraduate Medical School
Budapest, Hungary*

WE have investigated the formation and elimination of experimental acute inflammatory oedema in the hind paw of the rat. Most of our studies related to the early phase, the first 45 minutes of the inflammatory response, and to the use of a relatively mild stimulus. It has been found that certain inflammatory changes persist after the visible changes have disappeared, and the possibility should be considered that these delayed events might constitute a major feature of the inflammatory process (see also Wilhelm, 1962).

The experiments were carried out on male and female rats on a synthetic diet and weighing 150–175 g. Inflammation was induced by subplantar injection of bovine testicular extract containing 75 turbidity-reducing units of hyaluronidase in a volume of 0·1 ml. For moderate thermal injury the limb was immersed for 30 seconds in water at 51° C; for severe injury it was immersed for 60 seconds at 58° C. Untreated animals with a diminished response of undetermined origin were designated spontaneous systemic hyporeactors. Animals described as reinjected local hyporeactors were injected into the hind paw; 3–5 hours later, just as the visible swelling of the distal paw disappeared, they were reinjected.

Composition of inflammatory oedema fluid

The relative concentration of different macromolecules or particles in the oedema fluid produced by testicular extract was examined. It was observed that the concentration of albumin approximated to that of serum, whilst only small amounts of β-lipoproteins were present. On the other hand, in the course of inflammatory swelling particles as large as chylomicrons or even platelets passed through the vascular filter. Salicylates tended to diminish very slightly the concentration of macro-molecules and particles, but all plasma components were present in the oedema fluid and the concentration of platelets and platelet-like particles showed no change.

Courtice and Garlick (1962) presented data on the permeability of the capillary wall to different plasma lipoproteins before and after thermal injury, and recent electron microscope observations by Majno and Palade (1961) proved that in the course of the inflammatory response platelets escape from the capillary bed. These observations do not support the pore theory of permeability in acute inflammation and seem to suggest that, at least in the case of salicylate, inhibition of inflammatory swelling is not necessarily connected with a definite change in permeability. In this respect, we recall that examination of normal and inflamed small blood vessels of mice and rats failed to demonstrate significant differences (Florey, 1961).

It has been reported (Kelemen, 1960) that, although coagulation factors are present in the oedema fluid induced by testicular extracts, coagulation does not take place within the tissues, but if the oedema fluid is withdrawn it readily clots. The importance of fibrin formation in the acute inflammatory process has been emphasized by Jancsó (1961). We have demonstrated that heparin, at high dosage to prevent fibrin formation, repeated injections of thrombin to induce fibrinogen deficiency, and ε-aminohexanoic (ε-aminocaproic) acid to inhibit fibrinolysis, did not significantly reduce the swelling induced by testicular extract or moderate thermal injury. However, a marked inhibition of oedema induced by testicular extract was observed in animals pretreated with salicylate at high dosage.

For many years histamine was held to be responsible for the acute inflammatory reaction. More recently, other substances have been suspected of playing a role in the inflammatory process. Such substances include certain polypeptides, the plasma globulin permeability factor, 5-hydroxytryptamine, and, more recently, some plasma kinins. If any of these endogenous substances act alone in producing acute inflammation, it would be expected that oedema could be continuously transferred by oedema fluid. We have shown that this cannot be achieved when oedema is induced with testicular extract (Kelemen, 1957). Although results with thermal injury suggest that it is possible to transplant oedema, we have had no regular success in our attempts, although Spector (1956) has been successful. Therefore we have failed to prove conclusively that such endogenous substances are the main factors involved in acute inflammatory oedema. There may be certain factors that could prevent this transfer.

The formation of acute inflammatory oedema

Radio-iodinated serum albumin was used as a means of tracing the movement of albumin. [131]I serum albumin was prepared from human or rat serum. After injection and the attainment of equilibrium the radioactivity of the paws was determined. Testicular extract was injected on one side, and the increase in radioactivity and the development of oedema were followed. When the total radioactivity of the paw was at its peak, a sample of oedema fluid was aspirated. Radioactivity was determined again, serum samples obtained, and then the distal parts of both paws were amputated, weighed, dried, and a corrected weight calculated. The Table shows that the radioactivity of the distal part of the affected paw was increased as a result of the injection of testicular extract. Salicylate, hydrocortisone, and a local hyporeactor state diminished this increase, and the degree of swelling was also reduced. Similar results were obtained with ^{131}I human or rat serum albumin, and with rat serum albumin

DISTRIBUTION OF RADIOACTIVITY IN THE HIND PAW OF THE RAT AFTER
INTRAVENOUS INJECTION OF ^{131}I RAT SERUM ALBUMIN

The effects of treatment with anti-inflammatory agents on acute oedema induced by testicular extract. Mean results from groups of more than five animals. The radioactivity of the serum and of the paw before injection of testicular extract were taken to be 1·0.

Preparation	Relative radioactivity		Volume of oedema fluid in distal (amputated) part of paw (ml.)	Radioactivity in compartments other than circulating blood or oedema fluid (calculated) (%)
	Distal part of paw	Aspirated oedema fluid		
Control	3·50	0·80	0·31	26·8
Salicylate	2·80	0·80	0·19	32·3
Hydrocortisone*	2·65	0·61	0·13	29·4
Spontaneous systemic hyporeactor	4·83	0·64	—	40·6
Reinjected local hyporeactor	2·25	0·56	—	—

* The weight of these animals reached 200 g. at the start of the experiment.

marked with Evans Blue. Radioautographs of paper electrophoretic strips with samples of serum and oedema fluid showed that salicylate did not induce any remarkable change in the iodine-binding capacity of albumin. It is necessary to consider, at least in experiments using ^{131}I human serum albumin, that the administration of salicylate might cause a delay in the transfer of albumin. A slight decrease in albumin leakage was noticed in both untreated and salicylate-treated rats relative to that of the control animals.

Having obtained values for the total relative radioactivity of the distal part of the paws and of the oedema fluid, and knowing the volume of the oedema fluid, it is possible to calculate the percentage of radioactivity present in compartments other than the oedema fluid. Intravascular radioactivity did not contribute significantly. The observations that a rapid rise in radioactivity precedes visible swelling (cf. Aschheim & Zweifach, 1962) and that a remarkable residual activity can be detected several hours after the oedema has disappeared can now be related to the fact that in the untreated oedema 26·8 per cent of the total radioactivity was in compartments other than the circulating blood or oedema fluid.

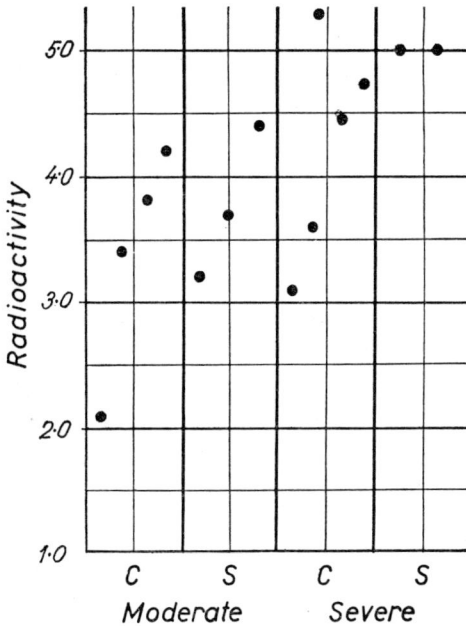

FIG. 1 INFLUENCE OF SALICYLATE ON INFLAM-
MATION INDUCED BY THERMAL INJURY
[131]I serum albumin was injected intravenously, and moderate or severe local thermal injury applied subsequently. The radioactivity of the distal part of the hind paw of the rat prior to thermal injury was taken to be 1·0, and the increase in radioactivity was observed in control animals, C, and in salicylate-treated animals, S.

The value for the salicylate treated rat was 32·3 per cent ($P < 0.05$). Figure 1 shows that there was also a significant increase in radioactivity in the paw when inflammation was induced by thermal means; salicylate had no influence on this increase, but it did have the effect of slightly reducing the swelling.

There are two unexplained observations reported in the literature. Jancsó (1955) and Kelemen (1960) noted that the local refractory state that may result from a previous inflammation still operates when the formation of oedema is inhibited by antihistamines. Furthermore, Gözsy and Kátó (1959) showed that no accumulation of Indian Ink or Trypan

Blue can be observed in the rat, and that no accumulation can be provoked by histamine or by substance 48/80 as long as the dextran-induced oedema persisted.

It has been found that testicular extract increases the elimination of locally injected molecules of ^{86}Rb or ^{131}I human serum albumin (Fig. 2). On the other hand, although elimination of ^{86}Rb was unchanged by salicylate administration, a slight delay in ^{131}I elimination was observed

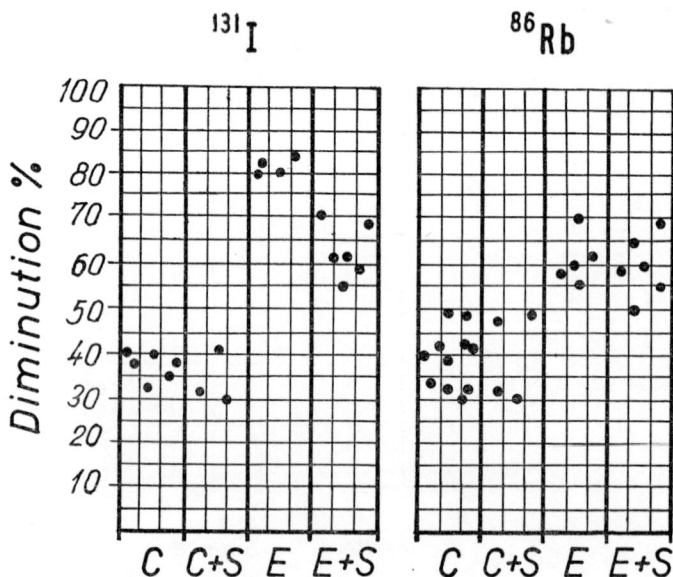

FIG. 2   EFFECT OF ACUTE INFLAMMATORY OEDEMA AND OF SALICYLATE
ON THE ELIMINATION OF LOCALLY INJECTED MOLECULES
^{131}I human serum albumin or ^{86} Rb was injected locally into the hind paw of the rat (C); the same injections were made, ^{131}I five minutes or ^{86}Rb ten minutes, after the administration of testicular extract (E); and the experiments were repeated during salicylate treatment (+S). Diminution of radioactivity was studied over two hours with ^{131}I, and over 25 minutes with ^{86}Rb.

in the salicylate-treated rats. Thus salicylate did not increase the elimination of ^{131}I serum albumin, and its anti-inflammatory action cannot be attributed to an enhanced elimination of the filtered material, a possibility otherwise worthy of consideration. Additional studies have suggested that the addition of ^{131}I to albumin did not appreciably change its immunological properties.

If our observations are correct, we may consider that whereas one phenomenon of the acute inflammatory response, namely swelling, is inhibited by salicylate or hydrocortisone, another effect, which apparently precedes the formation of oedema and which also persists after the disappearance of oedema, is not inhibited. If this is so, it is easier to understand the observation of Bywaters and Thomas (1962), that whilst salicylate and hydrocortisone are of value in supressing the clinical signs and symptoms of inflammation, they fail to prevent the subsequent development of tissue damage.

SUMMARY

Experiments concerning the formation of acute inflammatory oedema do not support the pore theory of permeability. No definite role could be assigned to fibrin formation, defibrination, or inhibition of fibrinolysis in the types of inflammatory swelling studied. Attempts to produce inflammatory swelling by oedema fluid induced by testicular extract mostly failed, and it was concluded that endogenous humoral substances cannot be regarded as the main factors of acute inflammatory changes. However, successful transfers occurred with severe thermal injury.

Two types of inflammatory stimuli applied to the rat's hind paw elicited a three to fourfold increase in the ^{131}I serum albumin content of the distal part of the paw. Determination of both the amount and the radioactivity of the oedema fluid revealed that about a quarter of the accumulated radioactivity was not accounted for by that present in the circulating blood or the oedema fluid.

It is suggested that, at least in certain types of acute inflammatory oedema, there is an increased uptake of some plasma proteins by the tissues. This uptake precedes visible swelling and persists after the swelling has subsided. The precise location could not be determined, and the significance of this protein accumulation remains unknown. This component of the inflammatory process was uninfluenced by salicylate or hydrocortisone.

Dr. A. Rédei and Dr. G. Simon of Budapest participated in this work.

REFERENCES

Aschheim, E., & Zweifach, B. W. (1962). *Amer. J. Physiol.*, **202**, 554.
Bywaters, E. G. L., & Thomas, G. T. (1962). *Brit. med. J.*, **ii**, 221.
Courtice, F. C., & Garlick, D. G. (1962). *Quart. J. exp. Physiol.* **47**, 221.
Florey, H. W. (1961). *Quart. J. exp. Physiol.*, **46**, 119.
Gözsy, B., & Kátó, I. (1959). *Experientia (Basel)*, **15**, 391.
Jancsó, N. (1955). 'Speicherung. Stoffanreicherung im Retikuloendothel und in der Niere.' Budapest: Akadémiai Kiadó.
Jancsó, N. (1961). *J. Pharm. Pharmacol.*, **13**, 577.
Kelemen, E. (1957). *Nature (Lond.)*, **180**, 710.
Kelemen, E. (1960). 'Permeability in acute experimental inflammatory oedema in the light of the action of salicylates', pp. 161 & 178. Budapest: Hungarian Academy of Sciences.
Majno, G., & Palade, G. E. (1961). *J. biophys. biochem. Cytol.*, **11**, 571.
Spector, W. G. (1956). *J. Path. Bact.*, **72**, 367.
Wilhelm, D. L. (1962). *Pharmacol. Rev.*, **14**, 251.

6*

CLINICAL IMPLICATIONS OF THE ANTI-INFLAMMATORY EFFECTS OF SALICYLATE

E. G. L. BYWATERS

Medical Research Council Rheumatism Research Unit
Taplow, Buckinghamshire, and Postgraduate Medical
School of London

ANTIPHLOGISTIC therapy in inflammatory diseases like rheumatic fever has been advocated for centuries, but from Sydenham's time, the seventeenth century, to the time of Bouillaud in 1840 it consisted mainly of repeated bleedings. This depletory approach was only gradually discarded in the latter half of the nineteenth century. Antiphlogistic is still rather a blanket term, since there are many stages in the development of the inflammatory process and therapeutic interference could be made at several different levels. It would be most valuable to have a sequence of steps for inflammation as clearly defined as those worked out for the clotting process; this would make it possible to understand, for example, if the anti-inflammatory effects of steroid and salicylate were additive or not. Do they act on the same or on different levels ? They are very often given together in an attempt to reduce the dosage of steroid, but I know of no adequate statistical proof of the success of this combination. Holt and co-workers (1954) have claimed that the results of giving salicylate and cortisone together in rheumatic fever are better than giving salicylate alone, but my own feeling is that, apart from severe cases of rheumatic carditis, neither steroid nor salicylate make much difference to the end result, compared with cases treated by bed rest alone, despite the dramatic effects of both drugs on fever and joint inflammation. In the more severe cases, which are rare nowadays, steroids may be useful, whereas salicylates are potentially dangerous as they may occasionally produce heart failure and precipitate pulmonary oedema (Bywaters & Thomas, 1961).

Steroids seem more powerful anti-inflammatory agents than salicylates and yet even steroids fail to suppress rheumatic inflammation in the heart, as shown by left auricular biopsy by Robles Gil, Rodriguez and Ibarra (1955) and by Décourt and co-workers (1961). It seems unlikely as a corollary, therefore, that salicylate suppresses the rheumatic granulomata and, in fact, Aschoff bodies have been seen in salicylate-treated patients.

The teleological role of inflammation

However, it is agreed that salicylates are to some extent anti-inflammatory. Is their use always a good thing? To the patient, the suppression of dolor, tumor, rubor, stupor, rigor, clamor, and calor is impressive and welcome, but teleologically inflammation is a defence mechanism of the body. Can we by-pass it with impunity? If the aim of inflammation, teleologically speaking, is accelerated disposal or neutralization of foreign and noxious agents, the suppression of inflammation might well lead to prolongation of the total course of the disease. Occasionally it seems possible that this might occur in rheumatic fever. It is well known that when a course of steroid therapy is stopped, a rebound is sometimes seen; the disease flares up and then in a few days settles down again. The same effect is also seen occasionally after stopping salicylate treatment.

Several explanations have been offered for this phenomenon in rheumatoid arthritis and rheumatic fever. Firstly, that it is due to resumption of the natural course of the disease. This can be tested by comparing the number of rebounds after a six week course with that following a 12 week course of steroid, which we have done; there seem to be less after 12 weeks. Another explanation is that it is due to adrenal-pituitary suppression, but it is difficult to account for the similar rebound following salicylates on this basis, since recent work has shown conclusively that salicylates, as given in man, do not effect the pituitary-adrenal axis. As a third possibility it would seem reasonable that a disease caused by reaction to irritant material and normally overcome by the body's defences might be prolonged if those defences were weakened. This is a useful field for thought and study. We tend to accept ancient and honoured shibboleths, like 'inflammation is a bad thing'.

If salicylate acts mainly as an antiphlogistic rather than as a central analgesic, should we use it so extensively for headaches, sciatica, and pains of many sorts that do not appear to be primarily inflammatory in origin? The implication of experimental results is that salicylate should be used for inflammatory pain. The implication of experience is that the answer may be in the suggestion that there are stages and degrees of inflammation.

REFERENCES

Bywaters, E. G. L., & Thomas, G. T. (1961). *Brit. med. J.*, i, 1628.
Décourt, L. V., Montenegro, M. R., Castiglioni, R., Sawaya, N., & Tranchesi, B. (1961). *A.I.R. Arch. interamer. Rheum. (Rio de J.)*, 4, 495.
Holt, K. S., Illingworth, R. S., Lorber, J., & Rendle-Short, J. (1954). *Lancet*, ii, 1144.
Robles Gil, J., Rodriguez, H., & Ibarra, J. J. (1955). *Amer. Heart. J.*, 50, 912.

DISCUSSION

R. DOMENJOZ (*Pharmacology Institute, Friedrich-Wilhelms University, Bonn, Federal German Republic*):

Mediators of the inflammatory reaction

Recent research on the polypeptides suggests that there are several groups of possible mediators of the inflammatory reaction:

(i) The so-called kinins, formed in the tissues by enzyme action.

(ii) The globulin permeability factors described by Miles and Wilhelm (1955), agents that have the characteristics of enzymes but the nature of which we do not know at the moment. Their action seems to be due to products of protein breakdown other than the kinins (Spector, 1960).

(iii) Certain metabolites of the polysaccharides (Spector, 1960), which might be considered in connection with KELEMEN's work.

Apart from these mediators there still remain histamine and 5-hydroxytryptamine (serotonin). Is this the moment to neglect them? Burckhardt (1962) used synthetic bradykinin and the analogous octa- and hexa-peptides, the two latter having bradykinin-like effects on capillary permeability but no stimulating action on smooth muscle. From the results obtained, I would like to mention two facts:

(i) in antagonizing the increase in capillary permeability caused by the polypeptides, the effect was apparent only in the rat and not in the guinea-pig;

(ii) the effect on capillary permeability caused by the hexapeptide and the octapeptide was antagonized in the guinea-pig by anti-histamines, and to a lesser degree by serotonin antagonists, and in the rat by serotonin antagonists, and to a lesser degree by anti-histamines.

Using pyribenzamine as an antihistamine, Burckhardt came to the conclusion that the effect of the polypeptides that structurally resemble bradykinin was an indirect one, due to the release of histamine and 5-hydroxytryptamine in the skin. In the literature on polypeptides it is generally stated that the action of bradykinin on capillary permeability is resistant to antihistamines. For this reason it must be argued that the effect of the octa- and hexa-peptides that Burckhardt observed is not identical with that of the nonapeptide, i.e. it is not 'bradykinin-like'.

It is incorrect for us to speak of salicylates; reference should be made to the substance used, aspirin or sodium salicylate. In my experience they are different in a qualitative as well as in a quantitative manner. If we examine their effect on formalin or dextran oedema in the rat we find distinct differences, sodium salicylate being more active against dextran and aspirin being more active against formalin inflammation (Domenjoz, 1955). Another interesting aspect concerns their action in the adrenalectomized rat. In the adrenalectomized animal sodium salicylate is only poorly active against formalin-induced oedema, whereas aspirin shows a reduced but still significant effect (Kornfeldt, H.: unpublished data).

I would be interested to learn if oedema in the rat's paw induced by formalin, dextran, or kaolin can be characterized or differentiated in respect of mediators significant for each of them. For example, is it possible to define the dextran oedema in terms of polypeptide activity? Wilhelm, Mill and Miles (1957) reported that dextran inhibits the *in vitro* activation of the permeability factor. Can this statement be applied to the dextran oedema of the rat?

The antagonism of the salicylates and the polypeptides is apparently a direct action that takes place in the inflamed region. Is there any possibility of including in this antagonism that component of the salicylate effect that is mediated by the adrenals?

REFERENCES
Burckhardt, D. (1962). *Helv. physiol. pharmacol. Acta*, **20**, 135.
Domenjoz, R. (1955). *Naunyn-Schmiedeberg's Arch. exp. Path. Pharmak.*, **225**, 14.
Miles, A. A., & Wilhelm, D. L. (1955). *Brit. J. exp. Path.*, **36**, 71.
Spector, W. G. (1960). *In* 'Polypeptides which Affect Smooth Muscle and Blood Vessels', p. 317. ed. Schachter, M. Oxford: Pergamon Press.
Wilhelm, D. L., Mill, P. J., & Miles, A. A. (1957). *Brit. J. exp. Path.*, **38**, 446.

LEWIS: There is no doubt that the kinins do not release histamine, a fact that has been shown by many investigators; neither are they sensitive to the action of antihistamines. I can think of two alternative explanations of the results of Burckhardt. Firstly, MacIntosh and Paton ([1949]. *J. Physiol.*, **109**, 190) showed that the release of histamine can be initiated by many basic substances, such as amides and amines, that might well be impurities formed during the synthesis of these peptides. Secondly, one of the factors that many investigators fail to consider in experiments involving antagonism of permeability changes is that many of these substances lower the blood pressure. When the blood pressure is lowered to values of 40–50 mm. Hg or less, there is not a sufficiently high capillary pressure for oedema formation, which is the evidence for an increase in capillary permeability. This inevitably leads to misleading conclusions.

COLLIER: In the rat, non-steroidal anti-inflammatory agents do not reduce the hypotensive actions of kinins. In the guinea-pig we find that mepyramine readily antagonizes the skin wealing caused by histamine, but not that caused by bradykinin. Therefore bradykinin does not act in the skin by releasing histamine.

Regarding the connexion with the adrenals, bradykinin-induced bronchoconstriction in the guinea-pig is not inhibited by corticoids, while its inhibition by non-steroidal anti-inflammatory agents can be demonstrated in the bronchial tree *in vitro*. We therefore do not think that the adrenals have much to do with the antagonism of bradykinin by aspirin-like drugs in guinea-pig lungs.

MILES: When we reported that dextran sulphate inhibited the activation of the permeability factor, either when administered to the animal or put into the test-tube, we were, I am afraid, being a little too confident on insufficient work. In those days we were allowing one hour for the glass-activation of the permeability factor *in vitro*, and after this period plasma treated with dextran sulphate was inactive. But dextran sulphate, the large-molecule kind, is an activator of the permeability factor. What actually happens is a very quick activation and decline of the factor within 15–20 minutes so that, after the hour taken for the ordinary slow glass activation, nothing active was left.

Turning to BYWATERS, if he regards the notion that inflammation is a bad thing as a shibboleth, the idea that inflammation is a good thing is equally a shibboleth. I would accuse him of a logical fallacy and of metaphysical timidity in these matters. His logical fallacy lies in assuming that inflammation is a single thing, whereas this term covers a multitude of phenomena. He is metaphysically timid because he doesn't go far enough with his teleological argument. If he argues that inflammation must be a good thing because we have inflammatory reactions to noxious agents, he might well go a little further and say 'Look how well we all are, because we obviously have the capacity to get rid of inflammation when it occurs'. On this basis inflammation is teleologically a bad thing, since all animals try to get rid of it rather than endure it.

A PERIPATETIC CORRESPONDENT: The speaker was accused of faulty metaphysics, but then he was just a physician; he laid no claim to being a metaphysician or even a paraphysician; ortho—like aspirin—was good enough for him. But why did he only think of such a neat rejoinder driving home?

Reproduced by permission of the Editor, *Lancet* [1962]. **ii**, 718.

VAN CAUWENBERGE: We have observed the effects of ε-aminohexanoic acid on some inflammation tests (Lefèbvre, P., Salmon, J., Lecomte, J., & van Cauwenberge, H. [1962]. *C.R. Soc. Biol. (Paris)*, **156**, 183). ε-Aminohexanoic acid, which inhibits fibrinolytic systems, reduces the increase of vascular permeability induced by histamine. It also reduces the intensity of purpura produced in the mouse by subcutaneous injection of croton oil. This suggests the participation of the fibrinolysis phenomena, or at least of a non-specific proteolysis, in the pathogenesis of some inflammatory reactions. On the other hand, ε-aminohexanoic acid has no effect on the other inflammatory tests we have studied.

We have studied the comparative effects of cortisone, ACTH, salicylate, and antihistamines on different experimental tests of inflammation (Roskam, J., Lecomte, J., van Cauwenberge, H., & Hugues, J. [1959]. VI Congr. Int. Ther., p. 81. Strassburg). We observed two important points:

(i) the effects of salicylate on some experimental inflammatory reactions often superpose those of ACTH;

(ii) salicylates also have some other effects, such as antihistaminic and anti-hydroxytryptaminic effects. Those effects observed in the adrenalectomized animal are probably in relation to a direct action of the drug.

We have also observed that in some cases, for instance in the inhibition of oedema induced in the paw of the rat by dextran, salicylates have an anti-oedematous action only in the normal rat or in the adrenalectomized rat treated with corticosteroid (van Cauwenberge, H., Lapière, C. M., & Lecomte, J. [1960]. C.R. Soc. Biol. (Paris), 154, 440). The action of the corticoids is in this case analogous to the one described by Ingle ([1953]. Recent Progr. Hormone Res., 8, 143) as a permissive action.

Salicylates in rheumatoid arthritis

In relation to BYWATERS's paper, Lefèbvre, Betz and I ([1960]. J. belge Méd. phys. Rhum., 15, 120) have obtained samples of synovium by punch-biopsy from the knee of patients with rheumatoid arthritis. Biopsies were taken before and after treatment with salicylate alone or in combination with corticosteroids (Plate I, facing p. 160). After treatment we observed a very important reduction of the histological signs of inflammation, even in patients treated with salicylate alone.

CALABRO: We have studied a number of patients with active rheumatoid disease who were treated with 5·4 g. daily of aspirin, o-(β-ethoxyethyl)salicylamide, and a placebo (Calabro, J. J., LoPresti, P. J., & Nosenzo, C. J. [1962]. Arthr. and Rheum., 5, 286). Each patient in turn received all treatments, each for a period of eight weeks. Improvement, as assessed by both the American Rheumatism Association's grading (Steinbrocker, O., Traeger, C. H., & Batterman, R. C. [1949]. J. Amer. med. Ass., 140, 659) and the Lansbury Index (Lansbury, J. [1958]. Arthr. and Rheum., 1, 505), was shown by 78 per cent of the patients when treated with aspirin, by 27 per cent when treated with o-(β-ethoxyethyl)-salicylamide, and by 11 per cent with placebo. This suggests that aspirin has more than an analgesic effect, and may imply an anti-inflammatory effect.

Does BYWATERS consider that the so-called anti-inflammatory effect of aspirin is achieved by the use of larger doses than those normally used for its analgesic action, and does he believe that there is a difference between aspirin and sodium salicylate?

BYWATERS: I do not see why it should not be the same property responsible for both effects. We generally tend to prefer aspirin to sodium salicylate, and I think it is probably more useful.

How many biopsies of the inflamed rheumatoid joint did VAN CAUWENBERGE take? The significance of any changes observed calls for the application of statistical methods, particularly in view of the variability of the synovial membrane even in the same knee.

VAN CAUWENBERGE: Four or five specimens of tissue were examined, both before and after treatment, from twelve patients. The pathologist was not aware of the individual case histories.

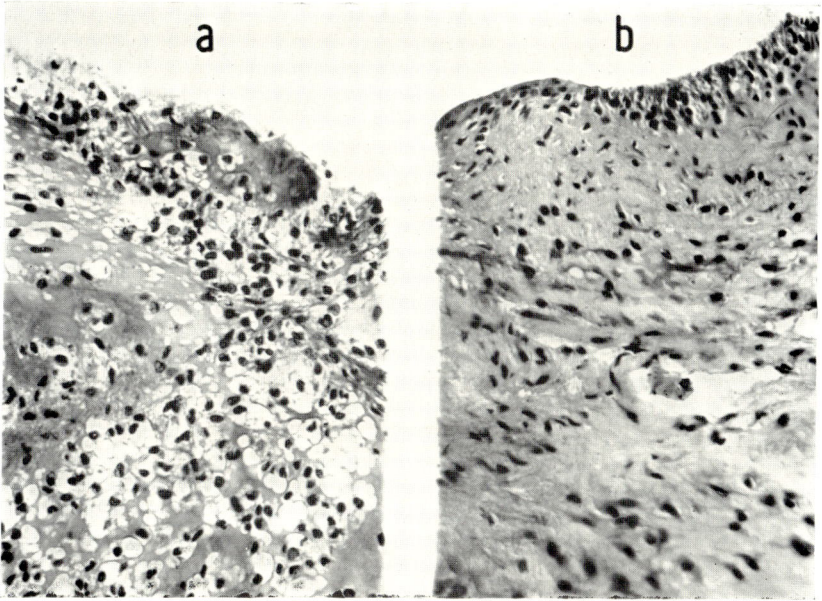

Plate I (van Cauwenberge)   Punch Biopsy Specimens taken from the Knee
of a Patient with Rheumatoid Arthritis

Specimens taken before, 'a', and after five weeks treatment with sodium salicylate, 4 g. daily, 'b'. There is a marked reduction in the histological signs of
inflammation in 'b'; clinical improvement was also manifest. (cf. p. 159).
Magnification × 200.

[*To face p.* 160

IMMUNOLOGICAL ASPECTS OF SALICYLATE
ACTION—A REVIEW

K. Frank Austen

*Departments of Medicine, Harvard Medical School and
Massachusetts General Hospital, Boston, Massachusetts, U.S.A.*

The ability of sodium salicylate or acetylsalicylic acid to suppress a variety of *in vivo* and *in vitro* antigen–antibody reactions has been recognized for many years. Some of the published work contains only fragmentary experimental detail or inadequate control data, but the information available does suggest that this is an important area of salicylate action.

Suppression of in vivo *antigen–antibody reactions*

The *in vivo* immunological phenomena suppressed by salicylate administration include: systemic anaphylaxis, the reverse passive Arthus reaction, and serum sickness in the rabbit; the reverse passive Arthus reaction and allergic encephalomyelitis in the guinea-pig; and serum sickness in man. The Shwartzman phenomenon in the rabbit is also suppressed.

Anaphylaxis. In 1948, Campbell reported that acetylsalicylic acid, 0·3 g. three times orally in 20 hours, protected nine rabbits completely and two rabbits partially against systemic anaphylaxis due to intravenous challenge with egg white. Each of ten controls developed shock, and in two instances this was followed by death. Three weeks after discontinuing salicylate the rabbits were challenged again, and both groups exhibited a similar degree of shock, indicating that the salicylate effect was reversible. Salicylates did not protect the rabbits against histamine shock. The protective effect of salicylates in rabbit anaphylaxis was confirmed by Lepper and co-workers (1950) and by McIntire, Richards and Roth (1957). In the experiments of Lepper and co-workers the plasma salicylate level ranged from 11·5 to 20 mg. per 100 ml. with acetylsalicylic acid and 18 to 26 mg. per 100 ml. with sodium salicylate.

Smith and Humphrey (1949) found that the guinea-pig was not protected against systemic anaphylaxis by salicylates even though the plasma salicylate level exceeded 40 mg. per 100 ml. at the time of challenge. On the other hand, these same animals were protected by antihistamine, and so the situation in the guinea-pig with respect to salicylate and antihistamine is the reverse of that observed in the rabbit.

Arthus reaction. Neither the direct passive (Fischel, 1947) nor the direct active (Smith & Humphrey, 1949) Arthus reaction in the rabbit was appreciably modified by salicylate administration. However, Smith and Humphrey pursued the matter further and investigated the reverse passive Arthus reaction. In the latter, the intensity of the erythema and oedema is proportional to the amount of antibody injected intracutaneously but is independent of the antigen concentration administered intraveneously over a wide range. Smith and Humphrey used each rabbit or guinea-pig as its own control; after allowing 48 hours to terminate or institute salicylate therapy, the experiment was repeated. The interval was so short that the initial exposure to antigen had not yet produced detectable active sensitization. Salicylate administration reduced the mean area of oedema due to the Arthus reaction by about 50 per cent in both the rabbit and the guinea-pig. In further studies, in which guinea-pigs were injected with Pontamine Blue prior to eliciting the reverse passive Arthus reaction, salicylates completely prevented dye extravasation, while antihistamine in a concentration sufficient to prevent blueing by an injection of histamine phosphate was without effect.

Shwartzman reaction. The local Shwartzman phenomenon, produced in rabbits in the usual fashion by the intracutaneous injection of filtrates of *Escherichia coli* followed in 24 hours by the intravenous administration of the same filtrate, was also suppressed by parenteral salicylate administration (Smith & Humphrey, 1949). The most striking finding was a reduction in the severity of the local haemorrhage. Antihistamines were without apparent effect. These studies were confirmed by Shwartzman, Schneierson and Soffer (1950) using a meningococcus filtrate.

Serum sickness. In 1923, Boots and Swift reported that salicylates had little effect on the course of serum sickness in man when administered after the onset of clinical arthritis. In investigating the same problem Derick, Hitchcock and Swift (1928) administered acetylsalicylic acid, 5–6 g. per day, or neocinchophen, 8–10 g. per day, 24 hours after the last injection of horse antipneumococcal serum, and continued therapy for 10–14 days. The results with the two drugs apparently were indistinguishable and so were pooled for comparison with the control series. The incidence of mild to moderate arthritis was approximately 15 per cent in both groups. A real difference was noted in the number developing severe arthritis, 32 per cent of the controls and only 3 per cent of the treated group. The incidence and severity of urticaria was not influenced by treatment. The salicylate-treated group developed a lower anti-horse-serum precipitin titre than the controls.

Some 20 years later, Sullivan, Parker and Hibbert (1948) and Smull, Wissler and Watson (1948) reported that salicylate administration suppressed the development of experimental serum sickness in rabbits following the injection of horse serum. Smull, Wissler, and Watson carried out two sets of similar experiments in which rabbits received two intravenous injections of 10 ml. per kg. of horse serum. In the first experiment the most striking lesion in the controls was a necrotizing arteritis, while in the second experiment a proliferative change in the valve leaflets was more prominent than the arteritis. Based on assigned values of 0 to 4+, the arterial lesions in the control rabbits averaged 3+ in the first experiment, and the valvular lesions in the control group averaged 2+ in the second experiment; the corresponding lesions in the salicylate-treated group, receiving 0·225–1·1 g. per kg., were less than 1+ in both experiments. The precipitin titre against horse serum was moderately reduced in the salicylate group.

A similar study was carried out by Roberts, Crockett and Laipply (1949) employing three 10 ml. per kg. injections of horse serum. Salicylates, 0·5 g. per kg. daily, did not interefere with the development of vascular or myocardial lesions. It may be that the use of three rather than two injections of horse serum overwhelmed the protective effect of salicylate.

Cellular hypersensitivity. There is only meagre data on the influence of salicylates on allergic reactions that cannot be transferred by serum. Fischel (1947) studied the skin reactions in man to the purified protein derivative of tuberculin (PPD) and to a nucleoprotein fraction of the haemolytic streptococcus. A blood salicylate level ranging from 15 to 53 mg. per 100 ml. failed to influence the skin reaction to either antigen, but it must be noted that the hypersensitivity state was established prior to the initiation of treatment.

Good, Campbell and Good (1949) investigated the effect of salicylates and *p*-aminobenzoic acid (PABA) on the development of experimental allergic encephalomyelitis in guinea-pigs due to immunization with homologous brain tissue emulsified in Freund's adjuvant. Paterson (1960) has demonstrated the passive transfer of this lesion with lymph node tissue. In the study of Good, Campbell, and Good, 19 out of 22 control guinea-pigs developed encephalomyelitis and seventeen, or 77 per cent, died. Neither sodium salicylate, 0·2 g. per kg., nor PABA, 0·5 g. per kg., altered the incidence or course of the disease, but a combination of the two reduced the incidence and mortality to 15 per cent. This combination was only beneficial when instituted prior to the fifth day following brain-adjuvant injection, whereas the onset of clinical disease occurred between days 13 and 27. Sodium salicylate alone afforded moderate protection in a dose of 0·3 g. per kg.

Suppression of in vitro antigen–antibody reactions

In vitro studies of the effect of salicylates on antigen–antibody reactions have been concerned with antigen-induced histamine release from sensitized tissue, immune haemolysis, and the antigen–antibody reaction *per se*.

Histamine release. Trethewie (1951), using perfused whole guinea-pig lung, and Ungar and Damgaard (1955) and Mongar and Schild (1957), using chopped lung, have reported that salicylates inhibit antigen-induced histamine release. However, according to Mongar and Schild the effective concentration is in excess of 160 mg. per 100 ml. Ungar and Damgaard attributed the salicylate effect to inhibition of a fibrinolytic enzyme, but the subsequent studies of Austen and Brocklehurst (1961) with guinea-pig lung, and Austen, Becker and Marcus (1959) with serum, have failed to uncover evidence of an antigen–antibody-activated plasmin-like enzyme.

In view of the ability of salicylate to protect against systemic anaphylaxis in the rabbit, Haining (1956) investigated the effect of salicylate on horse-serum-induced histamine release in sensitized rabbit blood. The concentration of sodium salicylate required to reduce histamine release from cells to plasma by 50 per cent was 27·5 mg. per 100 ml. (2 mM). To show that salicylate did not irreversibly alter the cells, the author demonstrated that cells washed free of salicylate responded to antigen in the usual fashion. In contrast, McIntire, Richards and Roth (1957), using egg albumin, reported that sodium salicylate or acetylsalicylic acid in a concentration of 20 mg. per 100 ml. did not inhibit antigen-induced histamine release from rabbit blood. It would be of interest to know the antibody titres in the two groups of rabbits.

Immune haemolysis. Cushman, Becker and Wirtz (1957) observed that sodium salicylate in a concentration of 20 mM failed to inhibit immune haemolysis. Mills and Levine (1958) noted that a concentration of 0·5 mM salicylaldoxime (*o*-hydroxybenzaldoxime) produced 50 per cent inhibition of immune haemolysis while 3·3 mM sodium salicylate (*o*-hydroxybenzoate) was without effect. Modification of the carboxyl group of salicylic acid, as in methyl salicylate or salicylamide, yielded a compound giving 50 per cent inhibition in a concentration of 3·3 mM. Mills and Levine demonstrated that these compounds produce a reversible inhibition by interfering with the interaction of the third component of complement, C_3', and the sensitized cell carrying the first, second, and fourth components of complement, $EAC_{1,4,2}'$. More recently van Oss, Friedmann and Fontaine (1961) have reported that acetylsalicylic acid is also an active inhibitor of immune haemolysis.

Antigen–antibody interaction. In 1943 Coburn and Kapp reported that sodium salicylate interfered with specific precipitation of rabbit anti-egg-albumin by crystalline egg albumin. In the equivalence zone 50 per cent inhibition was achieved with a salicylate concentration of roughly 3,000 mg. per 100 ml. Friend (1953) investigated the action of salicylate on the reaction between rabbit antisera and egg albumin or type III pneumococcus and, in agreement with Coburn and Kapp, concluded that salicylate inhibition was primarily due to interaction with the antibody.

Dilution alone had little effect on precipitation, but in the presence of a constant salicylate concentration dilution greatly increased the inhibition of the precipitin reaction, suggesting that salicylate altered the solubility of the antigen–antibody complex. This would also be consistent with the finding that salicylates partially dissociate preformed immune precipitates (Friend, 1953) or tissue bound antibody (Spar, Bale & Goodland, 1957). Unfortunately, the concentration of salicylate required for inhibition of aggregation is more than fifty times that achieved clinically.

The studies of Grant (1959, 1960) on inhibition of specific precipitation by dioxan are very pertinent because dioxan, like salicylate, readily forms intermolecular hydrogen bonds capable of reacting with the hydroxyl, carboxyl, or imino groups of various proteins. Grant (1959) studied five antigen–antibody systems and concluded that inhibition was due to reversible inactivation of antibody, perhaps due to hydrogen bonding.

Antibody formation and end-organ protection

Before applying the *in vitro* observations to a consideration of the *in vivo* data, two other aspects of salicylate action must be mentioned, the effect of salicylate on antibody production and the possibility of specific or non-specific end-organ protection.

Antibody formation. The overall data on antibody formation suggest that salicylate administration will depress antibody production to a minimal or moderate extent in man and the rabbit when administered in high doses early in the sensitization period. In 1922 Swift presented evidence that in some experiments salicylate administration to rabbits immunized with *Streptococcus viridans* or a type I pneumococcus reduced antibody formation by about one-half. It was subsequently shown in studies of serum sickness that salicylate administration during the sensitization period diminished the precipitin titre in man (Derick, Hitchcock & Swift, 1928) and in the rabbit (Smull, Wissler & Watson, 1948). Jager and Nickerson (1947) administered typhoid vaccine to 18 controls and 14 salicylate-treated subjects with a blood level maintained at 20–41 mg. per 100 ml. and noted a definite depression in the mean antibody response to H antigen but only a borderline effect on the anti-O titre. Homburger (1946) reported that salicylate administration prevented formation of anti-Rh agglutinins in guinea-pigs and rabbits, but Scherer (1948), following a similar protocol, failed to confirm this. In patients with streptococcal pharyngitis, salicylate administration has not been found to modify the antistreptolysin titre response (Coburn & Moore, 1942; Rantz, Boisvert & Spink, 1946).

Whether salicylates diminish antibody production directly or indirectly through some action on the reticuloendothelial system is not known. It may simply be that in high doses the negative nitrogen balance (Beisel, Austen & Rubini, 1960) that accompanies uncoupling of oxidative phosphorylation (Packer, Austen & Knoblock, 1959) is associated with a general impairment of γ-globulin synthesis.

End-organ protection. Swyer (1948) found that pretreatment of rabbits with salicylate decreased the capillary damaging effect of intradermal snake venom or histamine. Smith and Humphrey (1949) found that the stabilizing action of salicylates on capillary permeability was not based on an antihistamine-like action. In the rat, salicylates suppress arthritis due to either an intra-articular passive Arthus reaction (Ungar, Damgaard & Hummel, 1952) or the injection of silver nitrate (LaBelle & Tornaben, 1951). Spector and Willoughby (1959), based on studies of chemical inflammation, concluded that salicylates interfere with the action of the permeability producing globulins. It is apparent that salicylates stabilize capillary permeability in the face of either immunological or non-immunological damage.

Implications

In considering the mechanism whereby salicylates suppress clinical antigen–antibody phenomena, it is necessary to recall that salicylates are effective in two general situations:

(i) in acute phenomena dependent on the interaction of antigen with already established antibody concentrations, as in systemic anaphylaxis in the rabbit or the reverse passive Arthus reaction in the guinea-pig or rabbit;

(ii) in subacute or chronic phenomena produced by relatively large doses of antigen which both sensitize and elicit the reaction, as in serum sickness in man or the rabbit and allergic encephalomyelitis in the guinea-pig.

Possible sites of salicylate action include: interaction with antigen in such a manner as to impair its antigenicity; direct suppression of antibody formation; impairment of antigen–antibody interaction; inhibition of some antigen–antibody-activated step; specific competition with some pharmacological product of the antigen–antibody reaction; and non-specific end-organ protection.

Irrespective of the mechanism, the extent of antibody suppression is at best moderate. The data on impairment of antigenicity is only preliminary (Swift, 1922). A depression in antibody synthesis would not be a factor in limiting the immediate reactions associated with pre-existing antibody. On the other hand, the definite evidence that salicylate is only effective during the early sensitization phase could mean that in allergic encephalomyelitis (Good, Campbell & Good, 1949) salicylate interferes with the formation of a factor essential to cell-type hypersensitivity. It would be of interest to know the time limits for its beneficial action in serum sickness.

Salicylates, by interfering with antigen–antibody aggregation (Coburn & Kapp, 1943), could theoretically have a suppressive effect on both serum sickness in the rabbit and man and systemic anaphylaxis in the rabbit. A study by Dixon in 1953 led to the suggestion that antigen–antibody pulmonary thrombi play an important role in rabbit anaphylaxis and, as recently reviewed by Weigle (1961), serum sickness seems to be a result of circulating antigen–antibody complexes. Unfortunately, the salicylate concentration apparently required for the *in vitro* effect is many times the concentration found effective *in vivo*, and so the clinical pertinence of the finding that salicylates interfere with antigen–antibody aggregation is not established. It is also possible that the interaction of salicylate with certain antigens is important, since there are data in man and the rabbit that indicate that salicylates bind to serum albumin in preference to the globulins (Reynolds & Cluff, 1960).

The inability of salicylates to protect the guinea-pig against systemic anaphylaxis is not surprising because histamine is the predominant chemical mediator in this species; salicylates do not have an anti-histamine-like action (Smith & Humphrey, 1949) and in a reasonable concentration do not suppress antigen-induced histamine release from guinea-pig lung (Mongar & Schild, 1957). The relative contribution of pharmacological factors (Waalkes et al., 1957; Brocklehurst & Lahiri, 1962) and immunological pulmonary thrombi (Dixon, 1953) to systemic anaphylaxis in the rabbit is unknown. Thus the significance of the studies demonstrating that salicylates inhibit antigen-induced histamine release from sensitized rabbit blood remains to be determined (Haining, 1956).

The importance of the finding that acetylsalicylic acid (van Oss, Friedmann & Fontaine, 1961) inhibits immune haemolysis must await a better understanding of the possible role of complement in allergic phenomena. Sodium salicylate, which did not inhibit immune haemolysis, was as effective as acetylsalicylic acid in suppressing the immunological events just reviewed.

The possibility that salicylate is effective due to end-organ protection is supported by its ability to stabilize capillary permeability and suppress inflammation in the presence of either immunological or non-immunological insults.

At present, no single site of action adequately explains the diverse immunological phenomena suppressed by salicylate administration.

SUMMARY

Salicylate administration is effective against two general types of immunological phenomena: acute phenomena dependent on the interaction of antigen with an already established antibody concentration, as in systemic anaphylaxis in the rabbit or the reverse passive Arthus reaction in the rabbit or guinea-pig; and subacute or chronic phenomena produced by a relatively large dose of antigen that sensitizes and then elicits the reaction, as in serum sickness in man or the rabbit and allergic encephalomyelitis in the guinea-pig.

There is data indicating that salicylates can act at a number of different sites. Established actions include suppression of antibody production, interference with antigen–antibody aggregation, inhibition of antigen-induced histamine release *in vitro*, and stabilization of capillary permeability in the presence of either immunological or non-immunological insults. At present, no single site of action adequately explains the diverse immunological events suppressed by salicylate administration.

The author is a Research Career Development Awardee of the United States Public Health Service. This work was supported by a P.H.S. research grant (AI-04536-01) from the National Institute of Allergy and Infectious Diseases, U.S. Public Health Service.

REFERENCES

Austen, K. F., Becker, E. L., & Marcus, D. M. (1959). *Brit. J. exp. Path.*, **40**, 482.

Austen, K. F., & Brocklehurst, W. E. (1961). *J. exp. Med.*, **113**, 521.

Beisel, W. R., Austen, K. F., & Rubini, M. E. (1960). *Metabolism*, **9**, 905.

Boots, R. H., & Swift, H. F. (1923). *J. Amer. med. Ass.*, **80**, 12.

Brocklehurst, W. E., & Lahiri, S. C. (1962). *J. Physiol. (Lond.)*, **160**, 15P.

Campbell, B. (1948). *Science*, **108**, 478.

Coburn, A. F., & Moore, L. V. (1942). *J. Pediat.*, **21**, 180.

Coburn, A. F., & Kapp, E. M. (1943). *J. exp. Med.*, **77**, 173.

Cushman, W. F., Becker, E. L., & Wirtz, G. (1957). *J. Immunol.*, **79**, 80.

Derick, C. L., Hitchcock, C. H., & Swift, H. F. (1928). *J. clin. Invest.*, **5**, 427.

Dixon, F. J. (1953). *J. Allergy*, **24**, 547.

Fischel, E. E. (1947). *Proc. Soc. exp. Biol. (N.Y.)*, **66**, 537.

Friend, C. (1953). *J. Immunol.*, **70**, 141.

Good, R. A., Campbell, B., & Good, T. A. (1949). *Proc. Soc. exp. Biol. (N.Y.)*, **72**, 341.

Grant, R. A. (1959). *Brit. J. exp. Path.*, **40**, 551.

Grant, R. A. (1960). *Brit. J. exp. Path.*, **41**, 45.

Haining, C. G. (1956). *Brit. J. Pharmacol.*, **11**, 357.

Homburger, F. (1946). *Proc. Soc. exp. Biol. (N.Y.)*, **61**, 101.

Jager, B. V., & Nickerson, M. (1947). *Amer. J. Med.*, **3**, 408.

LaBelle, A., & Tornaben, J. A. (1951). *Science*, **114**, 187.

Lepper, M. H., Caldwell, E. R., Smith, P. K., & Miller, B. F. (1950). *Proc. Soc. exp. Biol. (N.Y.)*, **74**, 254.

McIntire, F. C., Richards, R. K., & Roth, L. W. (1957). *Brit. J. Pharmacol.*, **12**, 39.

Mills, S. E., & Levine, L. (1958). *Immunology*, **2**, 368.

Mongar, J. L., & Schild, H. O. (1957). *J. Physiol. (Lond.)*, **135**, 301.

van Oss, C. J., Friedman, J. C., & Fontaine, M. (1961). *Nature (Lond.)*, **189**, 147.

Packer, L., Austen, K. F., & Knoblock, E. C. (1959). *Proc. Soc. exp. Biol.* (*N.Y.*), **100**, 239.
Paterson, P. Y. (1960). *J. exp. Med.*, **111**, 119.
Rantz, L. A., Boisvert, P. J., & Spink, W. W. (1946). *Science*, **103**, 352.
Reynolds, R. C., & Cluff, L. E. (1960). *Bull. Johns Hopk. Hosp.*, **107**, 278.
Roberts, R. C., Crockett, K. A., & Laipply, T. C. (1949). *Arch. intern. Med.*, **83**, 48.
Scherer, W. F. (1948). *Amer. J. med. Sci.*, **215**, 33.
Shwartzman, G., Schneierson, S. S., & Soffer, L. J. (1950). *Proc. Soc. exp. Biol.* (*N.Y.*), **75**, 175.
Smith, W., & Humphrey, J. H. (1949). *Brit. J. exp. Path.*, **30**, 560.
Smull, K., Wissler, R. W., & Watson, J. M. (1948). *J. Lab. clin. Med.*, **33**, 936.
Spar, I. L., Bale, W. F., & Goodland, R. L. (1957). *Proc. Soc. exp. Biol.* (*N.Y.*), **94**, 803.
Spector, W. G., & Willoughby, D. A. (1959). *J. Path. Bact.*, **77**, 1.
Sullivan, C. J., Parker, T. W., & Hibbert, R. W. (1948). *Proc. Soc. exp. Biol.* (*N.Y.*), **67**, 508.
Swift, H. F. (1922). *J. exp. Med.*, **36**, 735.
Swyer, G. I. M. (1948). *Biochem. J.*, **42**, 28.
Trethewie, E. R. (1951). *Aust. J. exp. Biol. med. Sci.*, **29**, 443.
Ungar, G., & Damgaard, E. (1955). *J. exp. Med.*, **101**, 1.
Ungar, G., Damgaard, E., & Hummel, F. P. (1952). *Amer. J. Physiol.*, **171**, 545.
Waalkes, T. P., Weissbach, H., Bozicevich, J., & Udenfriend, S. (1957). *J. clin. Invest.*, **36**, 1115.
Weigle, W. O. (1961). *Advanc. Immunol.*, **1**, 283.

HYPERSENSITIVITY TO ASPIRIN

R. S. BRUCE PEARSON

King's College Hospital, London

ATTENTION was first directed to the clinical importance of aspirin allergy by Storm van Leeuwen in 1924. Since this time many references have been made to this condition. The manifestations considered to be of allergic origin include anaphylactic shock, asthma, rhinorrhoea, angioneurotic oedema, urticaria, and purpura. Of these asthma is by far the commonest to receive attention. However, it is doubtful if it is more common than skin manifestations, to which less attention has been paid. Gross and Greenberg (1948), in reviewing the literature, reported that in patients with allergic sensitivity to aspirin, skin eruptions were present in 54·6 per cent, oedema in 35·6 per cent, asthma in 32·6 per cent, and other manifestations in 17·8 per cent.

In a review of drug sensitivity, Dominici, di Mattei and Serafini (1952) record that, of 33 drugs or groups of drugs, asthma may be precipitated by 19. Of these, aspirin is the only one to do so at all commonly. No figures are available for sensitivity among the population as a whole; its incidence must be exceedingly low when one considers that the American public consumes 20–30 tons of aspirin daily. It is rarely, if ever, the only precipitant of asthmatic attacks. Reported figures of the incidence from asthma and allergy clinics vary from 1 to 10 per cent. These figures are of small value since age and sex are generally agreed to influence the incidence in a striking manner. All observers are agreed that women are more commonly affected than men and that the highest incidence is in middle age. Thus a clinic with a high proportion of children or young adults is likely to provide lower figures than one with a larger number of middle-aged patients. van Leeuwen (1928) also pointed out that the incidence was higher in those patients with severe asthma that was resistant to treatment.

Incidence of allergy due to aspirin

Figures obtained from my own clinics at King's College Hospital and the Woolwich Group of Hospitals show that of 1,205 asthmatics of all ages 2·3 per cent were aspirin-sensitive. In 24 aspirin caused asthma, and in four angioneurotic oedema. In addition to these, seven cases (0·5%) had abdominal symptoms, pain or vomiting, which were not regarded as due to hypersensitivity and have not been included. In the same series, 16 cases (1·3%) were recorded as being penicillin-sensitive; of these three had asthma and 13 had rashes of various kinds. The incidence of aspirin-sensitivity and of asthma by age and sex is shown in the Table, which is compiled from an analysis of these figures.

Although 14 females (2·1%) were affected compared with ten males (1·8%), there is little difference in incidence between the sexes of this series. The percentage of aspirin-sensitive patients irrespective of sex is 1·1 below 40 and 4·1 above. These figures compare with 1·2 and 1·9 per cent for penicillin sensitivity.

INCIDENCE OF ALLERGY AND OF ASTHMA DUE TO ASPIRIN

A series of 1,205 asthmatic patients, analysed according to age and sex

Age group	Male		Female	
	Number of patients	Aspirin-sensitive cases (%)	Number of patients	Aspirin-sensitive cases (%)
ALLERGY TO ASPIRIN				
0– 9	55	0	35	0
10–19	183	1·1	142	0·7
20–29	89	0	123	1·6
30–39	75	2·7	129	3·1
40–49	71	7·0	114	2·6
50–59	63	3·2	73	5·5
60–69	14	7·1	32	6·2
70+	1	0	6	0
Total	551	2·2	654	2·3
ASTHMA DUE TO ASPIRIN				
0–39	402	0·75	429	1·4
40+	149	4·7	225	3·6

Of the 24 aspirin-sensitive asthmatics, nine had nasal polypi and two had been treated for antrum infection. Over a period of observation varying between six months and nine years, five of the aspirin-sensitive patients (21%) died in status asthmaticus; three of these had nasal polypi. No deaths were recorded due to the actual consumption of aspirin, though fatalities after small doses are well recognized (Lawson & Thomas, 1932; Dysart, 1933; Francis, Chent & Bullen, 1934). The aspirin-sensitive patients did not fall exclusively into the intrinsic group of asthmatics, as has often been claimed. Seven patients were also sensitive to pollen, two to dust, two to foods, and one to various alcoholic drinks.

These findings are reasonably consistent with other reported observations. In particular, the frequency of nasal polypi, the increasing incidence in middle age, and the high mortality are in agreement with other reported series. They differ in that although females outnumbered males, the incidence of aspirin allergy among males did not differ appreciably from that among females, and also that extrinsic allergy was relatively common. Walton and Randle (1957), who reported 81 cases of aspirin allergy in a population of 4,761 allergic patients, found 69 (2·7%) with aspirin asthma out of 2,580 asthmatics; in this series twice as many females were affected as males, but figures for incidence are not given. However, many patients had evidence of extrinsic allergy.

The mechanism of aspirin allergy

Little is known of the immunological basis of aspirin allergy. Positive skin tests to aspirin by intradermal, prick, or patch tests are rarely positive (Mathews, Lovell & Sheldon, 1950); Storm van Leeuwen (1924) failed to demonstrate sensitivity by skin tests; and Blamoutier (1954) found no positive tests or passive transfer tests in eight aspirin-sensitive patients. However, Salvaggio and Crane (1961) recorded a positive passive transfer (Prausnitz-Küstner) reaction in a girl of 15.

It is generally assumed that aspirin acts as complement and forms an antigen in combination with serum protein. In an attempt to elucidate this problem, Mathews, Lovell and Sheldon (1950) skin-tested six aspirin-sensitive patients with serum from patients receiving aspirin; in none was there any significant difference between the reactions caused by aspirin-containing sera and control sera. Serum from aspirin-sensitive patients injected intradermally into control patients who were receiving aspirin failed to give positive reactions, as also did the injection of aspirin-containing sera into areas of skin previously sensitized with serum from aspirin-sensitive patients. These authors concluded that the clinical history was the only satisfactory method of diagnosing aspirin allergy. This statement is still true.

It is a point of interest that some asthmatics state that their symptoms may be relieved or prevented by taking aspirin; such a statement was volunteered by six patients in my own series.

Aspirin allergy remains a somewhat mysterious clinical entity. How does aspirin produce these effects? Why are aspirin-sensitive patients so rarely sensitive to sodium salicylate, salicylic acid, or acetamide? Why is aspirin so prone to cause asthma whereas p-aminosalicylic acid, a far commoner cause of skin sensitization, rarely does so? What is the explanation of the curious association between nasal polypi and aspirin allergy? If we could answer these questions, we might illuminate the whole problem of allergic sensitivity in asthma.

SUMMARY

Aspirin is the only drug that gives rise to asthma as an allergic manifestation at all commonly. Nevertheless, the incidence of sensitivity is low and aspirin is rarely the sole precipitant of asthmatic attacks. The important features of aspirin-sensitive patients are the frequency of associated nasal polypi, the increasing incidence in middle age, and the high mortality of aspirin-sensitive asthmatics. A clinical history is the only satisfactory method of diagnosing aspirin allergy.

REFERENCES

Blamoutier, P. (1954). *Sem. Hôp.*, *Paris*, **30**, 1549.
Dominici, G., di Mattei, P., & Serafini, U. (1952). 53rd Congr. Soc. ital. Med. intern., Venezia, p. 155. Rome: Pozzi.
Dysart, B. R. (1933). *J. Amer. med. Ass.*, **101**, 446.
Francis, N., Chent, O. T., & Bullen, S. S. (1934). *J. Allergy*, **6**, 504.
Gross, M., & Greenberg, L. A. (1948). 'The Salicylates, a critical bibliographic review', p. 168. New Haven: Hillhouse Press.
Lawson, R. W., & Thomas, R. (1932). *J. Amer. med. Ass.*, **99**, 107.
van Leeuwen, W. S. (1924). *J. Pharmacol. exp. Ther.*, **24**, 25.
van Leeuwen, W. S. (1928). *Münch. med. Wschr.*, **75**, 1588.
Mathews, K. P., Lovell, R. G., & Sheldon, J. M. (1950). *J. Lab. clin. Med.*, **36**, 416.
Salvaggio, J., & Crane, E. (1961). *J. Louisiana med. Soc.*, **113**, 292.
Walton, C. H. A., & Randle, D. L. (1957). *Canad. med. Ass. J.*, **76**, 1016.

DISCUSSION

Miles: Austen's survey has pulled together many hitherto scattered facts and he has made an extremely well-balanced assessment of just what might be happening. However, he cited an experiment in which it appeared that salicylates affected the stimulus of different antigens differently. That was based on the agglutination tests with H and O, in which O titres were unaltered and the H titre depressed. I wonder whether the difference might be due to the technique used. With H suspensions the test is very sensitive, and with O it is highly insensitive. If serum antibodies had been measured by the amount of antibody nitrogen absorbed to the two types of suspension, diminution of both kinds of antibody might have been found.

Anderson: Austen's considerations rest partly on van Oss's report that aspirin inhibited immune haemolysis. It has since been reported (Anderson, K. W. [1961]. *Nature* (*Lond.*), **191**, 1012) that this may be attributed to a pH effect and that if the system is sufficiently buffered aspirin has no effect on the reaction. I would therefore endorse the remarks of Lewis, that those working with salicylates in *in vitro* systems should check the effect of salicylate on the pH.

Long: Austen argued that salicylates influence the early or immediate allergic responses. This is true. He also argued that salicylates depress the delayed, tuberculin-type, allergic response. This argument was based on the passive transfer in guinea-pigs of allergic encephalomyelitis with cells. It is true that with cells you can transfer fixed antibodies, but if the cells are at the same time producing circulating antibody you can transfer both types of antibody.

With cells derived from an animal producing both, I have never succeeded in transferring passively a fixed antibody without at the same time transferring circulating antibody. The particular effect of salicylates on allergic encephalomyelitis cannot, therefore, lead to the general statement that salicylates depress delayed, tuberculin-type, allergic responses. Moreover, every attempt I have made to demonstrate the effect of salicylates on the delayed allergic response in the guinea-pig has failed; not only with salicylate on its own, but I have failed to demonstrate any synergism with drugs that depress the delayed allergic response.

Whitehouse: Do antibodies, or even antigens, combine with sodium salicylate, and if so, does this affect the interaction of antigen with antibody?

Austen: Anderson's comment is important. Nevertheless, the fact that acetylsalicylic acid may have an alternative explanation in no way changes the fact that salicylaldoxime and related compounds are good inhibitors. Mills and Levine certainly did control pH in their work.

Concerning the inhibition of aggregation, pH was controlled, although in this instance it probably does not matter because we are considering concentrations 50 to 100 times greater than those of clinical significance.

I agree with LONG that, even when an entity has been transferred by lymph node tissue, tissue culture work has often demonstrated that the same tissue is capable of producing antibody. However, it has not been found possible to transfer allergic encephalomyelitis with serum alone. Therefore it is reasonable to presume that some other factor is involved in the elicitation of this particular disease entity. I was careful not to call it antibody but a factor critical to the development of cell hypersensitivity, and that is as far as we can go. I was not aware of any other published work on the effect of salicylates on what we might rightly consider to be delayed-type reactions.

It has been mentioned that salicylates combine with the albumins in preference to the globulins. The emphasis in the studies on immune aggregation was directed towards an effect on the antibody; further work in regard to an effect on the antigen is certainly indicated because there is very little data on this aspect. All three reports on the protective effect of salicylate against systemic anaphylaxis in the rabbit involved the same antigen, egg albumin. It would be interesting to know whether salicylates give the same protection when the antigen is a γ-globulin.

HUMPHREY: AUSTEN has emphasized that it was necessary to commence the administration of salicylate within five days of injecting the encephalitogenic mixture. This may mean that the salicylate was influencing the processes occurring at the site of the injection and affecting the degree of local inflammation and the whole series of cellular events that followed.

A way to eliminate this possibility might be to try to obtain a passive transfer of encephalomyelitis to a normal animal with cells from an animal that had been treated with salicylate throughout the sensitizing course. This might show whether the donor was actually sensitized but protected by salicylate against the development of allergic encephalomyelitis.

BACHMAN: The question has been raised whether sodium salicylate has any effect on arthritis. Noble has made a study of the effect of various anti-inflammatory agents on an experimental form of arthritis induced in the adrenalectomized rat by repeated injections of prolactin (Noble, J. S. [1962]. Lactogenic-Hormone-Induced Polyarthritis in the White Rat: A suggested method for the laboratory evaluation of anti-inflammatory agents. M.Sc.(Pharmacol.) Thesis, University of Oregon Medical School). He found that pretreatment with sodium salicylate or cortisone gave substantial and equal effects in suppressing the formation of this experimental form of arthritis. He also observed that the two drugs were equally effective in suppressing the arthritis after it had already developed. Phenylbutazone was less effective than sodium salicylate or cortisone in both respects.

EFFECTS OF SALICYLATES ON EPITHELIAL SURFACES

Chairman F. AVERY JONES

SALICYLATES AND WOUND HEALING

G. WILHELMI

J. R. Geigy SA, Basle, Switzerland

WOUND healing is regarded by Marchand (1901) and other patholo-
gists as a type of inflammation, since exudative processes with the escape
of blood and plasma from the vessels, migration of polynuclear leucocytes,
auto-enzymic decomposition of tissue and, finally, proliferative changes,
are associated with it.

Review of literature

It is therefore entirely plausible that the process of wound healing
should be amenable to influence by anti-inflammatory drugs. This group
includes, among other antipyretics, the salicylates (Gross, 1950;
Eichholtz, 1950; Muschaweck, 1950; Studer, 1950; Kelemen et al., 1950;
Mulinos & Hirschhorn, 1951; Labelle & Tornaben, 1951; Wilhelmi,
1950, 1952; Bacchus & Bacchus, 1953; Domenjoz, 1955). The properties
of the salicylates that may play a part in this anti-inflammatory effect
include an antihistaminic activity (Gohar & Makkawi, 1951; Wilhelmi,
1952), an inhibition of histamine release (Haining, 1956; Trethewie &
Morris, 1959), and an antiserotonin activity (Glover, Marshall & Whelan,
1957; Kelemen, 1960; Mörsdorf & Bode, 1959).

In addition to an inhibition of inflammation, the salicylates possess
other properties that may influence wound healing, for example a weak
growth-inhibiting activity such as has been observed on cell division in
tissue-culture (Saito, 1935; Schumacher, 1953), in tumour tissue *in vivo*
(Meletti, 1956) and, to some degree, in experimental granulomas (van
Cauwenberge & Lecomte, 1957; Viskocil, 1957; Collet & Daniel-
Moussard, 1959; Trnavsky, Trnavska & Malinsky, 1962). In the sea-
urchin egg, on the other hand, we found only a very slight inhibitory
action on cell division (Wilhelmi, 1957), and Selitto and Randall (1956)
found sodium salicylate to be inactive in the cotton pellet test.

Of significance for an influence on wound healing are, finally, the inhibitory effects of the salicylates on the growth of micro-organisms, first described by Kolbe in 1874. A number of species is concerned, including diphtheria bacilli (Brown, 1878), streptococci (Diernhofer, 1936), and tubercle bacilli (Küster & Wagner-Jauregg, 1944). Ivanovics (1942) ascribes this antiseptic action of the salicylates in part to an inhibition of the synthesis of pantothenic acid, a process which is of importance for the growth of certain bacteria.

An effect described by Antweiler (1957), which is not easy to assess as regards its overall effect on wound healing, is the distinct inhibition by acetylsalicylic acid, and the weaker inhibition by sodium salicylate, of phagocytic activity of the polymorphonuclear leucocytes in the rat. Furthermore, the keratolytic effect of salicylic acid on local application to the skin, an effect familiar to dermatologists, may exert an influence on epithelial regeneration.

It would exceed my terms of reference if I were to review the studies that are concerned with the influence of the salicylates on metabolic processes. I would mention here only the uncoupling effect of the salicylates on oxidative phosphorylation, demonstrable in tissue slices or in mitochondria (Brody, 1956; Panagopoulos et al., 1961), which leads to increased tissue oxygen requirement, and the inhibition of the sulphation of mucopolysaccharides (Boström & Månsson, 1955; Whitehouse & Boström, 1961; Whitehouse, 1962). Another aspect which must be briefly mentioned is the influence of the salicylates on glucose utilization and storage by tissue, in the light of Bullough's (1949) observation that the rate of cell division is dependent on the glucose level in the blood and the tissues. Another factor is the stimulant effect of the salicylates on protein breakdown (Reid, Watson & Sproull, 1950).

The antihyaluronidase activity of the salicylates should also be mentioned; it can lead, among other things, to a decrease in the distribution of bacteria in the infected wound by means of changes in the ground substance. This antihyaluronidase activity is not demonstrable *in vitro* (Swyer, 1948; Calesnick & Beutner, 1949), but can be demonstrated by several techniques *in vivo* (Guerra, 1946; Domenjoz, 1955; Dewes, 1955; Wilhelmi, 1956; Mathies, 1958).

Numerous observations have shown that high doses of salicylates delay blood coagulation. Many authors, including Rapoport, Wing and Guest (1943), report the production of a hypoprothrombinaemia *in vivo*, although prothrombin activity cannot be depressed by salicylates *in vitro* (Clausen & Jager, 1946). This hypoprothrombinaemia can be reversed by means of vitamin K (Shapiro, 1944). In this connexion we may cite the increase in mastocytes observed to be caused by salicylates (Mari & Rizzatti, 1951), possibly resulting in the liberation of heparin (Ferrari & Costa, 1953), with its effect on blood coagulation and its possible role in the inhibition of inflammation and in the antihyaluronidase effect.

7

To close the review of the general literature I would mention the much-discussed question of a possible stimulation of the pituitary-adrenal axis by preparations of salicylic acid. In favour of such activity are, among other phenomena, the liberation by salicylates of ascorbic acid and cholesterol from the adrenals and the decrease in anti-inflammatory activity in the adrenalectomized animal (van Cauwenberge, 1953; Domenjoz, 1955). The increase in the excretion of 17-hydroxycortico-steroids during salicylate therapy has been interpreted in this sense. If the hypothesis is correct and this activity is essential to the mechanism of the salicylate effect, it would be expected that these preparations would inhibit wound healing by this means also. The inhibition of regenerative processes by ACTH and cortisone has been described by Ragan and co-workers (1949a, b) and by many others. However, this hypothesis has not remained undisputed, in that Crampton and co-workers (1962), to cite only one article of recent date, in the course of *in situ* perfusion experiments in the dog saw no stimulation of hydrocortisone secretion by the salicylates.

In the light of all these considerations it might be assumed that the salicylates were capable of exerting a very profound effect on wound healing; and yet if one excludes the instances of systemic intoxication as a result of overdosage or drug allergy, the effects of the salicylates, especially harmful effects, are much smaller than expected. This state-ment can be made with some confidence because these preparations in a wide variety of forms have been used extensively for the treatment of wounds.

Galen used the leaves of willow, which contain salicin, for the treat-ment of haemorrhagic wounds and of ulcers and fistulae. In an anony-mous Swiss herbal, dated 1486, the willow, in the form of heated and pulverized bark, is recommended for the local treatment of wounds. Ryff (1573) mentions the plant wintergreen, which contains methyl salicylate, as an excellent herb for the treatment of wounds. When salicylic acid was synthesized by Gerland (1852) it was soon taken into use as an antiseptic for wounds instead of the phenol used hitherto (Thiersch, 1875; Wilson, 1915). Later, the salicylates were extensively used in surgery as analgesics and antipyretics by the oral route and sometimes by the parenteral route, but there were no reports of any pronounced incidence of disturbances in wound healing. There was, however, a mention of the increased incidence of secondary bleeding after the use of acetylsalicylic acid in tonsillectomy (Ersner, Myers & Ersner, 1934; Neivert, 1945; Singer, 1945).

Experimental Studies

In the course of activity-spectrum studies of antipyretics in our laboratories, we also investigated the effects of salicylates on wound healing. In early experiments we found that the process of regeneration in *Planaria gonocephala* was influenced but little by a variety of anti-pyretics, including sodium salicylate (Wilhelmi, 1954). Regeneration was measured in terms of the period elapsing from decapitation to the reappearance of the eyes. When the inhibitory action was being tested,

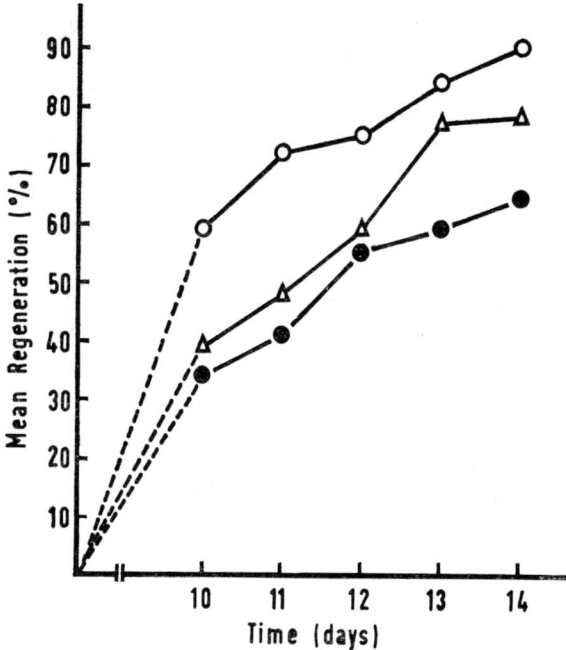

EFFECT OF SODIUM SALICYLATE ON REGENERATION IN
Amblystoma mexicanum

Each animal was immersed for 16 hours daily in a solution of sodium salicylate, at a concentration of 3 mg. per 100 ml. (open circles) or 10 mg. per 100 ml. (closed circles). Control animals are depicted by open triangles. Complete cure is recorded as 100 per cent regeneration.

Change in weight of regenerated tissue:

	Weight change (mg.)
Control	1·7
Salicylate, 3 mg. per 100 ml.	2·1
10 mg. per 100 ml.	1·4

the worms were immersed in solutions of sodium salicylate of varying concentrations for 48 hours. In this instance the number of animals that had regenerated the head on the seventh day after decapitation was determined, and thus the median effective concentration was calculated.

In an animal slightly higher in the evolutionary scale, *Amblystoma mexicanum*, further investigations of the effect of sodium salicylate on regeneration were carried out. Three or four holes were punched in the tail crest of each animal, and these were periodically inspected by eye and their degree of closure (nil, $\frac{1}{4}$, $\frac{1}{2}$, $\frac{3}{4}$, fully closed) was assessed. At the end of 14 days the regenerated tissue was again excised and was weighed. It was found that, unlike other antipyretics, sodium salicylate in high doses or high concentrations was capable of inhibiting healing, especially in the early stages. Smaller doses were ineffective, while weak concentrations promoted regeneration (Table 1 & Fig.; Wilhelmi, 1954).

We were also interested in determining whether, and to what extent, salicylates were capable of influencing wound healing in mammals, in this instance the rat. Pieces of the dorsal skin 1·5 cm. in diameter were excised

TABLE 1. EFFECT OF SODIUM SALICYLATE ON REGENERATION IN
Amblystoma mexicanum

Sodium salicylate was administered intraperitoneally. Complete closure of the punched holes is recorded as 100 per cent regenerative activity.

Preparation	Daily dose	Regenerative activity			Re-excised tissue 14th day (mg.)
		10th day (%)	12th day (%)	14th day (%)	
Drinking water	Control	55	68	92	2·80
	(mg./kg.)		(% change)		(% change)
Sodium salicylate	50	−19	− 2·4	+ 3·0	− 3·2
	100	−42	−20	−18	−32
	150	−65	−37	−26	−33

under anaesthesia in male albino rats weighing 120–150 g. each, and the course of healing was observed for 12 days. The diameter of the missing epithelium was measured on the first, fifth, ninth, and twelfth days, and its reduction in size was recorded. It was found that the smaller doses of sodium salicylate slightly stimulated regeneration initially, while the higher doses slightly inhibited it (Table 2). A degree of inhibition in the early stages was also observed when salicylic acid was applied locally in the form of an ointment (Table 2).

Histological preparations, for which I am indebted to Prof. Roulet of Basle, were examined in a special group of animals that were killed on the fourth day after the excision of skin. In the control animal a fairly broad layer of granulation tissue, originating largely from the edges of the wound, had already been formed. It was rich in cells and showed capillary shoots and round cells. In the animals receiving salicylic acid, 300 mg.

per kg. by mouth per day, there was only a narrow border of granulation tissue. The wound exudate was still present, but round cell infiltration was slight. The usual formation of capillary shoots was also visible. Other control groups of animals that were killed on the twelfth day after operation showed an advanced degree of epithelial regeneration, with dense granulation tissue and fibroblast proliferation and formation of fibres. The numerous capillaries mostly ran parallel to the surface. In the rats receiving salicylic acid, 300 mg. per kg. by mouth daily, examination

TABLE 2. EFFECT OF SALICYLATE ON THE REGENERATION OF RAT SKIN

The diameter of an area of excised epithelium was measured on the first, fifth, ninth, and twelfth days. Preparations were administered in divided doses twice daily.

Preparation	Daily dose	Mean diameter of wound before treatment	Mean reduction in diameter of wound		Change in regenerative activity	
			5 days	12 days	5 days	12 days
	(mg./kg.)	(mm.)	(mm.)	(mm.)	(%)	(%)
Control	—	15·86	3·68	12·05	—	—
Sodium	60 i.p.	16·79	4·79	11·59	+30	− 3·8
salicylate	210 i.p.	17·44	4·34	12·47	+18	+ 3·5
Salicylic acid	300 oral	14·46	3·10	8·56	−15	−29
Yellow Vaseline	0·1 ml. b.d.	15·1	4·3	10·1	—	—
Salicyl Vaseline	0·1 ml. b.d. 10%	14·9	3·6	9·5	−16	− 5·9
	20%	15·8	1·8	8·8	−58	−13

after 12 days also showed a fairly advanced degree of cell-rich granulation tissue with capillary shoots. The differences in the quantity of granulation tissue formed were much smaller in this late stage than they were in the early ones.

Finally, we used the gastric ulceration provoked by serotonin in the rat as an experimental wound. Such ulcers, of varying size, are found in the majority of rats a few hours after a single subcutaneous injection of 5-hydroxytryptamine. If the animals were treated for two days with sodium salicylate, the number of animals with a gastric ulcer and the mean intensity of ulceration in the individual animals were distinctly reduced. It was also observed that cicatrization was distinctly promoted even during the two days that sodium salicylate was given, although rather higher doses of this substance are themselves ulcerogenic. 5-Hydroxy-tryptamine also caused ulceration of the colon in a somewhat smaller number of animals, but on this type of ulceration sodium salicylate showed no effect that could be detected macroscopically (Table 3).

TABLE 3. EFFECT OF SODIUM SALICYLATE ON THE SEROTONIN ULCER IN THE RAT

Ulcers were induced with a single subcutaneous injection of 5-hydroxy-tryptamine, 40 mg. per kg. Sodium salicylate was injected subcutaneously in four divided doses over 30 hours; when both drugs were administered, salicylate injections were commenced 14 hours after the injection of 5-hydroxytryptamine. The intensity of ulceration was expressed on a scale from 0·5 to 3.

Preparation	Total dose (mg./kg.)	No. of animals	No. of animals with Gastric		Intensity of ulceration	No. of animals with Colonic	
			Ulcers	Scars		Ulcers	Scars
5-Hydroxytryptamine		19	15	4	0·71	9	2
5-Hydroxytryptamine + Sodium salicylate	200	20	7	13	0·33	8	3
Sodium salicylate	200	10	0	0	0	0	0
	800	10	6	4	0·5	0	0

Implications

Our experiments thus demonstrated stimulation as well as inhibition of regeneration by salicylates. A survey of the literature directly concerning wound healing must include the publications of Rudas (1960, 1962) and of Lindner and Rudas (1961). They found that, especially in the initial stages, skin regeneration in the rat is inhibited by sodium salicylate. This effect was achieved after only a single high dose of the substance, probably by slowing the inflammatory changes or by inhibiting the liberation of growth-promoting substances from the injured tissue. However, in their experiments the growth of the epithelium was hindered by the implantation of a plastic ring. Further investigations showed that the regeneration of experimental wounds was inhibited when air was excluded by means of a methyl methacrylate cover. However, this effect could not be enhanced by sodium salicylate. Another antipyretic, phenylbutazone, behaved in an analogous way. Sala (1954) was unable to achieve any significant alteration in the healing of sterile wounds of the rabbit's ear by means of fairly high doses of sodium salicylate—unlike what is observed with cortisone.

Kodicek and Loewi (1955) reported that the uptake of ^{35}S in the regenerating tendinous tissue of the guinea-pig was distinctly inhibited by sodium salicylate and somewhat less by acetylsalicylic acid, indicating that there was a reduction in the formation of mucopolysaccharide.

According to Weimar (1957), sodium salicylate applied locally inhibits the invasion of polymorphonuclear cells in the region of the experimentally injured cornea of the rat. However, the substance was effective only when it was used within the first two hours after operation.

As regards the influence of the salicylates on gastric ulcers in the rat, Pauls, Wick and MacKay (1948), by means of sodium salicylate and acetylsalicylic acid, were able to suppress to a considerable extent the development of ulcers in the rumen after pyloric ligature.

SUMMARY

Regeneration experiments in *Planaria gonocephala* showed no inhibitory action of salicylates on growth. In *Amblystoma mexicanum* regeneration was reduced by high doses, or by high concentrations applied by immersion; low concentrations increased regeneration.

In the rat the healing of gastric mucosal and of skin defects was accelerated by moderate doses of sodium salicylate. Ten to twenty per cent salicylic acid ointments, like high doses of salicylic acid and sodium salicylate (Rudas, 1960), inhibited the healing of experimental skin wounds, especially initially, except when the access of air was prevented (Rudas, 1962). Sodium salicylate was without influence on the regeneration of experimental defects in the rabbit's ear (Sala, 1954).

Review of the literature and of our own experiments thus shows that the effect of the salicylates on regenerative processes can be acceleratory or inhibitory according to dosage, mode of administration, experimental conditions, and species. The possibility of a beneficial effect of moderate doses of salicylates on wound healing might be a rewarding line of clinical investigation.

The literature on the salicylates goes back more than 100 years. The present review is surely incomplete, but it gives little grounds for supposing that this group of substances can in any way seriously disturb wound healing in man.

REFERENCES

Anonymous Swiss Herbal (1486). 'Herborius zu Deutsch: Gart der Gesundheit'. Augsburg: Johann Schönsperger. *See* Gross, M., & Greenberg, L. A. (1948). 'The Salicylates, a critical bibliographic review', p. 2. New Haven: Hillhouse Press.

Antweiler, H. (1957). *Klin. Wschr.*, **35**, 1087.

Bacchus, H., & Bacchus, A. (1953). *Fed. Proc.*, **12**, 7.

Bertolani, F., Bonati, B., Lorenzini, R., Bergamini, A., & Mari, E. (1953). *Folia endocr. (Pisa)*, **6**, 61.

Boström, H., & Månsson, B. (1955). *J. Pharm. Pharmacol.*, **7**, 185.

Brody, T. M. (1956). *J. Pharmacol. exp. Ther.*, **117**, 39.
Brown, G. (1878). *Naunyn-Schmiedeberg's Arch. exp. Path. Pharmak.*, **8**, 140.
Bullough, W. S. (1949). *Nature (Lond.)*, **163**, 680.
Calesnick, B., & Beutner, R. (1949). *Proc. Soc. exp. Biol. (N.Y.)*, **72**, 629.
van Cauwenberge, H. (1953). *C.R. Soc. Biol. (Paris)*, **147**, 1118.
van Cauwenberge, H., & Lecomte, J. (1957). *C.R. Soc. Biol. (Paris)*, **151**, 405.
Clausen, F. W., & Jager, B. V. (1946). *J. Lab. clin. Med.*, **31**, 428.
Collet, A., & Daniel-Moussard, H. (1959). *Arch. int. Pharmacodyn.*, **118**, 189.
Crampton, R. S., Black, W. C., Verdesca, A. S., Nedeljkovic, R. I., & Hilton, J. G. (1962). *Nature (Lond.)*, **194**, 295.
Dewes, R. (1955). *Arch. int. Pharmacodyn.*, **104**, 19.
Diernhofer, K. (1936). *Milchw. Forsch.*, **18**, 83.
Domenjoz, R. (1955). *Naunyn-Schmeideberg's Arch. exp. Path. Pharmak.*, **225**, 14.
Eichholtz, F. (1950). *Naunyn-Schmeideberg's Arch. exp. Path. Pharmak.*, **212**, 126.
Ersner, M. S., Myers, D., & Ersner, W. (1934). *Ann. Otol. (St. Louis)*, **43**, 114.
Ferrari, W., & Costa, E. (1953). Quoted by Bertolani et al. (1953).
Gerland, H. (1852). *J. chem. Soc.*, **5**, 133.
Glover, W. E., Marshall, R. J., & Whelan, R. F. (1957). *Brit. J. Pharmacol.*, **12**, 498.
Gohar, M. A., & Makkawi, M. (1951). *J. roy. Egypt. med. Ass.*, **34**, 110.
Gross, F. (1950). *Schweiz. med. Wschr.*, **50**, 697.
Guerra, F. (1946). *Science.*, **103**, 686.
Haining, C. G. (1956). *Brit. J. Pharmacol.*, **11**, 357.
Ivanovics, G. (1942). *Hoppe-Seylers Z. physiol. Chem.*, **276**, 33; & (1942). *Klin. Wschr.*, **15**, 343.
Kelemen, E. (1960). 'Permeability in acute experimental inflammatory oedema, in the light of the action of salicylates', pp. 13, 45, & 114. Budapest: Hungarian Academy of Sciences.
Kelemen, E., Majoros, M., Ivanyi, J., & Kovacs, K. (1950). *Experientia (Basel)*, **6**, 435.
Kodicek, E., & Loewi, G. (1955). *Proc. roy. Soc. B.*, **144**, 100.
Kolbe, H. (1874). *J. prakt. Chem.*, **10**, 89.
Küster, E., & Wagner-Jauregg, T. (1944). *Biochem. Z.*, **317**, 256.
Labelle, A., & Tornaben, J. A. (1951). *Science*, **114**, 187.
Lindner, A., & Rudas, B. (1961). *Hautarzt*, **12**, 539.
Meletti, O. (1956). *Nuovo G. Bot. ital.*, **63**, 46.
Marchand, F. (1901). 'Der Prozess der Wundheilung mit Einschluss der Transplantation.' Stuttgart: Enke.
Mari, E., & Rizzatti, E. (1951). *Arch. Maragliano Pat. clin.*, **6**, 1031.
Mathies, H. (1958). *Arzneimittel-Forsch.*, **8**, 233.
Mörsdorf, K., & Bode, H. H. (1959). *Arch. int. Pharmacodyn.*, **118**, 292.
Mulinos, M. G., & Hirschhorn, L. (1951). *Arch. int. Pharmacodyn.*, **88**, 115.
Muschaweck, R. (1950). *Naunyn-Schmiedeberg's Arch. exp. Path. Pharmak.*, **212**, 30.
Neivert, H. (1945). *Arch. Otolaryng.*, **42**, 14.
Panagopoulos, K., Kallistratos, G., Papantoniou, J., Oeconomopoulos, P., Vagougios, J., & Kontovassilis, P. (1961). *Med. exp. (Basel)*, **5**, 114.

Pauls, F., Wick, A. N., & MacKay, E. M. (1948). *Science*, **107**, 19.
Ragan, C., Grokoest, A. W., & Boots, R. H. (1949a). *Amer. J. Med.*, **7**, 741.
Ragan, C., Howes, E. L., Plotz, C. M., Meyer, K., & Blunt, J. W. (1949b). *Proc. Soc. exp. Biol. (N.Y.)*, **72**, 718.
Rapoport, S., Wing, M., & Guest, G. M. (1943). *Proc. Soc. exp. Biol. (N.Y.)*, **53**, 40.
Reid, J., Watson, R. D., & Sproull, D. H. (1950). *Quart. J. Med.*, N.S. **19**, 1.
Rudas, B. (1960). *Arzneimittel-Forsch.*, **10**, 226.
Rudas, B. (1962). *Arzneimittel-Forsch.*, **12**, 386.
Ryff, W. H. (1573). 'Reformierte deutsche Apoteck.' Strassburg: Josia Rihel.
Saito, K. (1935). *Folia pharmacol. jap.*, **20**, 269.
Sala, G. (1954). *R.C. Sci. Farmitalia*, **1**, 325.
Schumacher, H. (1953). *Ther. d. Gegenw.*, **92**, 167.
Selitto, J. J., & Randall, L. O. (1956). *Fed. Proc.*, **15**, 481.
Shapiro, S. (1944). *J. Amer. med. Ass.*, **125**, 546, 923.
Singer, R. (1945). *Arch. Otolaryng.*, **42**, 19.
Studer, A. (1950). *Z. Rheumaforsch.*, **9**, 356.
Swyer, G. J. M. (1948). *Biochem. J.*, **42**, 28.
Thiersch, K. (1875). *Samml. klin. Vorträge.* No. 84/85, p. 637.
Trethewie, E. R., & Morris, C. W. (1959). *Aust. J. exp. Biol. med. Sci.*, **37**, 567.
Trnavsky, K., Trnavska, Z., & Malinsky, J. (1962). *Arch. int. Pharmacodyn.*, **137**, 199.
Viscocil, J. (1957). *Brit. J. industr. Med.*, **14**, 30.
Weimar, V. (1957). *J. exp. Med.*, **105**, 141.
Whitehouse, M. W. (1962). *Nature (Lond.)*, **194**, 984.
Whitehouse, M. W., & Boström, H. (1961). *Biochem. Pharmacol.*, **7**, 135.
Wilhelmi, G. (1950). *Schweiz. med. Wschr.*, **80**, 936.
Wilhelmi, G. (1952). *Medizinische*, 1591.
Wilhelmi, G. (1954). *G. ital. Chemioter.*, **1**, 111.
Wilhelmi, G. (1956). *Helv. physiol. pharmacol. Acta*, **14**, C47.
Wilhelmi, G. (1957). *Pubbl. Staz. Zool. Napoli*, **30**, 168.
Wilson, A. (1915). *Brit. med. J.*, **i**, 331.

DISCUSSION

BUTTLE: I think we have all appreciated WILHELMI's masterly review of the literature on salicylates and wound healing. So far as our own experiments go, and they are confined entirely to the rat, we agree completely that salicylates have no significant effect on wound healing whatsoever.

ADAMS: Has WILHELMI done any experiments in cats or dogs?

ANDERSON: WILHELMI found that salicylates, at doses of 200 mg. per kg. intraperitoneally, actually aided the healing of the serotonin ulcer in the rat. At this dose sodium salicylate inhibits gastric secretion in small animals, and that may be why the ulcer was able to heal more quickly.

WILHELMI: No, I have not experimented with cats and dogs with salicylates.

7*

Salicylates do inhibit gastric acid secretion, but so do high doses of serotonin. I think that when salicylates are administered there is no chance for them to act in this manner with the serotonin ulcer. On the other hand, gastric juice formation is important with the pyloric-ligature ulcer (Shay) rat. If salicylates reduce acid secretion in this case, probably no ulcer will develop.

SALICYLATES AND THE GASTROINTESTINAL TRACT

A HISTORICAL PERSPECTIVE

ANDREW MUIR

AT the present time it is estimated that four thousand million aspirin tablets are swallowed annually in Great Britain. It is for this reason that the toxic effects of aspirin, even if individually uncommon, are of such importance.

As early as 1916 Gregersen detected occult blood in the faeces of patients taking oral salicylates. Twenty years elapsed before a series of observations indicated the probable source of this bleeding, and its potential danger. By gastroscopic examination of 16 subjects after the oral administration of aspirin, Douthwaite and Lintott (1938) found severe mucosal reactions in the vicinity of adherent portions of tablets in 13 of them. In one subject with a history of recurrent haematemeses they observed active bleeding from an intensely hyperaemic area underlying two adherent pieces of aspirin. These observations were extended by Hurst and Lintott (1939), and Hurst (1943) applied the findings to 51 cases of unexplained gastroduodenal haemorrhage and estimated that at least half were due to aspirin.

At the same time another series of observations appeared which apparently overshadowed the British work. Wolf and Wolff (1943) were unable to produce gastric lesions by direct application of aspirin to the mucosa of their gastrostomy subject, Tom. Gastroscopic examination of 107 subjects after aspirin administration by Paul (1943) showed no aspirin lesions. Caravati and Cosgrove (1946) repeated this work in twelve subjects, with similar results. These negative findings led Gross and Greenberg (1948) to suggest that any alimentary effects of salicylates were central, haematogenous, or both.

A hiatus of indifference followed until our own publication (Muir & Cossar, 1955), and since then a plethora of papers has appeared, agreeing in general with the earlier findings but differing greatly in method of study, theories of causation, and relative merits of salicylate preparations available. These extended observations have been based on chemical tests for faecal occult blood (Lange, 1957; Stubbé, 1958; Alvarez & Summerskill, 1958; Stubbé, Pietersen & van Heulen, 1962), radioactive chromate studies (Matsumoto & Grossman, 1959; Pierson et al., 1961; Scott et al., 1961; Wood, Harvey-Smith & Dixon, 1962), gastroscopic studies (Weiss, Pitman & Graham, 1961), post-gastrectomy studies (Muir & Cossar, 1959, 1961), and aspirin test meals (Schneider, 1957; Muir & Cossar, 1961).

A reasonable summary of the work to date is difficult to make because conclusions are often conflicting. However, it may help to attempt this, with the obvious proviso that few will believe all of it and some virtually none of it.

   (i) In approximately 70 per cent of patients salicylates cause a reproducible occult blood loss of 2–6 ml. per day. In an unspecified number the loss is much greater and anaemia may result.

  (ii) Salicylates may be a potent precipitating factor in 50 per cent of patients with overt gastroduodenal haemorrhage. The percentage is higher in the acute lesion group, i.e. those with no chronic dyspeptic history.

 (iii) The cause of bleeding is probably direct irritant action on the gastric mucosa. The mucosa of the bowel may also be affected, but to a lesser degree.

 (iv) The irritant action is controversial. It may be unrelated to the solubility of the formulation used, but particulate size, related to solubility, may be an important factor.

  (v) Hypoprothrombinaemia, increased capillary fragility, and decreased platelet adhesiveness are discounted as significant factors by most workers.

 (vi) The presence of a peptic ulcer or increased acid–pepsin potential is regarded as unimportant by some and as very important by others.

The references quoted are listed at the end of the next paper.

A REVIEW OF SOME OF THE FACTORS INVOLVED

JAMES L. A. ROTH

THE frequency with which the antecedent ingestion of salicylates has been associated with manifest or occult gastrointestinal bleeding and with exacerbations of ulcer symptoms has implicated these drugs in a causal or precipitating relationship. Numerous mechanisms have been suggested to explain the bleeding (Fig.), but some of them do not account for the suspected activation of gastroduodenal ulceration.

The gastric bleeding and ulceration seen in animals after the administration of salicylates parenterally suggested a hypothalamic–pituitary–adrenal systemic influence (Barbour & Dickerson, 1938; Volpato & Giro, 1955). The pharmacological properties of salicylates in many respects mimic those of cortisone (Hailman, 1952), but the evidence relating the release of cortisone to the action of salicylates on the pituitary-adrenal axis is conflicting (Roskam, van Cauwenberge & Mutsers, 1951; Bayliss & Steinbeck, 1954; Smith, Gray & Lunnon, 1954). A comprehensive review of the subject led Smith (1953) to conclude that the majority of the effects of salicylates are due to their intrinsic properties, rather than due to secondary endocrine influences.

It is also unlikely that the principal mode of action is a stimulation of acid secretion because a recent study (Winkelman & Summerskill, 1961) indicated that plain aspirin by mouth in conventional doses has no effect on the secretion of hydrochloric acid; soluble aspirin may act as only a weak stimulus, and sodium salicylate may inhibit secretion. Furthermore, there is no evidence that acid *per se* is the cause of ordinary peptic ulceration.

Drug idiosyncrasy or allergy has been considered to be the basis for non-gastrointestinal bleeding secondary to aspirin, such as epistaxis and ecchymoses (Honisberger, 1943). It has been attributed to increased capillary fragility (Frick, 1956), thrombocytopenia (Rappaport, Nixon & Barker, 1945), or decreased platelet adhesiveness with prolonged bleeding time (Beaumont, Willie & Lenègre, 1955). However, a systemic allergic mechanism would not account for the frequency of localized gastric mucosal effects. Moreover, manifest gastrointestinal haemorrhage and the recrudescence of peptic ulcer symptoms after the ingestion of salicylates occur far more commonly than could be attributed to drug sensitivity alone.

Depression of prothrombin or the stable prothrombin conversion factor is only observed with relatively large and repeated doses of salicylates (Link et al., 1943; Meyer & Howard, 1943). Thus a significant

OCCULT BLEEDING

GROSS HAEMORRHAGE

(Decreased Mucosal Resistance)

Focal Erosion or Ulceration

Decreased Mucous Barrier

Decreased Mucus

Focal Mucosal Necrosis

Epithelial Desquamation

Mucus Denaturation

Hypothalamic–Pituitary–Adrenal Effects

Increased Free Hydrochloric Acid

Allergic Hypersensitivity
 — increased capillary fragility
 — thrombocytopenia
 — decreased platelet adhesiveness

Hypoprothrombinaemia

Undefined Haemorrhagic Mechanism

ASPIRIN

(soluble forms)

(rare)

(large doses)

(parenteral)

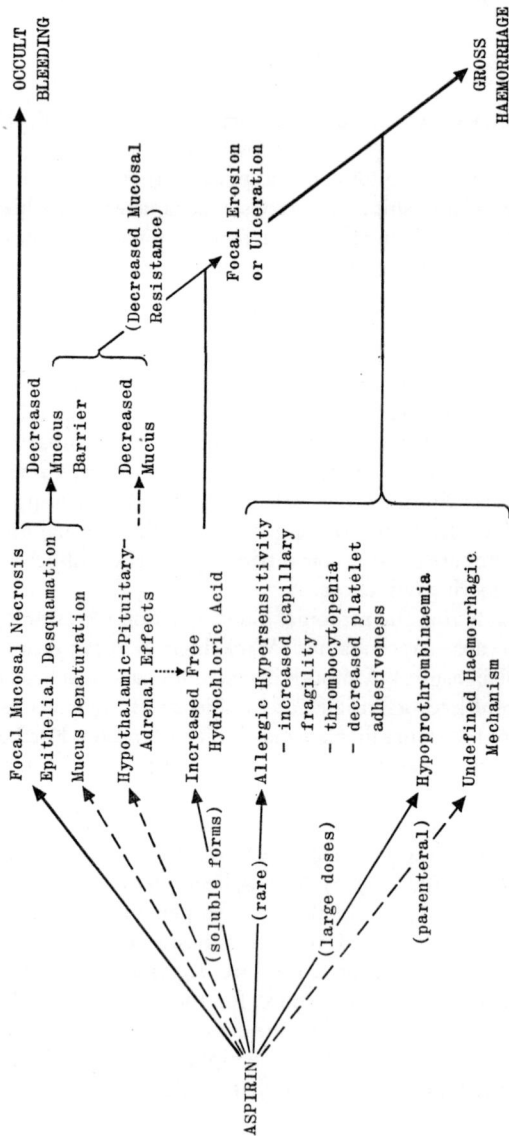

MECHANISMS OF SALICYLATE-INDUCED GASTROINTESTINAL EROSIONS AND HAEMORRHAGE. This summarizes the principal hypotheses. Definite effects are depicted by continuous arrows, whereas those effects that are not fully substantiated are shown by broken arrows.

effect upon these clotting factors does not account for the pathogenesis of the haemorrhage that is encountered with the commonly used doses of these drugs.

A central mode of action of salicylates has been implied (Caravati & Cosgrove, 1946). Recent studies by Grossman, Matsumoto and Lichter (1961) have shown that faecal blood loss occurs after intravenous aspirin, also suggesting that some as yet undefined central action may be important.

Not only has aspirin been considered a provocative cause of bleeding, but it has been held responsible for activation of peptic ulcer disease. This conclusion was reached because 20-40 per cent of patients had taken aspirin within 24 hours of the first symptoms of recurrent ulcer activity (Muir & Cossar, 1955; Kelly, 1956). Large gastric ulcers have been noted to develop while patients were under observation to study the role of aspirin in the development of anaemia (Martini, 1944; Stubbé, 1958). Prolonged oral administration of aspirin induced gastric ulceration in dogs (Thompson & Dragstedt, 1934), and large doses given orally or subcutaneously to rats have produced similar lesions (Shimamura & Aoki, 1939). A seasonal factor was noted by Barbour and Dickerson (1938); salicylate ulceration was produced readily in rats during September and April, but the lesions were encountered infrequently in the months of May and June. Peptic ulcer disease, however, is not an essential predisposing factor to salicylate bleeding, as demonstrated by the frequency with which faecal occult blood tests became strongly positive during experimental periods of salicylate administration in patients with X-ray negative dyspepsia, as well as in normal subjects (Lange, 1957; Stubbé, 1958; Alvarez & Summerskill, 1958). Such occult blood loss also has been found to be responsible for refractory and recurrent anaemias.

Although defective coagulation of the blood, hypoprothrombinaemia, or allergic reactions may be responsible for bleeding in only an occasional instance, one or more of these mechanisms may operate simultaneously with the local irritant effects of aspirin to provoke haemorrhage manifest by melaena or haematemesis. Gastroscopic observations (Douthwaite & Lintott, 1938; Hurst & Lintott, 1939; Jones, 1956), post-gastrectomy studies (Muir & Cossar, 1955, 1959), and the appearance of blood-stained mucus during fractional gastric analysis (Muir & Cossar, 1955; Schneider, 1957), all point towards the local irritant effects of aspirin upon the gastric mucosa. However, the topical action of salicylates cannot be regarded as the sole mechanism of bleeding. Contact of gross particles of salicylates is not essential for bleeding because occult loss of blood in the faeces occurs after the ingestion of solutions of aspirin. However, at gastric pH free acetylsalicylic acid would be likely to precipitate and the possibility that innumerable microscopic foci of mucosal necrosis are produced is under investigation. It has been suggested (Wood, Harvey-Smith & Dixon, 1962) that gastric absorption of undissociated acetyl-salicylic acid may be a factor concerned in blood loss. Furthermore, Grossman, Matsumoto and Lichter (1961) have suggested that some other as yet undefined parenteral mechanism may participate.

Many practising physicians seem to be indifferently complacent about these dangers. Patients are not informed and are not forewarned about these hazards. It is often stated that the ill effects of salicylates cannot be important if we consider their universal use and the tremendous quantities in which they are used. The relatively infrequent occurrence of melaena and haematemesis apparently induced by salicylates may be determined by the presence or absence of variable factors that permit the fortuitous occurrence of the topical action of salicylates. The likelihood of a tablet of medication getting caught in the mucosal folds, permitting prolonged local action, depends in part upon its disintegration time, dissolution rate, and mode of administration, including whether in solution, powder, or tablet; the amount of water used for ingestion; and whether the stomach was empty or the dose was taken after food. Hyper-trophied mucosal folds or the puckered scar or accessory pocket of previous ulcer activity are more likely to trap a particle of salicylate. Furthermore, the vulnerability of the mucosa to the topical erosive action of salicylate in an individual at a given time may also be increased by such factors as peptic ulcer diathesis, hypertrophic gastritis, an atrophic mucosa with reduced mucus barrier, and mucosal congestion secondary to alcohol, spices, or emotion. The chance occurrence of the topical damage to the mucosa may also be determined by seasonal influences on tissue resistance.

This review is based on a paper by Roth, J. L. A., and Valdes-Dapena, A. (1963), *in* 'Pathophysiology of Peptic Ulcer', ed. Skoryna, S. C. Montreal: McGill University Press.

REFERENCES

Alvarez, A. S., & Summerskill, W. H. J. (1958). *Lancet*, **ii**, 920.
Barbour, H. G., & Dickerson, U. C. (1938). *Arch. int. Pharmacodyn.*, **58**, 78.
Bayliss, R. I. S., & Steinbeck, A. W. (1954). *Lancet*, **i**, 1010.
Beaumont, J.-L., Willie, A., & Lenègre, J. (1955). *Bull. mem. Soc. méd. Hôp. Paris*, **71**, 1077.
Caravati, C. M., & Cosgrove, E. F. (1946). *Ann. intern. Med.*, **24**, 638.
Douthwaite, A., & Lintott, G. A. (1938). *Lancet*, **ii**, 1222.
Frick, P. G. (1956). *Amer. J. med. Sci.*, **231**, 402.
Gregersen, J. P. (1916). *Ugeskr. Laeg.*, **78**, 697, 1197, 1260.
Gross, M., & Greenberg, L. A. (1948). 'The Salicylates, a critical biblio-graphic review', p. 98. New Haven: Hillhouse Press.
Grossman, M. I., Matsumoto, K. K., & Lichter, R. J. (1961). *Gastro-enterology*, **40**, 383.
Hailman, H. F. (1952). *J. clin. Endocr.*, **12**, 454.

Honisberger, M. (1943). *Brit. med. J.*, **ii**, 57.
Hurst, A. (1943). *Brit. med. J.*, **i**, 768.
Hurst, A., & Lintott, G. A. (1939). *Guy's Hosp. Rep.*, **89**, 173.
Jones, F. A. (1956). *Gastroenterology*, **30**, 166.
Kelly, J. J. (1956). *Amer. J. med. Sci.*, **232**, 119.
Lange, H. F. (1957). *Gastroenterology*, **33**, 770, 778.
Link, K. P., Overman, R. S., Sullivan, W. R., Huebner, C. F., & Scheel, L. D. (1943). *J. biol. Chem.*, **147**, 463.
Martini, T. (1944). *Pren. méd. argent.*, **31**, 561.
Matsumoto, K. K., & Grossman, M. I. (1959). *Proc. Soc. exp. Biol. (N.Y.)*, **102**, 517.
Meyer, O. O., & Howard, B. (1943). *Proc. Soc. exp. Biol. (N.Y.)*, **53**, 234.
Muir, A., & Cossar, I. A. (1955). *Brit. med. J.*, **ii**, 7.
Muir, A., & Cossar, I. A. (1959). *Lancet*, **i**, 539.
Muir, A., & Cossar, I. A. (1961). *Amer. J. digest. Dis.*, N.S. **6**, 1115.
Paul, W. D. (1943). *J. Iowa med. Soc.*, **33**, 155.
Pierson, R. N. Jr., Holt, P. R., Watson, R. M., & Keating, R. P. (1961). *Amer. J. Med.*, **31**, 259.
Rappaport, A. E., Nixon, C. E., & Barker, W. A. (1945). *J. Lab. clin. Med.*, **30**, 916.
Roskam, J., van Cauwenberge, H., & Mutsers, A. (1951). *Lancet*, **ii**, 275.
Schneider, N. M. (1957). *Gastroenterology*, **33**, 616.
Scott, J. T., Porter, I. H., Lewis, S. M., & Dixon, A. St. J. (1961). *Quart. J. Med.*, N.S. **30**, 167.
Shimamura, M., & Aoki, A. (1939). *Folia pharmacol. jap.*, **27**, 19.
Smith, M. J. H. (1953). *J. Pharm. Pharmacol.*, **5**, 81.
Smith, M. J. H., Gray, C. H., & Lunnon, J. B. (1954). *Lancet*, **i**, 1008.
Stubbé, L. Th. F. L. (1958). *Brit. med. J.*, **ii**, 1062.
Stubbé, L. Th. F. L., Pietersen, J. H., & van Heulen, C. (1962). *Brit. med. J.*, **i**, 675.
Thompson, H. E., & Dragstedt, C. A. (1934). *Arch. intern. Med.*, **54**, 308.
Volpato, G., & Giro, M. (1955). *Chir. ital.*, **8**, 291.
Weiss, A., Pitman, E. R., & Graham, E. C. (1961). *Amer. J. Med.*, **31**, 266.
Winkelman, E. I., & Summerskill, W. H. J. (1961). *Gastroenterology*, **40**, 56.
Wolf, S., & Wolff, H. G. (1943). 'Human Gastric Function', p. 165. London: Oxford University Press.
Wood, P. H. N., Harvey-Smith, E. A., & Dixon, A. St. J. (1962). *Brit. med. J.*, **i**, 669.

STUDIES IN MAN

STUDIES OF OCCULT BLEEDING CAUSED BY SALICYLATES AND RELATED COMPOUNDS

PHILIP H. N. WOOD

Department of Medicine (Rheumatology)
Postgraduate Medical School of London

THE object of these studies was to find out how much people vary in the amount of blood lost after taking aspirin, and to see how this bleeding could be modified. Aspirin bleeding in any one subject is a relatively constant and reproducible phenomenon. The gastric mucosa appears to be in a state of constant susceptibility, and there is no evidence of a period of refractoriness to this action of aspirin.

Variation in occult bleeding

The variation in bleeding was studied in 226 individuals with normal digestive tracts. A few people showed no blood loss after aspirin, the majority lost between 2 and 6 ml. per day, and a small proportion was extremely sensitive. The fact that this proportion is small probably explains why aspirin bleeding is seldom of obvious importance in clinical practice. Analysis of this group in terms of a number of factors that might be supposed to affect the susceptibility to bleeding showed that age, sex, general health or coexistent disease, nodular seropositive rheumatoid arthritis, erythrocyte sedimentation rate, blood group, prothrombin level, plasma salicylate level, and a personal or family history of allergic diathesis, were unrelated to the resultant bleeding after aspirin. There was also no relation between occult bleeding and dyspeptic intolerance of aspirin. Dyspepsia, therefore, is not good evidence of direct harm to the bowel mucosa and must be regarded as an unrelated phenomenon.

The 226 subjects with normal digestive tracts were used as a reference population. The susceptibilities of groups of patients with alimentary disease can be compared with the variation in bleeding seen in the reference sample. By this means we found that groups of patients suffering from pernicious anaemia, with confirmed histamine-fast achlorhydria, and from active duodenal ulceration, such patients often having a high acid-pepsin secretion, did not differ significantly from those with a normal bowel in their susceptibility to aspirin. This confirms the contention of Winkelman and Summerskill (1961) that acid secretion is not of importance in the production of bleeding. In screening other anti-inflammatory drugs and other drugs with actions similar to those of salicylates, we could not detect reproducible bleeding after cortico-steroids, phenylbutazones, chloroquines, codeine, paracetamol, phen-acetin, sulphinpyrazone, and tolbutamide—in contrast to the incidence of detectable bleeding after aspirin, which occurred in approximately 70 per cent of subjects studied. In addition, the simultaneous adminis-tration of corticosteroids did not alter the magnitude of aspirin bleeding.

Grossman, Matsumoto and Lichter (1961), using radioactive chromate techniques, appeared to find bleeding after administering aspirin intravenously. Two points were noteworthy. First of all, there was a barely significant difference between faecal radioactivity during the control period and the period of intravenous therapy. Secondly, they gave a large dose over a short period of time. Although they did not report plasma salicylate levels, these must have been considerably higher than those obtained with conventional oral therapy. In the presence of a high concentration in the plasma it is quite possible that some aspirin could enter the cells of the gastric mucosa from the blood stream. That bleeding occurs without direct relation to the concentrations of salicylate in the plasma during conventional oral therapy is shown by the considerable reduction in the magnitude of blood loss observed when an enteric coated preparation of aspirin is substituted for the B.P. tablets, even though the same plasma salicylate level was maintained throughout. This suggests that there is no need to invoke some hypothetical parenteral or central action of aspirin; a local action on the cells of the gastrointestinal tract will account for all the data at present available.

A number of studies have implicated the stomach as the major site of susceptibility, and Levy (1961) has analysed the factors contributing to the presence of concentrations of aspirin in the stomach that greatly exceed those elsewhere in the gut. Thus in normal conditions the stomach bears the brunt of the assault by aspirin. The reduced loss after enteric coated preparations may be due to imperfections in the coating but, on the other hand, it may represent blood loss distal to the stomach. I think the latter is the most probable explanation, and that the concen-tration factors enumerated by Levy govern the reduction in the apparent susceptibility of the small intestine.

Modification of bleeding

Soluble aspirin, and preparations where aspirin is dispersed or dissolved in water before administration, cause as much bleeding as do tablets of plain aspirin (Wood, Harvey-Smith & Dixon, 1962). Other factors which did not affect the magnitude of bleeding were the state of the stomach, whether full or empty, and the bulk of the dose, i.e. a tablet as compared with the administration of a considerable bulk of fluid, which might provoke more rapid gastric emptying. We have not succeeded in establishing a critical dose level to produce bleeding. On the other hand, the administration of aspirin in two divided doses is associated with less bleeding than when the same total amount daily is divided into four doses. Other procedures associated with less bleeding are the simultaneous administration of a very large quantity of alkali, such as in effervescent aspirin, and formulations that delay the release of free aspirin, enteric coating and aloxiprin.

A number of workers have suggested that the irritant action of aspirin is due to the liberation of salicylic acid. Under physiological conditions hydrolysis of acetylsalicylic acid is not particularly rapid. Direct comparison of the effects of tablets of sodium salicylate and of salicylic acid showed that the resultant bleeding was identical and, in comparison with acetylsalicylate, salicylate was associated with much less bleeding; the magnitude of the reduction was greater than that observed with either aloxiprin or enteric-coated aspirin. We also studied two other salts of salicylic acid, choline salicylate and aluminium disalicylate, and a number of other derivatives of this acid—the amide, salicylamide; the alcohol, saligenin; and the amino derivative, p-aminosalicylic acid (PAS). Most of these appeared to resemble simple salicylate, although when the overall blood loss is small, as it is after non-acetylated salicylates, the significance of differences between different compounds is difficult to establish unless bleeding is virtually abolished. Salicylamide was exceptional in that it appeared to cause no bleeding. The only other preparation we have studied that was not associated with significant blood loss was enteric-coated sodium salicylate.

The idea that particulate aspirin has a local irritant action has received wide support. A B.P. tablet, a 'flash' dispersal preparation, and solutions of aspirin all cause the same degree of bleeding. This shows that tablet particles are not the essential feature in the development of bleeding. In addition, at the pH of the stomach the salts of aspirin would be converted into undissociated acetylsalicylic acid, and so the amount of undissociated aspirin available in the stomach from these different preparations need not be very different from that available from B.P. tablets of aspirin.

Bleeding is reduced by the simultaneous administration of a great excess of antacid. An excess of alkali promotes gastric emptying. The rate of gastric emptying is also modified by the bulk of material administered, especially if fluid, and also by the presence of other matter in the stomach. In fact, neither of these factors modified aspirin bleeding and, surprising though it is, it seems that the rate of gastric emptying is without significant effect on the bleeding induced. This suggests that antacid modifies the response by virtue of its neutralizing effect. By raising gastric pH it is highly likely that a large proportion of the aspirin would be ionized. Only undissociated acetylsalicylic acid is absorbed from the stomach (Hogben et al., 1957). Thus the excess of antacid could reduce gastric absorption of aspirin, suggesting that absorption of aspirin by the mucosal cells of the stomach is a necessary stage in the production of bleeding. This hypothesis would account for the fact that particles do not play an essential role in causing bleeding, and also for the fact that delaying the release of free aspirin reduces the resultant bleeding.

The mucosal absorption hypothesis is based on inference, and direct proof is difficult to obtain in the absence of techniques to differentiate aspirin absorbed from the stomach from that absorbed more distally. Overall absorption rates into the plasma do not necessarily provide a reliable index of the contribution of these two sites of absorption. Nevertheless it seems that at present this hypothesis is the only one that can account for all the data I have presented. Perhaps the most paradoxical observation, that gastric emptying rate does not influence bleeding, can be explained on this basis as well. The gastric mucosa exemplifies pH-dependent absorption. Because of the intrinsic interest of this process we may have exaggerated its importance. Gastric absorption of aspirin probably accounts for only a very small part of the overall absorption of an administered dose. CROFT has found that mucosal cells are shed within a few minutes, showing that aspirin produces at least part of its effect with remarkable rapidity. Thus if gastric mucosal absorption is limited but rapid, gastric emptying would need to be extremely quick to overcome this effect.

Levy (1961) has suggested that sodium salicylate causes less bleeding because it is more soluble than aspirin. At gastric pH sodium salicylate would be converted into undissociated salicylic acid—and salicylic acid is *less* soluble than acetylsalicylic acid. It is possible that, by altering this variable in Fick's equation, the rate of absorption from tablets of salicylic acid is slower than that from tablets of acetylsalicylic acid. Thus in a given time there would be less absorption in the stomach, and the concentration in the mucosal cells both in the stomach and in the small intestine would therefore be lower. This lower concentration in the mucosa of the small intestine could be less than the critical level required to produce damage, which would explain the virtual lack of bleeding associated with enteric-coated sodium salicylate. Salicylamide could represent a further example. It is neutral and very insoluble, and therefore its absorption by pH-dependent mechanisms would be even slower.

SUMMARY

Aspirin bleeding is very variable from one individual to another, and is relatively constant in any given individual. It appears to be unrelated to age, sex, or coexistent disease. The stomach is the major site of blood loss, but neither gastric acid secretion nor changes in blood coagulation appear to be related to the development of aspirin-induced bleeding.

We suggest that absorption of salicylate by the mucosal cells is the first stage in the development of haemorrhagic lesions, and that procedures that delay gastric absorption are associated with a reduction in the amount of blood loss. Variations in the effects of different salicylates may be related to differences in their physical properties.

These studies were supported by the Nicholas Research Institute Ltd.

The present address of the author is State University of New York at Buffalo Medical School, Buffalo, N.Y., U.S.A.

REFERENCES

Grossman, M. I., Matsumoto, K. K., & Lichter, R. J. (1961). *Gastro-enterology*, **40**, 383.
Hogben, C. A. M., Schanker, L. S., Tocco, D. J., & Brodie, B. B. (1957). *J. Pharmacol. exp. Ther.*, **120**, 540.
Levy, G. (1961). *J. pharm. Sci.*, **50**, 388.
Winkelman, E. I., & Summerskill, W. H. J. (1961). *Gastroenterology*, **40**, 56.
Wood, P. H. N., Harvey-Smith, E. A., & Dixon, A. St. J. (1962). *Brit. med. J.*, **i**, 669.

GASTROSCOPIC STUDIES OF THE EFFECT OF
SALICYLATES ON THE HUMAN STOMACH

ERNEST R. PITMAN, ALEX WEISS, AND EMERSON C. GRAHAM

City Hospital at Elmhurst
Elmhurst, New York, N.Y., U.S.A.

CRITICAL review of former gastroscopic studies raises a reasonable doubt as to the justification of the conclusions drawn due to failure to obtain comparative control examinations. None of the previous workers compared the state of the gastric mucosa before and after the administration of aspirin. Douthwaite (1954) recognized this objection but disposed of it as a theoretical consideration. However, clinical experience with numerous diagnostic gastroscopies has repeatedly revealed minor vascular changes in the absence of any known gastric irritant. In the light of these considerations, an investigation was undertaken to ascertain by gastroscopic observation the immediate effect of single doses of 0·6 to 0·9 g. of acetylsalicylic acid on the gastric mucosa, each subject serving as his own control (Weiss, Pitman & Graham, 1961).

Gastroscopic appearances

The control gastroscopic examinations revealed a total of 23 pathological changes in 16 of 30 subjects. Thirteen subjects had haemorrhagic areas ranging from a minute pinpoint of fresh blood to areas covering a few centimetres. Some of these areas were considered to be traumatically induced by the introduction of the aspirating Ewald tube. Three patients had scattered petechiae. Three had small localized areas of gastritis, two atrophic and one hypertrophic; two had scattered superficial erosions; and two had benign mucosal polyps. The site and character of these lesions were carefully noted and observed to be distinct from those attributed to the action of aspirin itself. The remaining fourteen subjects showed no abnormalities.

The aspirin, visualized in all but one case, was seen to have disintegrated into a pulverized state and in some instances into small scattered discrete fragments, having broken up in the layer of gastric juice remaining in the stomach. Frequently it appeared as a white gelatinous mass of granules adherent to the mucosa in the region of the cardia, but in many cases it was scattered more distally in the antrum and around the angulus. The mucosa remained either flat or heaped up in rugose folds about the aspirin. Following the introduction of aspirin there was no change in 17 patients (57 per cent). In seven patients (23 per cent) there was slight congestion of the mucosa surrounding the aspirin. This consisted of a noticeable increase in redness and distinct hyperaemia confined to the folds around the aspirin fragment, demarcating this zone from the orange-pink mucosa surrounding it. No break in the mucosa or blood ooze could be detected in these instances. More intensive changes were seen in six patients (20 per cent), four with the aspirin lying in a lake of fresh or altered blood, haemolysed by gastric hydrochloric acid, and two with an increase in bleeding over that seen at the time of the control gastroscopy. The aspirin fragment consisted of an agglutinated gelatinous mass suspended in a lake of blood mixed with fresh mucus in some of

COMPARISON OF CONTROL GASTROSCOPIC FINDINGS BETWEEN PATIENTS
WITH A NEGATIVE AND A POSITIVE REACTION TO ASPIRIN

Gastroscopic findings	Number of patients		
	Negative	Positive	Total
Normal	9	5	14
Varying degrees of haemorrhage	5	3	8
Chronic patchy gastritis (including haemorrhage in one)	2	2	4
Polyp (also showing haemorrhage and petechiae in negative case)	1	1	2
Gastric erosions (both with haemorrhage)	0	2	2
TOTAL	17	13	30

these six patients. No instances of erosion or ulceration were seen in any of the thirty subjects after the introduction of aspirin. However, in the patients with bleeding the mucosa underlying the aspirin was obscured by the blood lake, so that the possibility of an erosion could not be excluded.

The Table compares the control gastroscopic findings in the subjects with no reaction to aspirin, designated as negative, with those showing a change after aspirin, designated as positive. A higher incidence of inflammatory change after aspirin was found among patients showing some pathological condition at the time of the control gastroscopy, indicating that perhaps the person with a gastric mucosal abnormality may be more susceptible to injury produced by aspirin. There also appeared to be a greater susceptibility to aspirin-induced irritation in patients with peptic ulcer, especially gastric ulcer. Six of ten patients with peptic ulcer showed haemorrhage or congestion, whereas only seven of twenty patients without ulcer showed these changes. Of three patients with gastric ulcer, two showed a positive reaction, while three of seven patients with duodenal ulcer showed some vascular change. Almost half of the positive reactors were patients with peptic ulcer; the tendency to bleed after ingestion of aspirin was twice as great in the patient with peptic ulcer disease.

Twenty-eight patients gave a history of aspirin ingestion in the past, four frequently, seven moderately, and 17 occasionally. Seven patients gave a history of symptoms of intolerance, such as epigastric discomfort, gnawing pain, heartburn, nausea, vomiting, and bloating. Two of these reacted positively to aspirin, and five were from the group that reacted negatively. The symptoms were more severe in the negative group. Of the six patients with the more severe haemorrhagic reaction to aspirin, only one experienced ill effects from the drug and he described it as mild nausea. None of the thirty patients had previously experienced gastro-intestinal bleeding of presumed aspirin origin. Of the five patients discharged with a diagnosis of gastrointestinal haemorrhage of undetermined aetiology, none showed any reaction to aspirin gastroscopically and only one gave a history of mild epigastric distress with use of the drug.

Implications

Douthwaite and Lintott (1938) preceded their gastroscopic examinations by aspiration with a stomach tube. The extent of congestion and haemorrhage induced thereby remains unaccounted for in their analysis, but may explain the smaller percentage of vascular changes found after aspirin in the present study. They reported an incidence of vascular change of 80 per cent after aspirin, as compared with 43 per cent in this investigation, although the incidence of more severe degrees of vascular change was higher in our study, 20 per cent compared with 13 per cent.

The disparity between our results and those of Paul (1943) may be explained by two factors. First of all, Paul did not aspirate the gastric contents prior to gastroscopy, perhaps thereby leaving greater protective layers of mucus strengthening the defensive mechanism of the mucous membrane of the stomach. In many of our positive cases a recognizable lake of mucus accumulated, intimately mixed with the small gelatinous mass of blood, indicating possibly an induced protective reaction. Secondly Paul, not performing control gastroscopies, may have designated a variety of pathological mucosal changes that he called 'chronic gastritis' as not being caused by aspirin, when in fact they may have been due to ingestion of the drug. Recent mucosal biopsy studies indicate the lack of specificity of 'chronic gastritis' and demonstrate that certain changes, such as oedema, haemorrhage, and mucus secretion, are common to both the acute and chronic phases.

Many workers have stressed the fact that the site of most intense action in the stomach is the lesser curvature. However, in the present investigation no greater susceptibility of one region over another was found. Rotation of our subjects through 360° provided for dispersion of the aspirin fragments on the gastric wall, demonstrating the ability to irritate all areas of the gastric mucosa. In a number of patients exhibiting a positive reaction to aspirin the haemorrhagic changes took place around very small and almost completely disintegrated particles; conversely, whole unbroken and unpulverized tablets were seen in negative reactors without any mucosal alteration. This is at variance with the assertion made by some observers (Cronk, 1958; Rubin, Pelikan & Kensler, 1959; Levy & Hayes, 1960) that gastric irritation due to aspirin is a function of its rate of dispersion, dissolution, and disintegration within the gastric lumen.

The precise mechanism of aspirin-induced gastric bleeding is not known. The discrete mucosal haemorrhages and areas of congestion observed at the sites of contact with aspirin support the impression that the noxious action is locally produced. It could consist of direct vascular injury involving the capillaries of the lamina propria. Haemorrhage from this capillary plexus, which lies directly beneath the surface epithelial layer, could lead to hypoxia and subsequent necrobiosis of the neck stratum of the gastric gland tubule and would then result in an erosion. This sequence of changes could explain the mucosal haemorrhages reported here, and the erosive changes described by other workers. Haemorrhagic and erosive gastritis have been demonstrated to result from a variety of noxious agents exerting a deleterious action on the intricate capillary plexus in the lamina propria of the stomach. This inherent susceptibility is due to the unusual arteriovenous shunt mechanism in this layer (Palmer, 1954). Further elucidation of the precise histological changes occurring at the site of aspirin injury would be enhanced by the use of the gastroscope with an attached suction biopsy device enabling the operator to obtain a specimen from a desired visualized area.

SUMMARY

The effects of aspirin on the gastric mucosa were observed gastroscopically in thirty subjects. Forty-three per cent of the subjects reacted with congestive and haemorrhagic changes of the gastric mucosa. These effects occurred predominantly around areas in contact with and in close proximity to the drug. Evidence is presented that objective evaluation of the local effects of a drug by gastroscopy requires comparison with preliminary control observations of the gastric mucosa. Patients with peptic ulcer were slightly more susceptible to mucosal injury with aspirin, as were those subjects with pre-existing minor mucosal changes.

There was no correlation between symptoms of intolerance of aspirin and the occurrence of haemorrhagic phenomena.

This paper is based on material already published in the *American Journal of Medicine*.

REFERENCES

Cronk, G. A. (1958). *New Engl. J. med.*, **258**, 219.
Douthwaite, A. H. (1954). *Lancet*, **ii**, 917.
Douthwaite, A. H., & Lintott, G. A. M. (1938). *Lancet*, **ii**, 1222.
Levy, G., & Hayes, B. A. (1960). *New Engl. J. Med.*, **262**, 1053.
Palmer, E. D. (1954). *Medicine (Baltimore)*, **33**, 199.
Paul, W. D. (1943). *J. Iowa med. Soc.*, **33**, 155.
Rubin, R., Pelikan, E. W., & Kensler, C. J. (1959). *New Engl. J. Med.*, **261**, 1208.
Weiss, A., Pitman, E. R., & Graham, E. C. (1961). *Amer. J. Med.*, **31** 266.

EXFOLIATIVE CYTOLOGY OF THE STOMACH AFTER THE ADMINISTRATION OF SALICYLATES

D. N. Croft

Department of Medicine
St. Thomas's Hospital, London

Observations on gastrectomy specimens after the administration of soluble aspirin suggested that aspirin might act on the gastric mucosa by causing exfoliation of epithelial cells. This phenomenon has been observed in the dog gastric pouch (Hollander, 1946; Hollander, Stein & Lauber, 1946), in the human stomach (Wolf & Wolff, 1946, 1947), and in the dog small intestine (Creamer, Shorter & Bamforth, 1961), in response to various chemical and physical stimuli.

Exfoliation of gastric mucosal cells in man has been studied by the following technique. The subject lies inclined slightly to the left, with a latex gastric tube passed so that the tip just enters the stomach. Each specimen is obtained by washing the stomach with 500 ml. of warm normal saline. Four specimens are obtained: A, the fasting washout; B, the control washout, after 50 ml. of normal saline has been in the stomach for twelve minutes; C, after 1 g. of pure powdered calcium aspirin dispersed in 50 ml. of normal saline has been in the stomach for five minutes; and D, the washout after a second dose of 1 g. of calcium aspirin has been in the stomach for twelve minutes. Specimens C and D are usually more opaque and contain suspended particles. Cytological examination shows that these particles are composed of gastric mucosal nuclei and cells (Plate II, opposite). According to Schade (1960), gastric mucosal cells and nuclei are not usually found in gastric washout specimens from subjects with a normal gastric mucosa.

A quantitative method of estimating exfoliation was required. Deoxyribonucleic acid (DNA) is the essential constituent of the genes, and there is a constant amount per nucleus for the different tissues of any one species (Davidson, Leslie & White, 1951). Therefore the amount of DNA in a gastric washout specimen is directly proportional to the amount of nuclear material in the lumen of the stomach. We have estimated DNA by the diphenylamine method (Burton, 1956; Slater & Lovell, 1961). A healthy medical student was studied in this manner on two occasions. In the first experiment three dummy tablets of soluble aspirin were administered instead of calcium aspirin before specimens C and D. The DNA content of these specimens was not increased after the administration of tablets that contained no aspirin. In a separate experiment using aspirin, results similar to those shown in the figure were obtained.

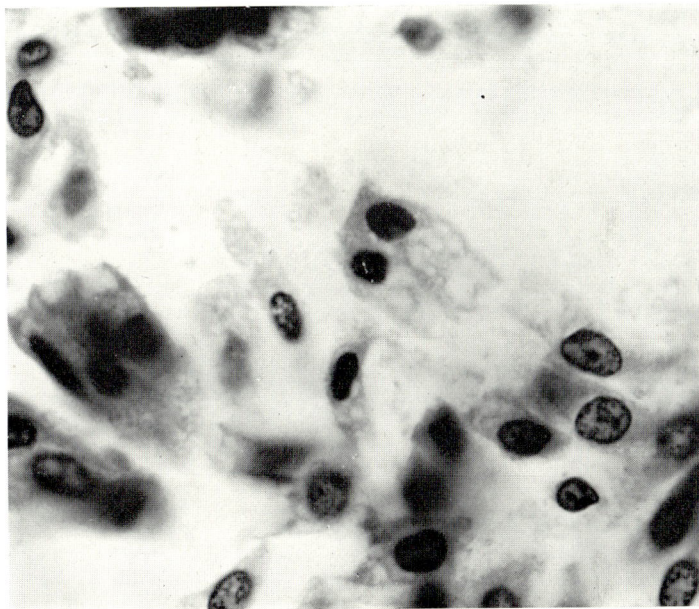

PLATE II (CROFT)   EXFOLIATED GASTRIC EPITHELIAL CELLS

Some of the intact cells are rectangular in shape and are recognizable as gastric columnar epithelial cells. The nuclei are oval or round, and have a thin distinct nuclear membrane and a fine chromatin network. This is typical of gastric epithelial nuclei.

Magnification × 1,000.

[*To face p.* 204

The time during which DNA can accumulate in the stomach varies for each specimen; therefore it is better to present results as the rate of DNA accumulation per minute. This rate is obtained by dividing the total DNA content of each specimen by the number of minutes from the end of the previous washout to the end of the washout concerned. Specimen A, the fasting washout, contains cells (and therefore DNA) that may have

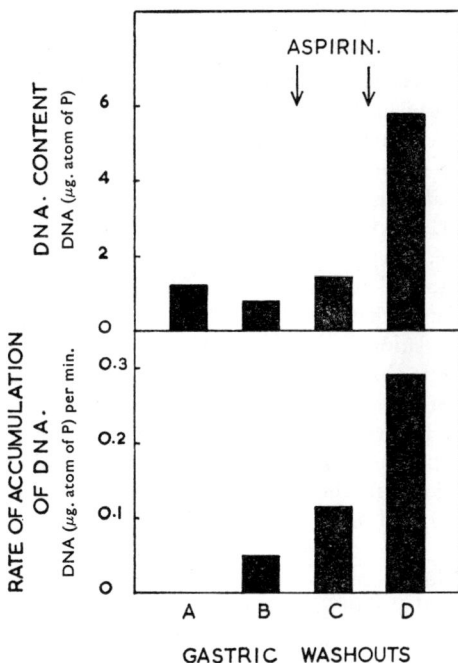

EXFOLIATION OF GASTRIC MUCOSAL CELLS AFTER
THE ADMINISTRATION OF ASPIRIN

This has been measured by estimating the content and rate of accumulation of DNA in gastric washout specimens. Washouts are designated fasting, A, control, B, and after the administration of dispersions of calcium acetylsalicylate, $1 \cdot 0$ g., C and D.

accumulated during an unknown period of time from swallowed saliva, sputum, from the oesophagus, and probably from the gastric mucosa. The rate of accumulation of DNA, therefore, cannot be calculated for this specimen. The figure shows the results obtained from one of the studies with aspirin. The upper part, the series of DNA estimations, shows a marked increase in the DNA content of the second post-aspirin specimen, D. When these are converted into the rates of accumulation of

DNA, the lower part of the figure, it can be seen that there is also a definite increase in DNA accumulation in the first post-aspirin sample, C. This increased rate of accumulation of DNA after the administration of aspirin represents exfoliation of cells from the gastric mucosa.

Exfoliation and susceptibility to aspirin bleeding

We have studied a selection of subjects whose salicylate bleeding had been estimated by the radioactive chromate technique at the Postgraduate Medical School, as described by WOOD. Six of these subjects were big bleeders, having been shown to lose more than 11 ml. of blood per day of treatment with aspirin. In four of these patients there was an increase in the rate of DNA accumulation after calcium acetylsalicylate similar to that seen in the figure. In one patient the rate of DNA accumulation appeared to fall after aspirin; in this patient the total DNA content of the fasting washout, specimen A, was the highest value obtained in any experiment done. It is possible that not all the DNA present in the fasting state had been washed out with specimen A, causing the apparently high rate of accumulation that was observed in specimen B. The apparent fall in DNA accumulation in specimens C and D was in relation to the unusually high rate observed in specimen B. The sixth patient showed no change in the rate of accumulation of DNA after the administration of calcium aspirin. This response is what is common in non-bleeders. Since the bleeding studies were done, two years ago, she has had a gastric biopsy. In view of the biopsy findings her gastric mucosa and bleeding potential may have altered, and further investigations are to be done to elucidate this.

Six non-bleeders were studied, five of whom lost up to 1 ml. per day after aspirin and the sixth lost up to 2 ml. of blood per day of treatment with aspirin. The latter patient is not truly a non-bleeder, and this may explain why there was a moderate rise in the rate of accumulation of DNA after administering aspirin. In four patients there was no rise in the accumulation of DNA after aspirin, three of them actually showing a reduction in the rate. In the sixth patient there was a significant rise in DNA accumulation. The striking feature of these results is that the majority of non-bleeders behaved differently from the majority of big bleeders, and also from all other apparently normal subjects studied. The four non-bleeders who showed no increase in DNA after aspirin also exhibited two other features. Cytological examination of their pre-aspirin washouts showed the presence of gastric epithelial cells and of polymorphonuclear leucocytes and other inflammatory cells. According to Schade (1960), exfoliated gastric epithelium is seen uncommonly except in patients with a pathological gastric mucosa, such as atrophic gastritis. The same is true of the associated inflammatory cells. These observations suggested that some of the non-bleeders had atrophic gastritis. It is interesting that the one apparently anomalous result, the non-bleeder who showed a marked rise in DNA after aspirin, did not have inflammatory cells in the pre-aspirin washouts.

Further evidence for the association between salicylate non-bleeding and atrophic gastritis has been obtained from another patient. Gastric biopsy by Dr. N. F. Coghill had shown that she had atrophic gastritis, and she had been shown to be a non-bleeder after salicylates. Exfoliation studies showed a fall in the rate of accumulation of DNA, and cytological examination of pre-aspirin washouts showed gastric epithelium and inflammatory cells. Thus this patient behaved in the same manner as did the majority of non-bleeders. This patient with atrophic gastritis, and some of the non-bleeders who on cytological evidence may have the same condition, may be exfoliating before aspirin is administered and aspirin appears not to increase this exfoliation.

SUMMARY

A technique for studying the exfoliation of gastric mucosal cells is described. In the majority of patients who are known to be aspirin bleeders aspirin appears to increase the rate of exfoliation of cells from the gastric mucosa. It is likely that this increased exfoliation causes some gastric lesion, of which an erosion is a severe example.

Patients who are aspirin non-bleeders and who have atrophic gastritis, or cytological appearances suggesting this, exfoliate before aspirin is given and do not appear to increase the rate of exfoliation after aspirin. The abnormal mucosa of these patients may have a rapid cell turnover, and may also have some property which prevents increased exfoliation after aspirin. Either one or both of these factors may prevent the development of the lesion that is responsible for salicylate bleeding.

Variations in salicylate-induced gastric epithelial exfoliation, and in gastric cell turnover, may be important factors in the mechanism of salicylate-induced bleeding into the gut.

This work was carried out during a period of study leave granted by the Governors of St. Thomas's Hospital.

REFERENCES

Burton, K. (1956). *Biochem. J.*, **62**, 315.
Creamer, B., Shorter, R. G., & Bamforth, J. (1961). *Gut*, **2**, 110.
Davidson, J. N., Leslie, I., & White, J. C. (1951). *Lancet*, **i**, 1287.
Hollander, F. (1946). In discussion after Wolf & Wolff (1946).
Hollander, F., Stein, J., & Lauber, F. U. (1946). *Gastroenterology*, **6**, 576.
Schade, R. O. K. (1960). 'Gastric Cytology', p. 25. London: Edward Arnold.
Slater, T. J., & Lovell, D. (1961). *Experientia (Basle)*, **17**, 272.
Wolf, S., & Wolff, H. G. (1946). *N.Y. St. J. Med.*, **46**, 2509.
Wolf, S., & Wolff, H. G. (1947). 'Human Gastric Function', 2nd Ed., p. 218. London: Oxford University Press.

DISCUSSION

PETER R. HOLT (*Gastroenterology Laboratory, St. Luke's Hospital, New York, N.Y., U.S.A.*):

The importance of the three papers we have just heard is that the studies have been done in human subjects by different techniques. The ease with which gastric lesions may be induced in some experimental animals by various stimuli made investigation in man imperative.

WOOD's studies have confirmed and expanded the observations of others using similar techniques. After hearing that most structural modifications do not abolish bleeding completely it would seem almost unnecessary to pursue differing chemical formulae much further, but rather to study some of the metabolically similar agents discussed previously. Even the more soluble salicylates cause bleeding, and the absence of particles does not confer immunity from this effect. However, I am sure most will agree that with large particles at the mucous membrane the local concentration of aspirin will be much higher, so that any damage to the mucosa related to concentration may be localized at that point. The radioactive chromate technique has provided so much background data that this must be the standard method with which future studies should be compared.

PITMAN has seen that salicylates in fine particulate form cause definite bleeding acutely, although the difficulties of the technique have not yet allowed him clearly to delineate the lesion. Although gastroscopic studies with premedication, patient apprehension, and gastric suction are not truly physiological, this does not in my opinion reduce the significance of his observations. I should like to see his studies compared with the radioactive chromate technique and with direct gastric biopsy.

CROFT has shown that there is a very rapid desquamation of mucosal cells in some subjects following aspirin and, although the results are very preliminary, that this occurs in patients who bleed. It may not occur in patients who do not bleed. These results reinforce my feeling that we must concentrate more on the non-susceptible population than on those who bleed. All workers in this field have been struck by the similar percentage of the population that is not susceptible. What is it that confers immunity on this group? CROFT observed that the non-susceptible may have a higher rate of shedding of mucosal cells before salicylate administration, and that this is not increased following the drug. When Hollander (1946) described the production of a cell-laden mucous secretion following the irritation of the gastric mucosa by various means, he ascribed a protective function to this process. Are we to believe, then, that the ability to shed mucosal cells rapidly protects the mucosa from salicylate damage? The patient with histologically proven atrophic gastritis, in whom DNA production before aspirin was very high, suggests that some forms of atrophic gastritis may be related to excessively high rates of cellular turnover. A similar mechanism has been suggested to account for the stunted villi in sprue (see Creamer, B. [1962]. *Gut*, **3**, 295). However, we must be cautious as this whole hypothesis rests on DNA estimations on a single patient with proven gastric atrophy, and WOOD's data on patients with pernicious anaemia suggest that the latter bleed as frequently as normals.

Thus we now believe that, to cause bleeding, salicylates enter the mucosal cells of the gastrointestinal tract, and that the stomach is most susceptible because of the higher concentration achieved there. Further histological evidence for diffuse damage to surface mucosal cells is needed from gastric biopsies and, hopefully, with electron microscopy, where perhaps early mitochondrial damage may be detected, linking up with a metabolic effect. Histochemistry may also be helpful. In addition, studies of cell turnover with thymidine labelling are necessary. It seems likely that from the pursuit of these studies we will learn much about pathological conditions of the stomach quite unrelated to the salicylates.

CREAMER: One of the big points of interest is whether CROFT can substantiate the suggestion that aspirin non-bleeders are people with atrophic gastritis. If this is true, then the question arises whether it can be explained in terms of cell turnover. We have only just started to look at specimens of gastritis for evidence of cell turnover, but some of them do have a high mitotic activity.

LEVY: WOOD concluded that the degree of bleeding after salicylic acid and salicylamide was inversely related to the rate of absorption of these drugs. In fact salicylic acid is twice as rapidly absorbed from the stomach as is aspirin, and salicylamide is even more rapidly absorbed than salicylic acid. Thus we are dealing with exactly the reverse of what his conclusions are based on.

There is evidently a difference of opinion whether the bleeding caused by salicylates is due to the contact of solid drug with the mucosa, or whether a solution can produce it. The degree of topical irritation and erosion is usually related to two factors; namely, concentration and time of contact. If it were possible to bring aspirin particles into contact with absolutely dry mucosa, I am quite certain that no irritation would occur. However, the mucosa is moist and salicylate particles become surrounded by a saturated solution of the drug. I believe that it is this solution that causes the irritation. The solid drug particles act as a reservoir and supply additional salicylate as part of the dissolved drug is absorbed. I am quite sure that application of a saturated solution of a salicylate to the gastric mucosa causes just as much irritation as application of drug solids for an equal length of time. When administering solid forms, reduction in the dose should decrease irritation because contact time is also reduced, due to the smaller depot of drug solids. One should be able to reduce blood

8

loss, if not prevent it, by administering salicylates in solutions that are diluted as much as possible. None of the data available seem to contradict this conclusion.

Wood: Levy apparently does not accept my finding that aspirin in aqueous solution in the absence of antacid is not associated with a reduction in gastrointestinal irritation. With regard to the different rates of absorption, I think Levy's data are based on studies in rats with ligated stomachs. This is hardly directly applicable to absorption from tablets in the intact human gastrointestinal tract.

Levy: Studies on the absorption of drugs from the stomach of the rat and the stomach of the human have yielded essentially identical results. Despite some histological differences, the absorption of these drugs appears to be essentially of the same character in both species.

Mucosal absorption

Martin: The work of Travell (1940) and the detailed studies of Brodie and co-workers (1957a, b, c) have given rise to the theory that the gastric mucosa is selectively permeable to the undissociated molecule, and that drugs are absorbed by passive diffusion of their lipid-soluble forms. Other workers have extended this theory to include transfer across other membranes in the body. Jacobs (1940) and others (Milne, Scribner & Crawford, 1958; Rall, Stabenau & Zubrod, 1959) have pointed out the striking effect that a pH gradient has on the concentration of certain drugs on the different sides of a membrane.

This theory does not appear to have been considered in detail in relation to the gastric mucosal cells when an acidic substance such as aspirin is absorbed from the stomach. The largest pH gradient of all would appear to be experienced by the gastric mucosal cells. The pH within these cells is of the order of 7·0, whereas the surface of the cell which borders the gastric lumen is in contact with the gastric fluid with a pH of about 2·0. Aspirin has a pK_a of 3·5, and at pH 2·0 about 97 per cent of that which is in solution will be in the undissociated form. The rate of entry into the mucosal cell will be high. On entering the mucosal cell only that small fraction which remains undissociated, about 0·03 per cent, will effectively contribute potential to the rate of removal of aspirin from the cell. There will therefore be a tendency for a high concentration of anion to accumulate in the mucosal cell. As a result, the mucosal cell may suffer damage long before a state of equilibrium is attained between the rates of entry and of removal of aspirin. Any damage of a non-specific nature might be attributed to a failure of the buffer system and a rise in hydrogen ion concentration, whilst the specific damage might be related to the character of the particular anion. This mucosal cell theory may be of significance in explaining the gastric damage that appears to be associated with the rapid absorption of aspirin from the stomach. In the less acidic conditions of the intestine its effect would be less apparent.

REFERENCES

Hogben, C. A. M., Schanker, L. S., Tocco, D. J., & Brodie, B. B. (1957a). *J. Pharmacol. exp. Ther.*, **120**, 540.
Jacobs, M. N. (1940). *Cold Spr. Harb. Symp. quant. Biol.*, **8**, 30.
Milne, M. D., Scribner, B. H., & Crawford, M. A. (1958). *Amer. J. Med.*, **24**, 709.
Rall, D. P., Stabenau, J. R., & Zubrod, C. G. (1959). *J. Pharmacol. exp. Ther.*, **125**, 185.
Schanker, L. S., Shore, P. A., Brodie, B. B., & Hogben, C. A. M. (1957b). *J. Pharmacol. exp. Ther.*, **120**, 528.
Shore, P. A., Brodie, B. B., & Hogben, C. A. M. (1957c). *J. Pharmacol. exp. Ther.*, **119**, 361.
Travell, J. (1940). *J. Pharmacol. exp. Ther.*, **69**, 21.

MILNE: These ideas may elucidate some of our difficulties. It is difficult to measure concentration in the gastric mucosa, but it has been shown that acids of the type of salicylic acid can be concentrated up to forty times between the gastric lumen and the mucosal blood plasma and so I imagine the amount in the cell is equivalent to the amount in the mucosal blood.

In relation to the pH gradients, one must remember that relatively small pH gradients can produce this effect. This may elucidate the difference between the pernicious anaemia patients and the patient with atrophic gastritis. In relation to differences between atrophic conditions of the stomach, it is important to measure not whether a large amount of hydrochloric acid is secreted, but what is the actual pH of the gastric juice. At pH 6·5 very little concentration will occur, but at pH 5·0 just as much concentration will occur as would at pH 1·0 or 1·5. One would like to see estimations of the salicylate content of exfoliated cells, but it would be difficult because the washout fluid would tend to remove the weak acids. This might be overcome by doing some of the estimations in undiluted gastric juice, without washes.

LEVY: Brodie and his colleagues studied the gastric absorption of aspirin and salicylic acid by placing solutions of these drugs in previously ligated rat stomachs, washing these out after one hour, and determining the amount of drug in the wash. We have used similar methods except that we excised the intact stomach at the end of one hour, homogenized it together with its contents, and determined the amount of drug in the homogenate. The percentage of drug absorbed was essentially identical by both methods, which suggests that there is no major concentration of aspirin or salicylic acid in the gastric wall. The pH in most of the cells of the gastric wall is probably quite similar to that of the blood, and there should be relatively rapid transfer of drug from the mucosal cells to the circulation.

VAN CAUWENBERGE: We have observed many cases of haemorrhage in patients treated with phenylbutazone, and also in those treated with prednisolone. I was surprised that WOOD found no blood loss after these drugs.

WOOD: Aren't you thinking of frank haemorrhage? I said that we did not find reproducible occult bleeding after these drugs. The dosage of phenylbutazone was not more than 300 mg. per day. I think that perhaps we might find even occult bleeding if we gave it in larger doses.

STUDIES IN ANIMALS

THE EFFECT OF VARIOUS SALICYLATES UPON THE DOG'S STOMACH: A GASTROSCOPIC PHOTOGRAPHIC EVALUATION

James W. Hurley and Lathan A. Crandall, Jr.

Kuno Rink, Elkhart, Indiana, U.S.A.

THE purpose of this investigation was to study the effect of various salicylates upon the gastric mucosa of the dog by means of gastroscopic photography. A standard gastroscope (Keever & Barborka, 1959) using Kodachrome film was employed. Healthy mongrel dogs were anaesthetized, the stomach washed out with 200 ml. of normal saline and the aspirate tested for blood, and then each animal was gastroscoped. Control studies were done on each animal prior to drug administration. Observations were carried out at various intervals after the twice daily administration of 0·6 g. of plain aspirin, effervescent aspirin, buffered aspirin, or sodium salicylate, which were dissolved or suspended in 150 ml. of water before being given by stomach tube. Similar doses of sodium salicylate were also given intravenously. Two control dogs were intubated twice daily to simulate salicylate administration and were examined five times over a 21 and 34 day period respectively; the stomachs of these two dogs remained normal.

Experimental Studies

Fifteen dogs were given plain aspirin and initially developed erosions and blood in the stomach within three to five days. Examinations were not carried out daily, and so more precise determination of the time of onset of gastric lesions was impossible. The erosions were usually located in the distal stomach or on the lesser curvature (Plate III, facing p. 216), whereas the intervening mucosa appeared normal. Microscopically, there was a loss of superficial epithelium and considerable engorgement of the mucosal blood vessels (Plate IV, facing p. 216). Another dog was given three doses of aspirin at eight-hour intervals, examined gastroscopically, and killed 36 hours after the initial dose of aspirin. A large antral ulcer with surrounding typical superficial erosions was seen. Microscopically the ulcer extended to the submucosa, and a surrounding leucocytic infiltration indicated the acute nature of the process. The only death in the series was a pregnant dog in whom lesions were observed on the fifth day of aspirin administration. At autopsy, on the ninth day, the stomach was normal.

In ten dogs there was clearing of the erosions and haemorrhage and the appearance of a gastroscopically normal mucosa within five to twelve days of the initial dose of aspirin, despite continued administration of aspirin. In eight dogs aspirin administration was discontinued for two to seven days and then reinstituted. When aspirin was withdrawn for only two days the erosive gastritis observed on resuming aspirin was less than that which had been noted originally. However, resumption of medication after omission of aspirin for four days or longer resulted in a vigorous return of typical gastric erosions. In three dogs aspirin was continued for an additional 93 days, and then withdrawn for two days or longer. When aspirin was omitted for only three days, resumption of the medication resulted in severe gastritis. In the one animal in whom aspirin was omitted for only two days the gastric mucosa remained normal.

Effervescent aspirin was given to eight dogs. Four examinations each, in eleven days, failed to disclose evidence of gastric pathology. In two dogs this preparation was discontinued and after a further 19 days plain aspirin was given; gastric erosions and haemorrhage typical of those seen after aspirin were observed. The gastric mucosa regained its normal endoscopic appearance by the fifth day of aspirin administration. To complete this cross-over type of experiment, plain aspirin was given to two other dogs and typical erosions appeared within three days. When the stomach had regained its normal appearance aspirin was discontinued, for 7 and 11 days respectively. Control studies were repeated and then effervescent aspirin was administered. Subsequent examinations of the stomach were normal on three occasions in one dog and on four occasions in the other dog.

Two dogs were given buffered aspirin, and within four hours of the initial dose both showed erosive changes in the gastric mucosa similar to those produced by plain aspirin. Erosions and blood had disappeared by the third day of administration. Four dogs received oral sodium salicylate. In each animal gastric erosions and haemorrhage were observed on the second day of medication, although in one dog the erosions were minimal in extent. Eight dogs received sodium salicylate intravenously and no animal developed gastric pathology. Six dogs were observed for at least eight days; the other two dogs died from undetermined causes at the fourth and sixth days and at autopsy their stomachs were found to be normal. Three animals were given oral aspirin after the ninth day of parenteral sodium salicylate; erosions developed in the stomach within 36 hours. Grossman, Matsumoto, and Lichter (1961) feel that salicylates may exert their effect on the gastrointestinal tract by way of a central action that ultimately produces haemorrhage. Our findings with intravenous sodium salicylate support a belief in a local cause of gastric pathology.

After control studies, six dogs were given plain aspirin in half the dosage, 0·3 g. twice daily, suspended in 150 ml. of water. Within two days all developed an erosive process similar to that produced by twice the dose. One dog was autopsied on the second day and demonstrated the typical small erosions with macroscopically normal intervening mucosa. In two of these dogs aspirin was discontinued for two days after the stomach had lost its reactivity to aspirin. Resumption of medication produced no detectable gastritis or bleeding on three examinations. One dog given this reduced dose of aspirin developed an antral ulcer after twelve days.

Plain aspirin was dissolved by heating to 100° c a suspension of 0·6 g. aspirin in 150 ml. of water. On cooling to 37° c the aspirin remained in solution without immediate hydrolysis. This preparation was given twice daily to four dogs, and on the second day typical gastric erosions measuring 1–3 mm. in diameter developed in the pars media. One dog was killed 15 minutes and another dog 90 minutes after receiving the aspirin solution; in both animals gastric lesions were noted. A control dog was given 150 ml. of water at 37° c twice daily in the same manner and was examined several times. No change in the gastric mucosa was noted. It has been suggested by Levy and Hayes (1960) that the local irritant action following aspirin administration is a result of particles of the drug acting upon the mucosa. This mechanism is unlikely, in the dog at least, in view of the fact that erosions could be produced by a solution of aspirin. The erosive action of aspirin may be related to the concentration within or at the cell membrane.

Implications

Effervescent aspirin contains a large amount of efficient buffering material, sodium citrate, which may be instrumental in protecting the gastric mucosa by neutralizing gastric acid. However, Winkelman and Summerskill (1961) have pointed out that the effect of aspirin upon the gastric mucosa does not depend on the acid secretion of the stomach. Buffered aspirin tablets, which are relatively insoluble, produced the same gastric pathology as plain aspirin. Rubin, Pelikan and Kensler (1959) have suggested that this may be the result of the insignificant amounts of buffering material contained therein.

The dose of salicylate averaged 186 mg. per kg. of body weight, well in excess of the average human dose. When the dose was reduced by 50 per cent the erosions still appeared, and in one animal a rather remarkable gastric ulcer appeared. Because of the dosage difference, no implication can be made of the frequency of erosive gastritis in humans after the administration of any of the various preparations.

After gastric erosions appeared, it is noteworthy that they then completely disappeared in spite of the continued administration of acetylsalicylic acid. Individual differences were noted in the time required to heal; most erosions disappeared within eight days of the initial administration of aspirin, but one required 13 days to heal. This phenomenon has not been recorded previously either in animals or in man. Interruption of medication after healing of erosions allows the stomach to regain its susceptibility to aspirin, although omission for only two days was not followed by erosions when the aspirin was resumed. The development of refractoriness of the gastric mucosa may be the result, to some degree, of acquired tolerance by the gastric epithelium. According to LeBlond and Stevens (1948), pyloric surface cells are replaced every 1·9 days in the rat. This period of time corresponds with the two day time lapse in the appearance of aspirin sensitivity in this study. When the epithelial replacement is sufficiently complete after aspirin has been discontinued, the new cells again demonstrate susceptibility to aspirin.

SUMMARY

An erosive gastritis was produced in dogs given aspirin, buffered aspirin, aspirin in solution, and sodium salicylate orally. Intravenous sodium salicylate and effervescent aspirin did not produce a noticeable gastric reaction.

The size of the aspirin particle in contact with the gastric mucosa is not the essential feature in the production of erosions because plain aspirin in solution produced similar lesions. Aspirin concentration at the cell membrane may be more important in causing disruption of the gastric epithelium and other mucosal changes.

The erosive gastritis produced by salicylates cleared in each animal in spite of continued medication. Interruption of medication for more than two days after disappearance of the lesion allowed the gastric mucosa to regain its susceptibility. After the mucosa became normal no additional gastritis was produced if aspirin was administered for less than two days. It is suggested that the turnover of gastric epithelium may allow the stomach to regain its susceptibility to aspirin.

REFERENCES

Grossman, M. I., Matsumoto, K. K., & Lichter, R. J. (1961). *Gastroenterology*, **40**, 383.
Keever, I. C., & Barborka, C. J. (1959). *Gastroenterology*, **36**, 743.
LeBlond, C. P., & Stevens, C. E. (1948). *Anat. Rec.*, **100**, 357.
Levy, G., & Hayes, B. A. (1960). *New Engl. J. Med.*, **262**, 1053.
Rubin, R., Pelikan, E. W., & Kensler, C. J. (1959). *New Engl. J. Med.*, **261**, 1208.
Winkelman, E. I., & Summerskill, W. H. J. (1961). *Gastroenterology*, **40**, 56.

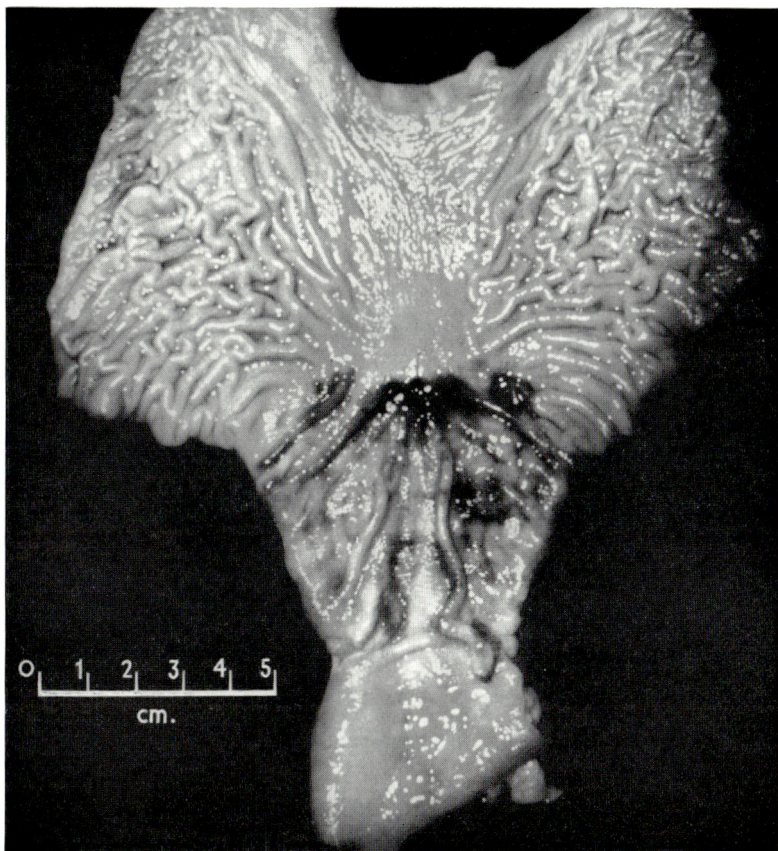

PLATE III (HURLEY)   GASTRIC EROSIONS INDUCED BY ASPIRIN IN THE DOG
Stomach of a dog killed four hours after a single dose of 0·6 g. of aspirin.
Erosions are seen largely in the antrum. (cf. p. 213).

[To face p. 216

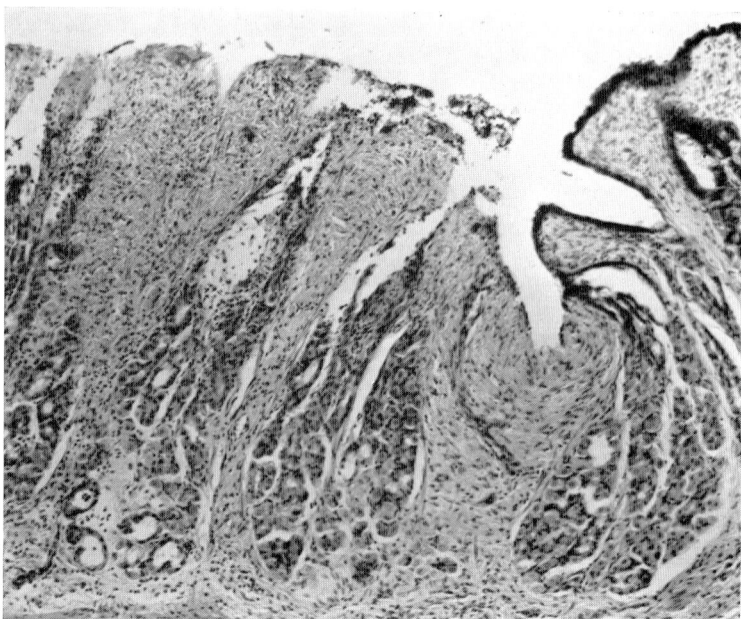

PLATE IV (HURLEY) HISTOLOGY OF ASPIRIN-INDUCED EROSIONS IN THE DOG
Section of gastric antrum of dog illustrated in Plate III. There is loss of super-
ficial epithelium and engorgement of blood vessels. (cf. p. 213).
Magnification × 100.

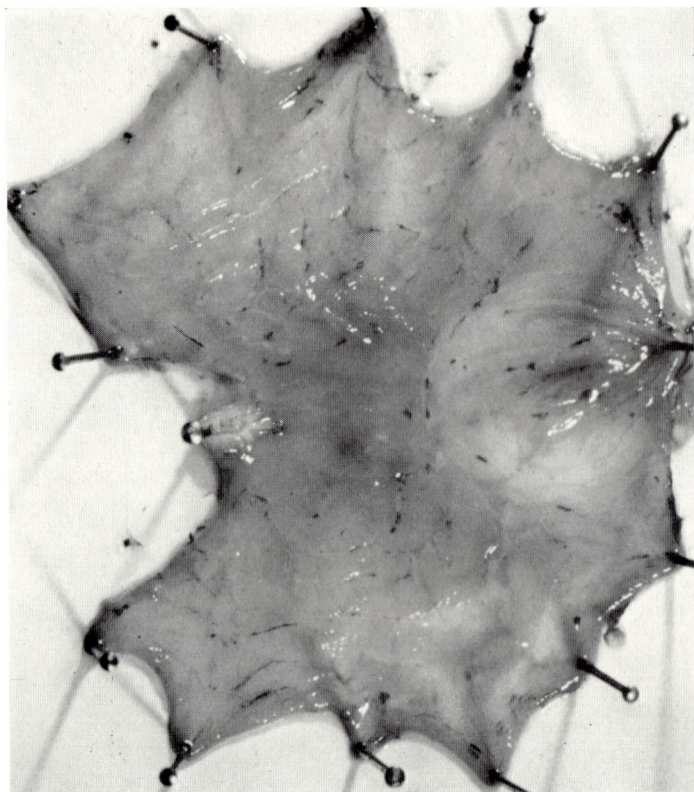

PLATE V (ANDERSON)   GASTRIC EROSIONS INDUCED BY ASPIRIN IN THE
GUINEA-PIG

Stomach of a fasted guinea-pig killed four hours after a single oral dose
of aspirin, 300 mg. per kg. The stomach has been opened along the greater
curvature. The black spots are typical punctiform and fissured mucosal
erosions, with altered blood adhering to their surface.

To face p. 217]

SOME BIOCHEMICAL AND PHYSIOLOGICAL ASPECTS OF SALICYLATE-INDUCED GASTRIC LESIONS IN LABORATORY ANIMALS

K. W. Anderson

*Nicholas Research Institute, Slough, Buckinghamshire, and
Nicholas Institute for Medical and Veterinary Research
Sherbrooke, Victoria, Australia*

SMALL focal gastric erosions and minor haemorrhage were observed in guinea-pigs, rabbits, dogs, and the glandular stomach of rats and mice, from thirty minutes to several hours after a single oral dose of aspirin (Anderson, 1958). These findings appeared likely to throw some light on the phenomenon of symptomless gastric bleeding in humans and prompted further studies in the guinea-pig. Guinea-pigs were fasted overnight and a single dose of aspirin, 10 to 500 mg. per kg., was administered through a soft rubber catheter. Animals were killed at selected intervals and their stomachs removed and opened along the greater curvature. The gastric contents were collected and their pH and acidity determined. After gently stretching out the mucosal folds, the stomachs were pinned on cork mats and scrutinized under a dissecting microscope at magnifications between 5 and 20 times (Plate V, opposite). Mucosal damage was assessed by counting the number of punctiform erosions seen during careful examination of the stomach. No attempt was made to evaluate the extent of epithelial exfoliation.

Gastric lesions in guinea-pigs

Within a few minutes of administration there was a widespread shedding of surface epithelial cells. Within the boundaries of these exfoliated areas erosion of the underlying glandular tissue was apparent half to one hour later, and was accompanied by bleeding from disrupted capillary vessels. The erosions were of heterogeneous shape, varying from pinpoint craters to longitudinal fissures up to 10 mm. in length. They appeared to be fully developed within 2–3 hours and by this time often penetrated deep into the lamina propria, but not into the muscularis mucosa. There was no significant evidence of vascular dilatation or ischaemia associated with their early development. In general, the lesions occurred in the body of the stomach and on the lesser curvature, only rarely being found in the fundus or pyloric mucosa and never distal to the pylorus. Evidence of tissue repair began after six hours, and there was

8*

little if any macroscopic evidence of mucosal damage in animals autopsied 24–36 hours after a single dose.

A comparison of animal studies and clinical findings with miscellaneous analgesic preparations suggested an excellent correlation between the two tests. As shown in the Table, those compounds or preparations that consistently caused gastric damage in the guinea-pig after single doses

THE POTENTIAL FOR MISCELLANEOUS ANALGESIC PREPARATIONS TO CAUSE
GASTRIC DAMAGE IN GUINEA-PIGS AND IN MAN AFTER ORAL ADMINISTRATION

Preparation	Smallest single dose required to produce damage in guinea-pigs (mg. per kg.)	Clinical assessment of bleeding	Reference
Plain aspirin	25	Positive	
Soluble aspirin	25	Positive	1, 2
Buffered aspirins	25	Positive	3
Calcium aspirin urea	25	Positive	1, 2
Aspirin-glycine	25	Positive	1, 2
Salicylic acid	25–50*	Slight	4
Sodium salicylate	25–50*	Slight	4
Aloxiprin	100–200	Moderate	1
Effervescent aspirin	100–200	Moderate	1
Aspirin anhydride	100–200	Positive	1, 2
Methyl salicylate	> 500	—	
Salicylamide	> 500	None	4
Paracetamol	> 500	None	4
Phenylbutazone	50	None†	4

* Considerable surface exfoliation but less bleeding than after aspirin.
† Known to be a potentially ulcerogenic drug.

[1] Wood, Harvey-Smith & Dixon, 1962.
[2] Stubbé, Pietersen & van Heulen, 1962.
[3] Lange, 1957.
[4] Wood, 1963.

of 100 mg. per kg. or less are reported to give clear evidence of gastro-intestinal bleeding at therapeutic dose levels in man. As the minimum dose for the induction of gastric damage in animals increased, so the preparation gave less significant clinical evidence of bleeding. Where no gastric damage could be seen in animals after single doses of 500 mg. per kg. the preparation appeared to cause no gastric bleeding in man.

By comparison with plain aspirin in suspension, the average number of mucosal erosions in fasted animals was significantly increased when aspirin was ball-milled to a mean particle size of 20 μ before adminis-tration. The degree of gastric damage was significantly less in unfasted animals irrespective of the particle size of the drug. When aspirin or calcium aspirin was given in solution at concentrations of 5 or 10 mg. per ml., the response was not significantly different from that observed with suspensions of the drug in a finely divided form (Fig.). However, when given at concentrations of 2·5 mg. per ml. there was little if any gastric damage.

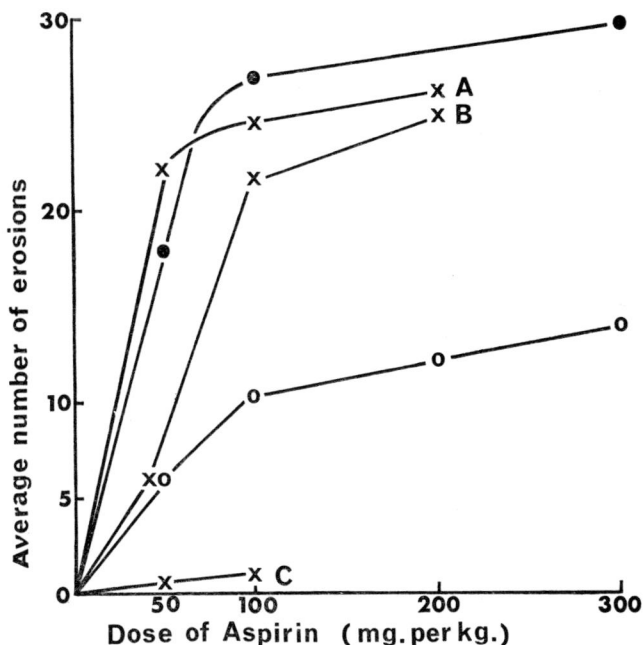

INCIDENCE OF GASTRIC MUCOSAL EROSIONS IN THE GUINEA-PIG AFTER ORAL DOSES OF ASPIRIN

The animals were fasted overnight and single doses of aspirin, 50 to 500 mg. per kg., were administered through a soft rubber catheter. Aspirin was administered as a suspension of plain aspirin, particle size 200–400 μ (open circles); as a suspension of aspirin that had been ball-milled to a mean particle size of 20 μ (closed circles); and as a solution of aspirin (crosses), in concentrations of 10 mg. per ml., A, 5 mg. per ml., B, and 2·5 mg. per ml., C.

No significant reduction in the extent of gastric damage occurred when gross amounts of antacid material were present in the gastric lumen with an undissolved preparation of aspirin. However, the administration of aspirin in solution with equal parts by weight of sodium bicarbonate reduced, and in many cases eliminated, gastric damage in the guinea-pig. In most animals the effect of the bicarbonate solution was to cause rapid and complete emptying of the gastric contents into the intestine. When gastric emptying did not occur, or when it was deliberately blocked by applying a pyloric ligature before administering the dose, the excess bicarbonate maintained the gastric contents at or close to pH 7·0. Under these conditions the amount of aspirin absorbed from the gastric lumen of pyloric-ligatured guinea-pigs in two hours was only approximately half of that absorbed when the same amount of plain aspirin was in a ligated stomach for two hours at pH values between 1·5 and 3·0. In the intact animal, therefore, bicarbonate reduced the gastric absorption of aspirin either directly or by promoting its removal to the intestine, and this could explain the absence of gastric erosions. It should be pointed out that proof of a relation between reduced gastric absorption and reduced gastric erosion could not be obtained directly in pyloric-ligatured guinea-pigs because salicylates rarely cause gastric damage in this preparation.

Histochemical and biochemical studies have not revealed any effect of aspirin on pepsinogen secretion nor on the peptic activity of the gastric contents. The peptic activity of the fasting secretion in untreated guinea-pigs was low, and gastric erosion often occurred in aspirin-treated animals where no *in vitro* peptic activity of the gastric contents could be shown. At low doses aspirin had no effect on the guinea-pig's basal acid secretion. At doses of 100 mg. per kg. or more it produced complete anacidity within an hour of administration. However, the effect was transient and gastric acidity gradually returned to its basal level over several hours, depending on the dose. It seemed, therefore, that neither hyperacidity nor peptic activity were involved in the pathogenesis of the lesions.

Some 200 compounds structurally related to aspirin have been studied in this manner. The results, briefly summarized, are:

  (i) most compounds only had gastric irritant potential when the carboxyl group was unsubstituted. Thus salicylamide and methyl salicylate had no effect on the gastric mucosa of the guinea-pig;

  (ii) only compounds that were reasonably well absorbed from the gastric lumen of pyloric-ligatured animals caused damage to the mucosa when administered to intact animals;

  (iii) among those compounds that possessed an unsubstituted carboxyl group and were well absorbed, the potential to cause gastric damage was modified by the nature and position of other ring substituents. For instance, gastric irritant potential increased in the series benzoic acid, salicylic acid, acetylsalicylic acid, methyl hydrogen phthalate, indicating the importance of the *ortho* substituents. Other ring substituents could change the order of this series, apparently according to their effect on the chemical charges on the *ortho* group or their effect on the gastric absorption of the molecule as a whole.

Implications

Gastric damage was reduced when aspirin was given in solution, either at very low concentrations or with sufficient sodium bicarbonate to maintain the gastric contents at pH 7·0. It has been established that gastric absorption of weak acids is proportional to the concentration of undissociated molecules at the lumen surface. Both procedures should reduce the gastric absorption of aspirin, by simple dilution or by reducing the percentage of undissociated drug in the gastric contents. Gastric absorption of aspirin in the pyloric-ligatured guinea-pig was shown to be considerably reduced at pH 7·0. Furthermore, a positive relation between gastric absorption and irritant potential was established amongst a wide range of benzoic acid derivatives. It is concluded, therefore, that aspirin-induced gastric damage depends on gastric absorption of the drug and probably originates at a cellular level when the rate of entry into the mucosal cells exceeds some critical value. Initially the surface epithelial cells are shed, and this is followed by necrosis of the underlying glandular but not muscular tissue. The erosion appears to be a direct effect of the drug and not due to intrinsic proteolytic agents in the environment.

With undissolved forms of the drug there is a relation between the number of particles in the stomach and the number of focal erosions. This is probably explained by the increased focal absorption of aspirin around particles that adhere to the mucosa as they dissolve. On the other hand, erosion also occurred with completely dissolved forms of aspirin unless fairly drastic measures were taken to reduce either the rate or the extent of gastric absorption. The evidence suggests that the critical rate of absorption for the generation of gastric erosions is of a low order. If it is of a similar order in man the avoidance of gastric erosions would be difficult with any formulation of aspirin where the whole of the dose was available for absorption from the stomach. The numerous clinical reports that fail to show any appreciable reduction in gastrointestinal blood loss with many modified formulations appear to support this contention.

The rate of entry of aspirin into mucosal cells has been cited as the contributing factor in the formation of gastric lesions, but this may be an oversimplification. MARTIN has pointed out that one would expect an enormous decrease in the rate of transfer as the drug crossed the various biological membranes that separate the gastric lumen at pH 1·5 from the blood at pH 7·3. The accumulation of aspirin at the surface of or within the cells along this pathway may therefore be the critical factor in the generation of erosions. One can only speculate on the biochemical mechanism whereby aspirin causes dysfunction and shedding of the gastric mucosal cells. It is important to note that the concentrations achieved in mucosal tissue during absorption could far exceed the levels attained in other body fluids. Some non-specific local effect such as a change in intracellular pH is therefore not excluded. However, the study of other derivatives of benzoic acid indicates that a particular spatial or chemical configuration around the carboxyl group is necessary for gastric irritant potential, irrespective of the acid strength of the compound. These studies suggest that the compound's ability to complex with cellular metal or to inhibit a specific enzyme is involved, but this question has not yet been resolved.

No evidence of erosion was seen in the lower tract of animals given single large doses of aspirin. This suggests that the stomach is the major, if not the sole, site of bleeding. In view of what has been said this seems reasonable, as the greatest concentration of aspirin after oral ingestion would be in the stomach. The potential to cause erosion would therefore decrease or disappear in the lower tract as the dose was dispersed by absorption and dilution. However, it is not inconceivable that some bleeding could occur at lower sites in man, especially with enteric-coated forms of the drug. It is of interest that aspirin has been shown to affect other epithelia besides that of the stomach, including the buccal mucosa (Roth et al., 1961) and renal tubular epithelium (Scott & Denman, 1961). Smith (1958) also reported the erosion of villi by salicylate with *in vitro* preparations of animal intestine. One wonders whether the action of salicylate in these situations was to cause cellular dysfunction by some common mechanism once a sufficient local concentration of the drug had been achieved.

SUMMARY

Aspirin and soluble aspirin cause small focal gastric erosions accompanied by minor haemorrhage within 30 minutes to several hours of an oral, but not parenteral, dose to fasted laboratory animals. Further study in the guinea-pig shows that some counterpart of these lesions could account for symptomless gastrointestinal bleeding caused by aspirin in man.

The evidence suggests that erosions are generated when the rate of absorption of aspirin, or its accumulation in the mucosal tissue, exceeds some critical value. The mechanism appears to involve an effect of the drug on the mucosal cells and is not obviously related to gastric hyperacidity or peptic activity.

Among substituted benzoic acids the potential to cause gastric erosion in animals is dependent upon gastric absorption of the compound, but it is favoured by particular spatial or molecular configurations around the carboxyl group.

REFERENCES

Anderson, K. W. (1958). *Communication to* XXXIII Congr. Aust. N.Z. Ass. Advanc. Sci., Adelaide.
Lange, H. F. (1957). *Gastroenterology*, **33**, 770.

Roth, J. L. A., Valdes-Dapena, A., Pieses, P., & Buchman, E. (1961). *Gastroenterology*, **40**, 691.

Scott, J. T., & Denman, A. M. (1961). X Congr. Lega int. Reum., **2**, 1405. Rome: Minerva Medica.

Smith, M. J. H. (1958). *Amer. J. Physiol.*, **193**, 29.

Stubbé, L. Th. F. L., Pietersen, J. H., & van Heulen, C. (1962). *Brit. med. J.*, **i**, 675.

Wood, P. H. N. (1963). *In* 'Salicylates, An International Symposium', p. 196. ed. Dixon, A. St. J., Martin, B. K., Smith, M. J. H., & Wood, P. H. N. London: Churchill.

Wood, P. H. N., Harvey-Smith, E. A., & Dixon, A. St. J. (1962). *Brit. med. J.*, **i**, 669.

TOPICAL ACTION OF SALICYLATES ON THE BUCCAL MUCOSA IN MAN AND ON THE STOMACH IN THE CAT

JAMES L. A. ROTH AND ANTONIO VALDES-DAPENA

Division of Gastroenterology and Department of Pathology
Graduate School of Medicine, University of Pennsylvania
Philadelphia, Pennsylvania, U.S.A.

THE frequency with which salicylates in any form locally will damage a mucous membrane is shown by their topical action on the lip (Roth, Nast & Vilardell, 1962; Roth et al., 1963). After contact with aspirin for 30 minutes the buccal mucosa is white, opacified, and wrinkled, and the slough peels off with the slightest manipulation. The appearance is reminiscent of the keratolytic action of salicylic acid in Whitfield's ointment when applied between the toes in athlete's foot. Buffering with antacids does not prevent this local damage to the mucosa, which under the microscope reveals acute superficial necrosis and destruction of the squamous epithelium. No topical irritant effect could be demonstrated with paracetamol.

The relative importance of the topical irritant effects of aspirin is also illustrated by studies on the gastric mucosa of the cat. Various grades of localized mucosal damage were observed in 38 of 45 cats (84 per cent) in which aspirin, plain or in compound formulation, was allowed to remain in contact with the gastric mucosa for 2–3 hours. Fourteen cats showed only apparent coagulation of the mucus, white opacification of the mucosa, and flattening of the rugal folds where aspirin had been in contact. In the absence of microscopic changes, this appearance was attributed to denaturation of the protective layer of mucus and desquamation of the surface epithelial cells. In the remaining 24 cats multiple gross haemorrhagic lesions were noted where particles of aspirin had been trapped by the rugal folds (Plate VI, opposite). Microscopically the affected area was sharply demarcated. The abrupt transition from normal mucosa to distinctly abnormal tissue was striking. The affected mucosa stained poorly with the nuclear stain, haematoxylin, indicating cellular death (Plate VII, facing p. 225). In some instances the outlines of the glands were preserved, giving a ghost image of the normal architecture; in others the distortion was greater, rendering the area more or less amorphous. A prominent feature was a deep greenish-brown colour which was not produced by the stains used. The foci of pigmentation did not give a positive reaction for iron, and therefore were not attributable to

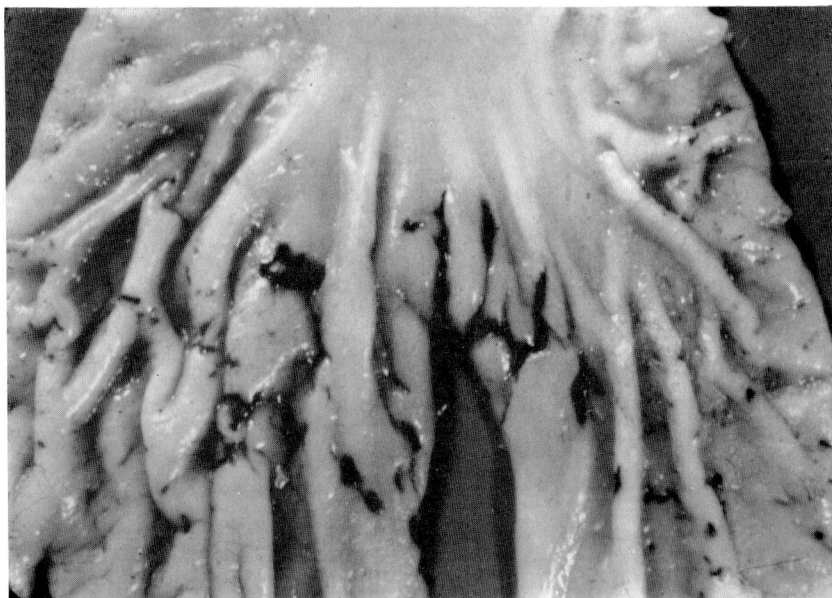

PLATE VI (ROTH)   GASTRIC EROSIONS INDUCED BY ASPIRIN IN THE CAT

Stomach of a cat removed two hours after placing a tablet of buffered aspirin on the mucosa. Note the multiple irregular erosions where particles lodged between folds.

[To face p. 224

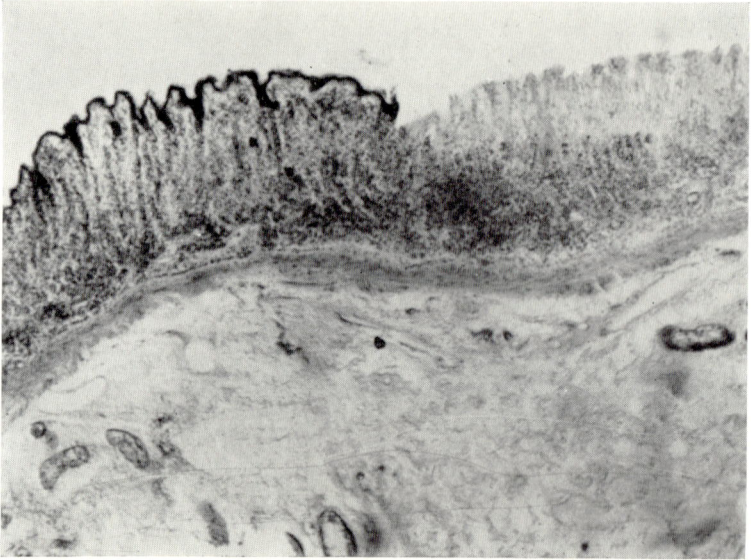

PLATE VII (ROTH)   HISTOLOGY OF ASPIRIN-INDUCED EROSIONS IN THE CAT

Section of gastric mucosa of a cat. The stomach was removed two hours after placing a tablet of aspirin on the mucosa. Note the abrupt transition from normal mucosa to the erosion, with loss of the superficial layers after contact with the drug (on right). A ghost image of the normal architecture is suggested by the outlines of the glands. (cf. p. 224).

Magnification × 72.

haemorrhage. The change in colour was interpreted as staining due to bile or sulphide, both of which tend to occur in dead tissues. The superficial nature of this focal mucosal necrosis and the lack of any marked secondary reaction would indicate that it represents an acute and recent event. Occasional thrombi were demonstrated in small vessels, but this finding could not be correlated with the area of focal necrosis. Such thrombi were also seen in the mucosa of some of the controls, and other non-specific changes included foci of leucocytic infiltration, a peculiar homogeneous appearance of the connective tissue layer at the base of the mucosa, occasional clusters of eosinophils, and oedema of the submucosa. It cannot be claimed, therefore, that we are dealing primarily with vascular damage. It is a valid assumption that the focal necrosis is determined by the presence of an agent that accomplishes its damage by direct contact.

It is surprising that the local irritant action of aspirin does not manifest itself more often considering the ease and frequency with which the mucosal changes were produced in the buccal and cat studies. Such changes may occur more commonly than are appreciated clinically, considering the frequency both of vague indigestion and of occult bleeding.

SUMMARY

The topical action of salicylates has been studied on the human buccal mucosa and on the stomach of the cat. Loss of the protective mucous barrier through chemical coagulation of the mucus, sloughing of the surface epithelium, and focal necrosis of the mucosa by aspirin probably decrease local tissue resistance and permit the free hydrochloric acid and pepsin to produce erosion or ulceration. Focal necrosis may thus give rise to occult bleeding. If focal necrosis occurs in a susceptible individual— someone with a lesion capable of bleeding, with increased acid-pepsin secretion, or with a coagulation or capillary defect—a massive haemorrhage may follow the ingestion of salicylates.

REFERENCES

Roth, J. L. A., Nast, P. R., & Vilardell, F. (1962). *Postgrad. Med.*, **32**, 442.
Roth, J. L. A., Valdes-Dapena, A., Pieses, P., & Buchman, E. (1963). *Gastroenterology*, **44**, 146.

DISCUSSION

JACK R. LEONARDS (*Department of Biochemistry, Western Reserve University School of Medicine, Cleveland, Ohio, U.S.A.*):

The suggestion that absorption of unionized aspirin from the stomach is a stage in the production of gastrointestinal bleeding is an attractive explanation of the facts. However, it is only a hypothesis and no data are available regarding the rate of absorption of this fraction from the stomach. Most people agree that the major reason for the bleeding is contact of a solution of acetylsalicylic acid (ASA) with the gastric mucosa, and that greater concentrations of this solution would exist around a particle that is dissolving locally at the mucosal surface. One way, therefore, to eliminate or reduce the concentration of ASA would be to give a preparation in solution as one of its salts. It must be stressed that the aspirin must be dissolved in water before being given. As LEVY has emphasized, the mere fact that a tablet disintegrates, or that it contains a soluble substance, does not mean that it will be in solution when it is next to the gastric mucosa.

For this reason we have chosen to study solutions of aspirin dissolved before ingestion, with regard to both bleeding and absorption in man. We measured blood loss with red blood cells doubly-labelled with ^{51}Cr and ^{59}Fe (Leonards, J. R. [1962]. *Fed. Proc.*, **21**, 452). Like others, we found that bleeding was markedly reduced after effervescent aspirin, as compared with the blood loss observed after plain aspirin in suspension in the same volume of water. Effervescent aspirin also buffers gastric pH and thus it is impossible to tell whether the lack of bleeding after the effervescent preparation is due to the drug being in solution or to the elevation of pH.

With regard to absorption studies, I must emphasize that it is what happens in the first 10–20 minutes that is important, not what happens in the next three or four hours. A rapidly disintegrating aspirin tablet did not yield maximal plasma salicylate concentrations even after one hour. A so-called buffered preparation, containing a small amount of alkali and which is not really buffered, had a higher dissolution rate and yielded somewhat greater plasma salicylate levels. When aspirin was administered in solution the plasma levels 10 and 20 minutes after ingestion were much greater. It made very little difference whether we used effervescent aspirin, aspirin dissolved in hot water, or pure sodium acetylsalicylate dissolved in water.

It is indeed unfortunate that the only preparation available in the United States that must be dissolved in water before ingestion contains too much sodium for anything more than occasional use or administration to patients in whom sodium retention is no problem. It cannot be tolerated in the very high dosage requirements of rheumatoid arthritics and patients with rheumatic fever, where sodium retention is important. I believe that the development of new pharmaceutical preparations similar to effervescent aspirin, but containing less sodium than this preparation, and that must be dissolved in water before administration, will give the most rapidly absorbed formulation and, I predict, would cause virtually no bleeding.

ANDERSON: LEONARDS did not report studies on gastric bleeding after the solution of aspirin in hot water. WOOD has checked gastric bleeding with solutions of pure aspirin dissolved in water at low concentrations and which do not precipitate aspirin particles. He found that such solutions cause gastric bleeding in man.

LEVY: LEONARDS found that the absorption rate of aspirin from solutions was the same, regardless of the presence of alkaline agents. This should indicate that delayed gastric absorption is not the mechanism responsible for the apparently lower incidence and magnitude of bleeding when aspirin is administered in alkaline solution. However, I believe that there may be another answer to this problem. We have compared the rate of gastric emptying after the administration of these solutions of aspirin and have found that it is more rapid with the alkaline solutions. Thus the potential gastric irritant is removed from the stomach more rapidly and brought to the intestine. This may well be the reason for the reduced bleeding.

DAVISON: I agree with LEONARDS that you cannot yet completely rule out irritation by the particulate form of aspirin. I have perfused gastric pouches in dogs with solutions and suspensions of aspirin, both at pH 1·0, and the suspensions produced a several-fold greater blood loss.

WOOD: I am not convinced that LEONARDS's data on overall absorption are necessarily relevant to bleeding. The appearance of salicylate in the plasma may be due to absorption from sites other than the stomach.

LEVY: In the first five minutes it should be from the stomach.

WOOD: I would question that assumption.

LEONARDS: I did not mean to imply that absorption is in any way related to bleeding. Nevertheless, having the drug in solution before ingestion is an important factor, both in bleeding and in absorption.

Refractoriness to aspirin

J. T. SCOTT: I think HURLEY's description of healing of erosions during continued administration of aspirin is the first mention of a refractory period in gastrointestinal studies. It may bear some relation to the similar phenomenon I have observed with human kidney cells. I hope HURLEY will go on to study occult bleeding in his animals. Presumably he should find that this occurs for only a few days. If he confirms this, it would indicate a species difference between dogs and man.

CROFT: With regard to the refractory period, I wonder whether the prolonged administration of salicylate might stimulate the turnover of gastric mucosal cells, in addition to causing exfoliation after short-term administration.

HURLEY: I have no specific data on occult bleeding. I have begun a similar gastroscopic study in humans, and there does not seem to be this refractory period in man. The incidence of erosions was similar to the incidence of lesions observed by PITMAN. I saw erosions throughout the two-week period that the subjects took aspirin.

LIM: Among the glandular cells of the gastric mucosa are chief cells that are composed of peptic and mucoid types, one secreting enzyme and the other mucinogen. Mucoid cells differ from the surface epithelium and are found mainly in the neck of the glands. The cells on the gastric side of a gastro-enterostomy revert to the mucoid type. The first cell to appear is a very primitive mucoid type—this is what one sees in the embryo before peptic and parietal cells develop.

Even a stimulus like a strong Martini will lift off some of the surface epithelium. I believe that the regeneration which takes place rapidly after the surface epithelium has fallen off passes through the mucoid stage and then differentiates back to the surface-protective mucin-secreting cell. Perhaps this is the explanation of the refractory period.

BACHMAN: In his animal studies ANDERSON seemed to use doses of salicylates that were greater than those usually administered to man.

HOLT: Are any animals insusceptible, at least to products that do cause bleeding?

ANDERSON: We can detect erosions at doses ranging from 10 mg. per kg. On a weight for weight basis this is equivalent to the administration of two tablets to man. Using doses of 10–25 mg. per kg. the incidence of erosions is higher than in control animals, but such studies must be carried out on very large numbers of animals to yield significant results. To avoid the difficulties of such large scale studies, we use high dose levels in smaller groups of animals. To our knowledge, all this does is to increase the number of mucosal erosions.

Rats are somewhat more refractory than other animals, but all the other species I mentioned are sensitive, including fistulated dogs. It is important to use fasted animals as the mucosa is much more susceptible to aspirin in this state.

JONES (Chairman): The hint which particularly appeals to me is the suggestion that we will get the answer from the study of a single cell, and I hope that work will be directed further in that direction.

WHITEHOUSE: I suggest that the answer may also come from studies of extracellular phenomena. Perhaps the stickiness of the gastrointestinal surface cell is destroyed by salicylate. It has been suggested that calcium has a lot to do with intercellular adhesion (Heilbrunn, L. V. [1952]. 'An

Outline of General Physiology', 3rd Ed., p. 530. London: Saunders). By binding some of the calcium perhaps salicylate could reduce this adhesion.

Calcium ions may also be involved in the secretion and formation of mucus. For example, extracorporeal fish mucins can be disaggregated and depolymerized by calcium-complexing agents like ethylenediaminetetraacetic acid (EDTA). Perhaps salicylate, by sequestering some metal ions like calcium, might interfere with the normal mucous coating of the intestine.

ANDERSON: We had the same idea and did administer EDTA in some animal experiments. There was no surface exfoliation, but of course it may not have been absorbed into the gastric mucosa.

CROFT: We tried to make some observations about the production of mucus during our exfoliation studies. The results were not conclusive, but there did not seem to be any marked differences in mucus production between big bleeders and non-bleeders.

CLINICAL IMPLICATIONS

SALICYLATES, DYSPEPSIA, AND
PEPTIC ULCERATION

ANDREW MUIR

Law Hospital, Carluke, Lanarkshire

OF a random group of 3,000 people, one in 15 could not take aspirin without risking dyspepsia—usually heartburn alone, but occasionally epigastric distress and vomiting. One in 20 became dyspeptic every time they took aspirin; the remainder often, but not always. Of the 150 people who invariably developed dyspepsia 77 suffered from peptic ulceration; of those who could take aspirin with impunity only 23 suffered from peptic ulcer. These figures indicate that peptic ulcer patients suffer more often from aspirin dyspepsia. In a group of 70 arthritics requiring heavy salicylate dosage seven could not take the optimum amount because of dyspepsia. On changing to soluble aspirin three were able to do so, salicylate blood levels reaching 30 mg. per 100 ml.

Out of 300 patients with a peptic ulcer, one third (68 duodenal, 21 gastric, and 7 stomal ulcers) developed dyspepsia after aspirin; in 72 heartburn alone, in the remainder their usual ulcer symptoms. No information on the activity of ulcer symptoms at the time these patients took aspirin is available. In spite of dyspepsia most patients continued to take aspirin. Of the 34 who changed to soluble preparations voluntarily 14 were able to take them with impunity. Of a group of 83 ulcer patients with clear-cut exacerbations of activity, each of whom could tell to the day when a bout started and finished, 33 admitted taking aspirin within 24 hours of their first symptoms.

In ten years 42 patients have been admitted to my wards for investigation of dyspepsia based on aspirin eating; the majority were neurotic women. All had been investigated more than once before, with negative results; eight had histories of overt gastroduodenal haemorrhage, and three had had diagnostic laparotomies. A history of aspirin taking was never volunteered; it was usually taken in formidable quantities, and rapid improvement on withdrawal was the rule.

Since 1950 we have questioned 384 consecutive cases of gastroduodenal haemorrhage admitted to hospital; 274 were suffering from probable peptic ulcer, 93 were in the acute lesion group, and 17 had miscellaneous diseases associated with a tendency to gastroduodenal haemorrhage. In

all, 57 per cent had taken aspirin within 48 hours of their initial haemorrhage, as compared with 14 per cent of a control group. After a careful
assessment of their previous histories, we considered that one in eight had
been caused by aspirin, although in the acute lesion group nearly half
were blamed on aspirin. In only two patients was a soluble formulation
incriminated. Fifty per cent of those whose bleeding was attributed to
aspirin had a past history of aspirin dyspepsia, not necessarily prior to
their current haemorrhage. In those with a confirmed chronic ulcer their
ulcer dyspepsia was not often worsened by the aspirin they had just taken,
but about half of the acute lesion group complained of dyspepsia
immediately before haemorrhage. In 78 patients with a perforated peptic
ulcer who were questioned similarly only two had taken aspirin within 48
hours of their perforation, compared with 14 in a control series.

Experimental studies

Aspirin, 10 gr. (648 mg.) uncrushed but in a little water, was introduced
into the stomach immediately after withdrawal of the fasting juice in a
standard caffeine citrate test meal. Specimens withdrawn later showed
heavy blood-staining in five of a group of 20 ulcer patients. This was
assumed to indicate marked gastric irritation. A comparison was made
between plain aspirin and calcium aspirin urea, using identical coded
tablets. In the first study 60 subjects were divided into two groups, half
of each group suffering from peptic ulceration. Each subject had one test
meal, one group receiving plain aspirin and the other calcium aspirin urea.
Seventeen patients reacted positively with each preparation, but bleeding
was less in the group given calcium aspirin urea. In the second study the
comparison was made in 20 eupeptic subjects with two test meals at
weekly intervals. Aspirin preparations were given in random order, 0·6 g.
of either being dispersed in 100 ml. of water. Thirteen positive reactions
occurred with plain aspirin and only one with calcium aspirin urea.
Therefore calcium aspirin urea in solution appears to produce much less
gastric irritation than plain aspirin in suspension.

We have studied 217 specimens obtained immediately after elective
gastrectomy for intractable duodenal ulcer. Only duodenal ulcer cases
were chosen because gastritis is uncommon in such patients, whereas it
is common with gastric ulcer and neoplasm. Twenty studies were made
without previous test drugs, and 197 after the administration of a
salicylate two hours pre-operatively. Stricter standards were adopted the
longer this work proceeded until we now accept only maximal lesions,
superficial or deep erosions shaped and occupied by adherent aspirin
particles, usually along the lesser curvature but sometimes widely spread
beneath congested rugae (for illustrations, see Muir & Cossar, 1961). In
one case the adherent particle penetrated the submucosa and showed the
appearances of a true gastric ulcer. This was one of our early specimens,

and the attempt to dislodge the particle with forceps instead of washing out gently with a wash-bottle made it unsuitable for histological examination. In the first series of experiments we compared plain aspirin, a specially prepared hard tablet of aspirin, and soluble aspirin, and made 20 observations after each preparation. Maximal lesions were seen in three specimens after plain and in five specimens after hard aspirin, but none were seen after soluble aspirin. In the second series we compared plain aspirin with calcium aspirin urea, using identical coded tablets. When the code was broken we had made 62 observations with the former and 75 with the latter. Five maximal lesions were found after plain aspirin and none after calcium aspirin urea. Therefore we have still to see a maximal lesion after soluble formulations of aspirin.

The conclusions to be drawn from this work are at variance with those of many workers on three main points—the relative safety of soluble formulations, the increased risk in ulcer patients, and the higher incidence of dyspepsia prior to bleeding. This might be explained partly by the entirely clinical approach adopted for much of this work.

SUMMARY

Dyspepsia caused by aspirin is not uncommon, and may be a real problem for patients with arthritis who need to take large doses. Dyspepsia occurs more frequently in patients with a peptic ulcer.

In a group of 384 patients with gastroduodenal haemorrhage, aspirin was a vital cause in 12·5 per cent. Aspirin was blamed for the haemorrhage in almost half of those with an acute lesion. The aspirin taken was almost exclusively in plain tablets or compound formulations. Dyspepsia in the ulcer patients was not often aggravated by the aspirin that contributed to the bleeding, but more than half the acute lesion group suffered from heartburn prior to the bleeding.

Experimental studies with aspirin test meals and post-gastrectomy specimens confirm the development of gastric bleeding and acute erosive gastritis after aspirin in a proportion of patients. Soluble formulations of aspirin cause less bleeding and have not produced a single instance of a maximal lesion in a gastrectomy specimen.

REFERENCE

Muir, A., & Cossar, I. A. (1961). *Amer. J. digest. Dis.*, N.S. **6**, 1119.

THE RELATIONSHIP OF ASPIRIN-TAKING TO OVERT GASTRODUODENAL HAEMORRHAGE

D. J. PARRY AND PHILIP H. N. WOOD

Departments of Medicine
West Middlesex and Hammersmith Hospitals, London

THE incidence of the ingestion of aspirin by patients admitted consecutively to two medical wards of a general hospital has been determined. Patients were questioned carefully and only those whose replies were unreliable or who were unable to reply were excluded. Of a total of 638 patients, 542 showed no signs of overt gastroduodenal haemorrhage whilst 96 were admitted because of haematemesis or melaena. In the former group 32 per cent had taken aspirin within the week before admission, whilst in the latter group 69 per cent had taken aspirin in the corresponding period.

Those patients admitted with overt bleeding were investigated as thoroughly as possible by the determination of the pH of the night gastric secretion, by gastroscopy, and by barium meal, all carried out within a few days of admission. A definite diagnosis was based on the results of the last two investigations. A wide variety of diagnoses was established in the 96 patients who bled. Those suffering from hiatus hernia, carcinoma of the stomach, oesophageal varices, and anastomotic ulcer were excluded from further analysis because the numbers in each category were small. There remained 15 patients with gastric ulcer, 30 with duodenal ulcer, six in whom an acute erosion was seen, and 29 in whom no definite site for the bleeding could be established.

Of the 45 patients with chronic peptic ulcers 23 had taken aspirin within the week before admission and 22 had not done so. When analysed according to the site of the ulcer this similarity in aspirin histories was again evident. This is perhaps suggestive that aspirin was a causal factor, because half of these patients had taken aspirin compared with only one third of those admitted with no overt bleeding. However, the numbers are small and the differences are not great. The susceptibility of another group of ulcer patients to aspirin has been estimated by radioactive chromate studies of occult bleeding. The blood loss after aspirin in 49 patients with a chronic peptic ulcer was similar to that observed in the reference sample of 226 subjects with a normal gastrointestinal tract. There was no difference in the response of those with chronic gastric ulcers from those with chronic duodenal ulcers.

All six patients with acute erosions had taken aspirin within 24 hours of their haemorrhage. It is interesting to note that acute gastric erosions were seen on only six occasions in a group of 35 patients in whom no other cause for the haemorrhage could be discovered. This might be due to delay in gastroscopy; although in most patients this investigation was carried out within 48–72 hours of admission, in a few cases it was delayed until 96 hours after admission.

The remaining group is comprised of 29 patients in whom no definite site for the bleeding could be established; 27 of these patients had taken aspirin within one week of the development of symptoms of acute blood loss. The two patients who had not taken aspirin and four of those who had done so had a highly acid night gastric secretion; in these patients duodenal ulceration may have passed unrecognized, although some normal people occasionally have a high night secretion of hydrochloric acid. Investigation of the patients in this group was not complete in every case; nine patients were not gastroscoped, old age and technical difficulty due to cervical spondylosis being the main reasons for the omission of this investigation.

The time of taking aspirin in relation to the day of bleeding or admission to hospital was noted in all cases. In the undiagnosed group 15 patients had taken aspirin within 24 hours of bleeding, and a further seven had taken it within the preceding 48 hours. Some patients had taken aspirin for a long period; one patient had taken 2 g. at night for more than five years because of insomnia. Analysis of the data showed that the time of taking aspirin before bleeding, or the period over which it was taken, bore no relation to the incidence of haemorrhage; indeed, the general pattern of aspirin ingestion was similar to that seen in the group of patients admitted without overt bleeding. In those patients admitted with bleeding the most frequently taken tablet was plain aspirin. However, some patients had taken soluble formulations and, in particular, one of the patients in whom an acute erosion was seen had taken effervescent aspirin.

Susceptibility to aspirin

Earlier studies of occult bleeding in patients admitted with major haemorrhage had shown that there was no striking difference from the reference population in the blood loss following aspirin. These studies were conducted on 25 patients in whom there was strong clinical evidence that aspirin might have precipitated the haemorrhage, and the provocative trial with aspirin was commenced as soon as their existing blood loss had ceased. Ten of these patients had chronic peptic ulcers, whilst in the remaining 15 the site of bleeding was not discovered. In view of this we attempted to study occult bleeding susceptibility after aspirin in those patients of the present series in whom acute erosions were seen or in whom no site of bleeding was discovered. Four of the former and seven of the latter have been studied so far, and the variation in blood loss was not strikingly different from that seen in the reference population sample of 226 patients with normal gastrointestinal tracts. This point is well illustrated by a tabetic patient who had a large haematemesis after taking aspirin for his lightning pains. No other cause for his haemorrhage could be found, and yet after a provocative trial with aspirin he lost no blood whatsoever in his stools.

The incidence of aspirin ingestion is high in patients with overt gastroduodenal haemorrhage, particularly in those with acute gastric erosions and in those in whom no site for the bleeding could be found after thorough investigation. Nevertheless the response of such patients to a course of oral aspirin is no different from that found in a control series of patients with a normal gastrointestinal tract. This suggests that aspirin is not the only factor, but that aspirin may precipitate a major haemorrhage in certain as yet undefined circumstances.

SUMMARY

The incidence of aspirin ingestion has been studied in 638 consecutive admissions to two medical wards in a general hospital. The incidence is much higher in those admitted with overt gastroduodenal haemorrhage, particularly those with acute erosions or those in whom no site for the bleeding could be found.

The susceptibility to occult blood loss after aspirin in such patients does not differ from that seen in subjects with a normal bowel. This suggests that in certain circumstances aspirin may precipitate a major haemorrhage, but that it is not the only factor involved.

THE ROLE OF ASPIRIN IN CAUSING
IRON-DEFICIENCY ANAEMIA

L. Th. F. L. Stubbé

Department of Rheumatology, University Hospital
Leiden, The Netherlands

IRON-DEFICIENCY anaemia occurs especially in young women. One of the causes can be occult blood loss from the gastrointestinal tract as a result of the use of aspirin. We have studied the frequency of occult bleeding after aspirin in 461 individuals, those with a history of stomach trouble being excluded. Bleeding during the administration of aspirin occurred in 288 (62·5 per cent) of these patients (in 56 per cent of 148 males and in 65·5 per cent of 313 females). In general the dose of aspirin was 1·5–3·0 g. daily. The occult blood loss was determined by the benzidine test. Although some claim the contrary, this method is reliable in hospitalized patients if done accurately. When no aspirin was administered we found a negative reaction in at least three successive lots of faeces in all 461 patients. Moreover, since our first report (Stubbé, 1957) many investigators have found the same percentage of aspirin-induced occult blood loss with radioactive chromate techniques as we did with the benzidine method.

Blood loss and iron-deficiency

The amount of blood loss may vary considerably. To obtain an idea of this variation we gave a few patients a small quantity of their own blood to drink. When 4 ml. of blood was administered there was a positive benzidine reaction, varying from slightly to distinctly positive. According to Roche and Pérez-Giménez (1959) 13–76 (mean 44) per cent of the iron lost with blood into the intestines is reabsorbed. In cases of chronic blood loss with incipient iron-deficiency the percentage of iron absorption may be higher. Nevertheless, if the benzidine reaction remains strongly positive for a long period one may conclude that the amount of iron lost can be considerable. With radioactive chromate methods more exact values are found for blood loss into the intestines, but not for the iron lost with the faeces. This may be one of the reasons why not every patient who seems to lose a considerable amount of blood in this way develops iron-deficiency anaemia. On the other hand we have often found a prolonged bleeding time after aspirin ingestion. However, we have the impression that after some days the bleeding time can become less prolonged in spite of continuation of the aspirin administration; from this it may also be possible that after a certain time of aspirin consumption the amount of blood loss becomes less.

Kelly (1956) and Summerskill and Alvarez (1958) have described five cases of severe iron-deficiency anaemia due to faecal blood loss associated with the taking of aspirin. Since then we have described a further 14 cases (Stubbé, 1961), and recently we have seen two more cases. In every patient the use of aspirin, even if not the sole cause, played an important role in the development of the condition. There were no indications of peptic ulcer, profuse menses, or haemorrhagic diathesis in any of these patients. It appears that the use of aspirin certainly need not be extravagant to play a predominant role. The main features of these 16 patients, all of whom developed strongly positive benzidine reactions after the administration of aspirin, were:

 (i) reason for taking aspirin: rheumatic complaints, 4; headache, 12;
 (ii) daily dose of aspirin 0·5–3 g. in 15;
 (iii) age less than 25 years in 9;
 (iv) sex: 15 females;
 (v) haemoglobin less than 9·0 g. per 100 ml. in 15.

One patient took about 20 tablets of aspirin daily. In this patient the benzidine reaction in the faeces was positive during the first three weeks after admission; however, all the other patients were hospitalized for investigation of their anaemia and in them a negative benzidine reaction was found. This can be explained by the fact that on the whole the blood loss disappears from the faeces some days after discontinuing the use of aspirin. As a rule aspirin is no longer given after admission, and so the role of this drug will often be masked and will therefore not be found unless one is conscious of this process.

Aspirin as a cause of anaemia

Since an occult blood loss is found after the use of aspirin in 50–70 per cent of people it is not so simple to prove the causal relationship between the use of this drug and iron-deficiency anaemia. This will often be possible only by a provocation with aspirin to check whether indeed an important amount of blood is lost. In all 16 patients we found strongly positive benzidine reactions after aspirin was given and a negative reaction, three times in succession, after the aspirin was stopped. Especially when it is a question of long medical histories with many iron injections, blood transfusions, and even laparotomies, as in three of our patients, such a provocation test under precautionary measures seems justifiable. By means of ^{51}Cr-labelled erythrocytes it was shown that the blood loss can be considerable; in two patients a loss of more than 80 ml. per day was detected. However, even when the daily blood loss is not profuse this can still be a factor in the development of iron-deficiency anaemia if aspirin is used chronically. A female patient was treated for anaemia for seven years; she took aspirin regularly for headaches. She lost 45 ml. of blood in six days during the administration of 1·5 g. of aspirin daily. Blood loss with the menses amounted to about 55 ml. This means that, including the menses, about 275 ml. of blood was lost monthly, which seems quite sufficient to explain the recurrent iron-deficiency anaemia.

Another proof that aspirin has been a causative factor may be found if, after withdrawing aspirin, the haemoglobin rises or remains within normal limits without iron therapy. This occurred in eight patients who were observed for over a year; four patients could not be followed up for more than three months, and in two the period of observation was also too short. In the remaining two patients the anaemia recurred, but we suspected both patients of taking aspirin again, which could be confirmed in one by a positive reaction for salicylate in the urine.

Whatever the primary disorder, long-term administration of aspirin should be accompanied by periodic haemoglobin estimations and tests for occult blood. This may help to distinguish patients who bleed severely, and if this appears to be the case it seems necessary to stop aspirin therapy. That it is not always enough to check the faeces for only one period became evident in a young girl with rheumatoid arthritis. In this patient the benzidine reaction was negative after a month of aspirin therapy. Aspirin was continued and three months later, when the haemoglobin had fallen, the benzidine reaction appeared to be strongly positive.

In order to prevent occult blood loss many investigators recently have tried to find an aspirin preparation with the same analgesic effect as ordinary aspirin but without its noxious effect. Our experiments with aspirin tablets of 250 mg. coated with approximately 40 mg. of cellulose acetatephthalate were favourable (Stubbé, Pietersen & van Heulen, 1962). Blood loss disappeared in 26 of the 30 patients studied, and in the remainder the loss became considerably less. Especially for chronic use, as in rheumatoid arthritis, this preparation seems to be very satisfactory. With these coated tablets blood disappeared from the stools in most of the patients, and at the same time good absorption from the gut could be proved. Thus we may conclude that aspirin leads to local irritation only of the gastric mucosa, and not of the intestinal mucosa. For occasional use as an analgesic, such as in the treatment of headache, we found effervescent aspirin suitable. Blood disappeared from the faeces in 31 of the 32 patients tested with this preparation. Leonards (1962), using erythrocytes doubly-labelled with ^{51}Cr and ^{59}Fe, found that gastrointestinal blood loss could be neglected with this preparation.

Recently, however, we saw a young girl who had severe iron-deficiency anaemia after having taken one or two tablets of aspirin regularly every day. Provocation with aspirin and with effervescent aspirin showed a considerable faecal blood loss of up to 46 ml. per day after each preparation. With aluminium aspirin to which 200 mg. of aluminium hydroxide had been added a blood loss as high as 115 ml. per day was detected. During the administration of all three preparations a distinctly prolonged bleeding time was found (Fig.). It may be assumed that, besides the local irritation of the gastric mucosa, this aspirin-induced prolongation of the

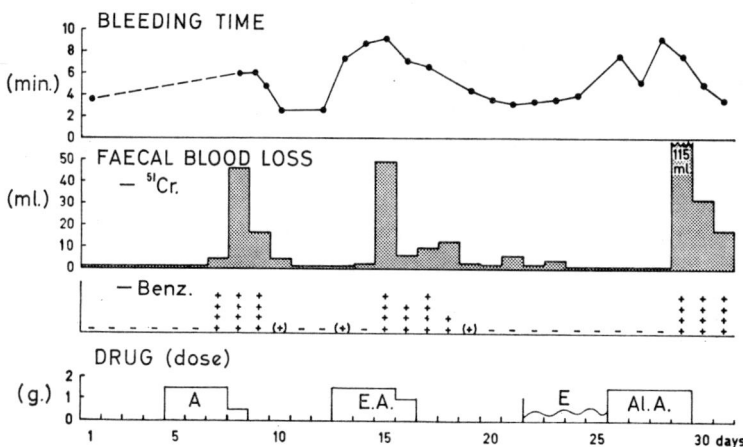

INFLUENCE OF ASPIRIN ON BLEEDING TIME AND FAECAL BLOOD LOSS

The same amount of acetylsalicylate was administered in different preparations to a 17-year-old female patient with iron-deficiency anaemia. Bleeding time was determined by the method of Ivy, and faecal blood loss was estimated by both radioactive chromate and benzidine methods.

Aspirin preparations: A, plain aspirin; E. A., effervescent aspirin; Al.A. aluminium aspirin.

The effect of the effervescent preparation prepared without aspirin, E, was also observed.

bleeding time will often play a prominent role in the quantity of blood lost.

It is striking that this group of 16 patients consisted mainly of young women. The question arises whether a distinctly prolonged bleeding time caused by aspirin occurs more often in young women. Another explanation may be the fact that many women live on the edge of their reserve of iron and often resort to the use of aspirin because of menstrual complaints. This can cause anaemia, which itself can cause headache and thus result in an even more frequent use of aspirin. It is most likely that an important part of the large number of women who are treated with iron for moderate anaemia belongs to this group.

SUMMARY

Occult loss of blood in the faeces occurred in 62·5 per cent of 461 persons to whom aspirin was administered. This blood loss can lead to a severe iron-deficiency anaemia.

In 16 cases the use of aspirin, even if not the sole cause, played an important role in the development of anaemia. By means of ^{51}Cr-labelled erythrocytes it was shown that the blood loss can be considerable. In hospital a negative benzidine reaction is often found because blood disappears rapidly from the faeces when aspirin is discontinued on admission. As patients often deny taking aspirin, a provocation test with this drug may be required.

In order to prevent occult blood loss with long-term use, tablets of aspirin coated with cellulose acetatephthalate seemed very satisfactory. For occasional use as an analgesic effervescent aspirin was found to be suitable. However, in one case of aspirin-induced iron-deficiency anaemia the blood loss after this preparation was as much as after plain aspirin; after aluminium aspirin the loss was even greater. During the administration of all three preparations a distinctly prolonged bleeding time was found. It may be assumed that, in addition to local irritation of the gastric mucosa, an aspirin-induced prolongation of the bleeding time may play a prominent role in determining the quantity of blood lost.

REFERENCES

Kelly, J. J. (1956). Amer. J. med. Sci., 232, 119.
Leonards, J. R. (1962). Fed. Proc., 21, 452.
Roche, M., & Pérez-Giménez, M. E. (1959). J. Lab. clin. Med., 54, 49.
Stubbé, L. Th. F. L. (1957). Occult Bloedverlies met de Faeces als gevolg van het gebruik van Acetylsalicylzuur. M.D. Thesis, University of Leiden.
Stubbé, L. Th. F. L. (1961). Ned. T. Geneesk., 105, 1673.
Stubbé, L. Th. F. L., Pietersen, J. H., & van Heulen, C. (1962). Brit. med. J., i, 675.
Summerskill, W. H. J., & Alvarez, A. S. (1958). Lancet, ii, 925.

DISCUSSION

N. F. COGHILL (Physician, West Middlesex Hospital, Isleworth, Middlesex):

As time is short I will make only one point. Listening to all these papers it is difficult to pick out a pattern into which all the different data will fit. I agree with JONES that the answer to the problem of how salicylates affect the stomach is likely to be found at the level of the gastric mucosal cell. Those working in specialized fields, for example cell function, should remember the diverse findings in the clinical field when formulating hypotheses about salicylate action on the stomach.

CROFT: We have done some post-gastrectomy studies similar to MUIR's. Because we thought we might find a larger proportion of mucosal lesions we gave aspirin for some days pre-operatively. Four patients were given 4 g. of soluble aspirin daily for 2–4 days. All four operative specimens showed macroscopic acute ulceration. Thus, unlike MUIR, we found that soluble aspirin did cause serious lesions. I must say that I think such studies are dangerous. One patient developed a severe and prolonged haemorrhage post-operatively, and we decided to stop this type of experiment.

PARRY suggested that some other factor might be involved in the precipitation of major haemorrhage. If exfoliation has anything to do with bleeding, many substances have been shown to cause this, including alcohol, mustard, clove oil, and hydrochloric acid. Patients who have had a massive haemorrhage apparently due to aspirin might be investigated to see whether they have had any other gastric insult in the preceding two days.

ROTH: We must make sure that our perspective of bleeding of an occult nature does not take us too far away from the more important clinical problem of massive bleeding. Possibly the mechanism of these two magnitudes of bleeding is not the same. Because a salicylate preparation is relatively safer from the standpoint of the low order of occult bleeding does not necessarily make if safer from the standpoint of provoking massive bleeding.

GLYNN: In view of the relationship between blood group and ulcer, has anyone studied the relationship between blood group and susceptibility to aspirin?

WOOD: Yes. There is no discernible relationship. I did mention this in my paper.

DUTHIE: Were serum iron levels low in the cases of anaemia that STUBBÉ attributed to aspirin?

STUBBÉ: Yes indeed, all 16 patients had a low serum iron and a high iron-binding capacity.

A SPEAKER: Has anyone studied the loss of other substances associated with the gastric hyperaemia and bleeding, particularly the possible loss of albumin? Is this the cause of hypoalbuminaemia in patients with rheumatoid arthritis?

HOLT: I did some work with polyvinylpyrrolidine (PVP) in Boston. Subsequently I looked up my controls for this study and found that two were rheumatics taking large doses of salicylates. In both of these the test was normal, but further studies may be worth while.

SALICYLATES AND THE KIDNEY

RENAL IRRITATION CAUSED BY SALICYLATES

J. T. Scott

Department of Medicine (Rheumatology)
Postgraduate Medical School of London

In the early years of this century there were several reports concerning the production of albumin, red cells, white cells, and casts in the urine of experimental animals following the administration of very large doses of salicylate. Similar changes were noted in patients starting salicylate therapy. These early observations were reviewed by Gross and Greenberg (1948). Recently an increase in the urine cell count during salicylate treatment has been noted concurrently by Clausen and Harvald (1961) and by Scott and Denman (1961).

Cells in the urinary sediment

The present communication describes the effect of salicylate medication on the urinary sediment, using the accurate estimation of leucocytes and non-squamous epithelial cells described by Houghton and Pears (1957). Urine cell counts have been carried out in 38 male subjects given aspirin or sodium salicylate, studying normal volunteers and patients with rheumatoid arthritis or rheumatic fever. No difference is apparent between the reactions of normal people and of hospital patients, nor between children and adults. On starting the drug an increase in the urine cell count is invariably seen, provided that the subject has taken no salicylate medication in the preceding month or so. The maximal cell count varies between individuals and with the dosage of salicylate; the highest count we have seen is 11,000,000 cells per hour (Normal: less than 200,000 cells per hour).

Figure 1 shows the effect on a normal subject of a single dose of aspirin. Two hours after the dose the serum salicylate level was 18 mg. per 100 ml., falling to zero within 24 hours. The urine cell count rose to reach a maximum of 1,700,000 thirty hours later, falling to normal levels in four days. This is a typical response, and a similar effect is obtained with sodium salicylate. In the example given the dose was 2·7 g. of salicylate. A smaller response is obtained with a single dose of 1·3 g., which gives a maximum serum level of about 12 mg. per 100 ml. However, I have seen a small but definite cellular response following only two tablets (648 mg.). It therefore appears that the cellular response is proportional to the dose and that there is no real threshold level. On a few occasions a heavy celluria has been accompanied by slight albuminuria.

When the salicylate is continued a rather curious phenomenon is seen. The urine cell count rises to reach a maximum on the second or third day

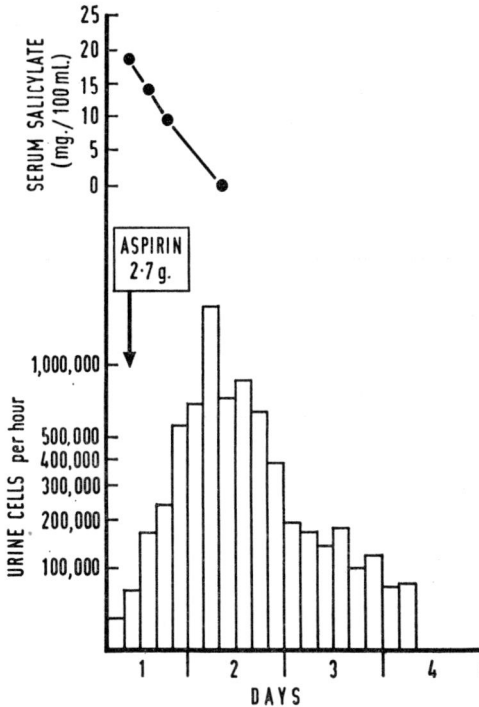

FIG. I   EFFECT OF ASPIRIN ON THE URINE CELL
COUNT

A single dose of 2·7 g. of aspirin was administered to a normal subject. Plasma salicylate concentrations are shown. The urine cell count, represented on the ordinate on a logarithmic scale, is
depicted as the hourly output of cells determined
from continuous four-hour collections over a four-
day period.

but then falls rapidly towards normal, though the characteristic type of cell continues to appear in the urine in small numbers for some days. Not only is the celluria not sustained while the patient continues to take salicylate, but after cessation of aspirin there is a refractory period during which repeated administration of the drug produces no effect, or only a diminished one. Figure 2 shows the effect of single doses of aspirin repeated at different intervals in three subjects. In the first subject there was a celluria of just over 1,000,000 cells per hour following the first dose. The second dose three days later, however, produced no response at all. In the second subject the initial cell count was likewise just over a million. The second dose of aspirin was given 12 days later; a celluria was seen, but with a count of only 200,000 cells per hour. In the third subject the initial count was 1,700,000 cells per hour. The second dose was given 28 days later and even after this period the response was less than the first, measuring in this instance 450,000 cells per hour.

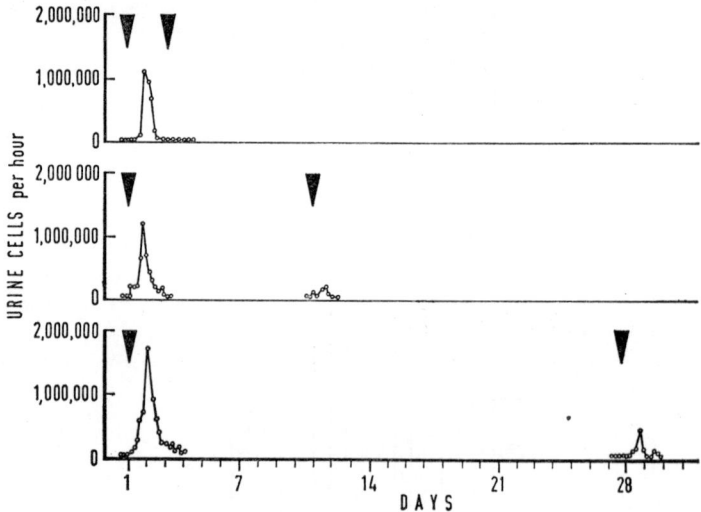

FIG. 2   EFFECT OF REPEATED DOSES OF ASPIRIN ON THE URINE CELL COUNT
     Single doses of 2·7 g. of aspirin (shown by arrows) were repeated at different intervals in three subjects.

The cells concerned in this phenomenon appear to be of one type and have a characteristic appearance. They are intermediate in size between leucocytes and bladder squamous cells. They are circular or oval in shape, but often irregular, and the cytoplasm is coarsely granular. Often no other morphological details are visible, but sometimes an eccentric nucleus can be made out. As time passes they become increasingly degenerate and distorted and are sometimes fused together in cellular or granular casts. Staining confirms the morphological appearance of a round or oval cell with an eccentric nucleus. This is the characteristic appearance of renal tubular cells in the urine (Rofe, 1955), and a clear morphological resemblance is apparent between these cells and desquamated tubular cells in sections of human kidney and rat kidney (Plate VIII, opposite). Examination of the cells histochemically, using the

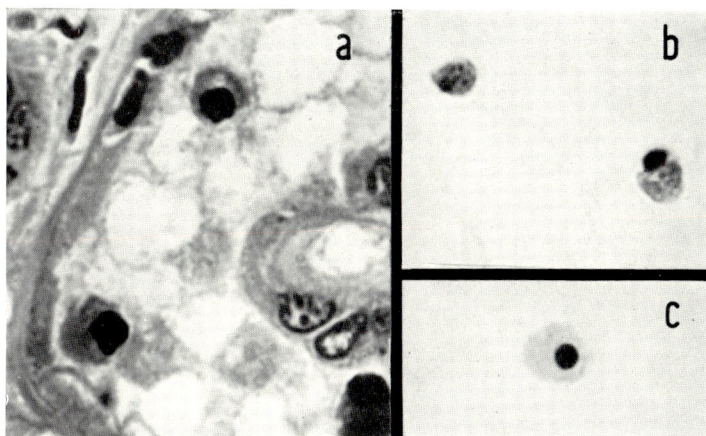

PLATE VIII (SCOTT) RENAL TUBULAR EPITHELIAL CELLS

All specimens stained with haematoxylin and eosin. Compare the appearances in a histological preparation, showing tubular cells lying in the lumen of the renal tubule, 'a', with aspirin cells, the cells seen in the urine after the ingestion of salicylate, 'b', and with a trypsinized rat kidney cell from a preparation used for tissue culture, 'c'.

Magnification × 1,000.

[*To face p.* 244

coupling azo dye method for alkaline phosphatase and the plasmal reaction (Pearse, 1960) showed that about 30 per cent are positive for alkaline phosphatase and 90 per cent positive with the plasmal reaction. This indicates that some cells are derived from the proximal convoluted tubule and some from lower down the nephron (Wachstein, 1955). However, one must remember that the histochemical properties of these cells may have been profoundly disturbed by salicylate. In any case, the cells are exfoliated and damaged, and the autolytic or ischaemic kidney has been shown to lose various enzymatic activities (Cameron & Spector, 1961). The histochemical findings must therefore be interpreted with caution. It seems very probable, however, that we are dealing with renal tubular cells derived from a considerable length of nephron.

Implications

What is the mechanism whereby salicylate causes transient desquamation of renal tubular cells? One possibility is that it is a speeding up of normal cell turnover due to a non-specific elevation of metabolic rate by salicylate. If this is the explanation one would expect to find a similar effect with fever. In fact, no increase in urine cells follows artificial fever in normal subjects studied over the course of a few hours (Pears & Houghton, 1959) or several days (Houghton, B. J., personal communication), and so this hypothesis lacks confirmation. A second interesting possibility presented itself by the observation that just before the cells appear the urine is often full of urate crystals. Renal damage caused by uric acid is a subject of current interest (Duncan & Dixon, 1960); could the increase in urine cells in our experiments be due to a load of urate passing through the kidney in response to a uricosuric dose of salicylate (Yü & Gutman, 1959)? A coincident study of urine urate and urine cells in a subject starting to take aspirin, 5·3 g. daily, showed that the serum salicylate rose over the first three days, with a sharp fall in the serum urate. This was attended by a peak in the excretion of uric acid immediately preceding the urine celluria. Support appeared to come from an infusion of lithium urate which raised the serum urate to 9·8 mg. per 100 ml. The rise in urine uric acid was accompanied by a high peak of urine cells of identical appearance to those appearing after aspirin. A control infusion of lithium chloride, however, produced an identical effect; it was evident that the urine cells could not be attributed to the urate. In other experiments the serum urate was raised to about 10 mg. per 100 ml. in a different way, by complete fasting. When the fast was broken the serum urate fell, but the resulting uricosuria was not accompanied by an increase in urine cell output. Similarly, a good uricosuric response in two gouty subjects who were starting treatment with probenecid was not attended by any increase in urine cells. Thus this hypothesis is also unconfirmed, and we remain ignorant of the exact mechanism whereby salicylate induces this tubular exfoliation. It may well be related to its desquamating action on gastric mucosa, but until more is known about the precise effect of salicylate on cellular biochemistry and enzymology this must remain speculative.

Finally, what is the practical significance of this phenomenon? It should be widely known because the presence of albumin and large numbers of renal tubular cells and casts in the urine otherwise may be attributed to serious kidney disease. I have seen the occurrence of urine cells and albumin in a case of Still's disease (juvenile rheumatoid arthritis) attributed to injections of gold, possibly correctly, but where it may equally well have been due to the aspirin that the patient had just started taking. It is doubtful if any serious damage is done to the kidney by salicylates in normal therapeutic doses, even after long periods. There has been no clinical evidence of this over the many years that aspirin has been in use. I have followed the urine cell counts in two patients over a period of several weeks, and in both cases the cell counts returned completely to normal after three or four weeks. In both these cases the mean cell count in the final week was no higher than that before aspirin was started. There is no indication, therefore, of persistent celluria or of chronic renal damage. This may still be an open question but I cannot as yet see any indication from this study that the use of long-term salicylates, the basic treatment for rheumatoid arthritis, should be in any way modified.

SUMMARY

The administration of salicylates causes an increase in the urine cell count, the cells having the characteristics of renal tubular cells. Despite continued administration of salicylate the celluria diminishes within a few days. After cessation of aspirin medication there is a refractory period during which further salicylate produces little effect on the urine cell count.

There is no indication that salicylates cause persistent celluria or chronic renal damage. The presence of albumin and large numbers of renal tubular cells and casts in the urine may be due to the ingestion of aspirin, and this should be borne in mind before attributing these abnormalities to serious kidney disease.

Since the presentation of this paper a slightly more detailed account of this work hase been published in the *Lancet* ([1963], i, 344).

REFERENCES

Cameron, R., & Spector, W. G. (1961). 'The Chemistry of the Injured Cell', p. 99. Springfield: Thomas.
Clausen, E., & Harvald, B. (1961). *Acta med. scand.*, **170**, 469.
Duncan, H., & Dixon, A. St. J. (1960). *Quart. J. Med.*, N.S. **29**, 127.

Gross, M., & Greenberg, L. A. (1948). 'The Salicylates, a critical biblio-graphic review', p. 99. New Haven: Hillhouse Press.
Houghton, B. J., & Pears, M. A. (1957). *Brit. med. J.*, i, 622.
Pears, M. A., & Houghton, B. J. (1959). *Lancet*, ii, 1167.
Pearse, A. G. E. (1960). 'Histochemistry, Theoretical and Applied', 2nd Ed., pp. 866 & 868. London: Churchill.
Rofe, P. (1955). *J. clin. Path.*, 8, 25.
Scott, J. T., & Denman, A. M. (1961). X Congr. Lega int. Reum., 2, 1405. Rome: Minerva Medica.
Wachstein, M. (1955). *J. Histochem. Cytochem.*, 3, 246.
Yü, T. F., & Gutman, A. B. (1959). *J. clin. invest.*, 38, 1298.

DISCUSSION

Dixon: Scott knows that a similar phenomenon has been reported with phenacetin, which supports his idea that renal cell shedding is not due to uricosuria but to the type of drug. I do not know of valid statistics that enable one to be sure that the incidence of chronic renal disease in patients on long-term aspirin therapy is not increased. In looking up the causes of death in a series of patients with rheumatoid arthritis I was struck by the number who died with, although not necessarily of, chronic pyelonephritis.

J. T. Scott: One does not see the high peak of renal tubular cells soon after a dose of phenacetin. It may be that if you followed patients on long-term phenacetin you would find some rise in the urine cell count, but this is another matter. There is very strong circumstantial evidence that phenacetin, in high dosage over a long period, causes chronic renal damage. We are faced with the paradoxical situation that phenacetin causes renal damage and yet no detectable celluria, while aspirin causes a florid exfoliation of kidney cells but in normal dosage is probably harmless.

THE TOXICITY OF SALICYLATES

Chairman M. D. MILNE

BIOCHEMICAL CHANGES IN LIVER, KIDNEY, MUSCLE, MYOCARDIUM, AND THE ADRENALS, FOLLOWING THE ADMINISTRATION OF VARIOUS DOSES OF SALICYLATES

TEOPHIL RUDOLPH NIEDERLAND

III Medical Clinic and Research Laboratory of Pharmacobiochemistry Komensky University Medical School, Bratislava, Czechoslovakia

MOST of the experiments which have been performed to elucidate the biochemical effects of salicylates have been following one, or only a few, doses of the drug. On the other hand, patients treated with salicylates are given repeated doses on a long-term basis. In our experiments we wanted to create conditions similar to those in clinical practice. We studied the effects of salicylates not only after a single dose, but also after continuous short- and long-term administration of various doses to animals. This enabled us to follow the biochemical changes in various organs in a dynamic way.

The experiments were carried out on male and female white Viennese blue-eyed rabbits weighing about 2 kg. A 10 per cent solution of sodium salicylate was injected subcutaneously. The daily dose was administered in three portions, injected at eight-hour intervals. The control animals were injected with normal saline at the same intervals. Five experimental models were employed:

    (i) peracute. A single dose of 0·81 g. per kg. body weight. Most of the rabbits died within eight to ten hours.

   (ii) acute. 0·69 g. per kg. daily. Two types of experiment were made:

      (*a*) The terminal stage occurred within 36–48 hours and was very characteristic in most animals, with bleeding from the nostrils, generalized tremor, jerks, and sometimes also spasmodic contractions. At this stage the animals could be handled easily, and were killed.

(*b*) Animals were sacrificed after 12, 24, and 36 hours. The results were almost identical with those obtained in the subacute experiments.

(iii) subacute. 0·45 g. per kg. daily. Rabbits were killed, simultaneously with the corresponding control animals, after 12, 24, 48, 96, and 120 hours.

(iv) chronic. 0·23 g. per kg. daily for six weeks. The animals were killed after 42 days.

(v) chronic-intermittent. 0·23 g. per kg. daily for three weeks, then an interval of one week without treatment, and then another three weeks of salicylate administration; five such periods of salicylate were given. After 19 weeks, at the end of a three-week salicylate period, the animals were killed.

All rabbits were killed by a blow on the back of the neck. The organs were removed immediately, and the following analyses made:

(i) glycogen in liver, myocardium, and muscle;
(ii) lipid fractions (fatty acid esters, free fatty acids, lipid phosphorus, and cholesterol) in liver and kidney;
(iii) total protein in liver;
(iv) cholesterol and ascorbic acid in the adrenals.

Glycogen

Glycogen disappeared almost completely from the liver at the terminal stage of life, and in peracute and acute experiments only traces could be found. The results in muscle and myocardium were similar (Niederland, Gvozdják & Brixová, 1958). In the subacute model liver glycogen began to decrease after 12 hours, and this change was more marked after 24 hours (Fig. 1). On the following days, despite continued administration of salicylate, a slight trend towards higher values was observed, although after 120 hours the liver contained only minimal traces of glycogen. There was a statistically significant difference between these values and the control observations. Muscle glycogen was reduced in the first three days, but thereafter values did not differ significantly from control observations. In the final stages of life, however, muscle glycogen was significantly reduced. Glycogen in the myocardium varied in both control and experimental animals, but it diminished terminally in the salicylate-treated animals (Niederland, Brixová & Gvozdják, 1959).

Both free and bound glycogen were reduced in the liver and in muscle after chronic administration. In myocardium there were similar changes, although only the reduction in bound glycogen was of significant extent (Niederland, Gvozdják & Dobiš, 1961). In the liver of the chronic-intermittent models bound glycogen was unaltered, but free glycogen was increased (Niederland, Brixová et al., 1961). Both fractions were

9*

increased in muscle and myocardium, but only the increase in free glycogen was significant in myocardium (Niederland, Gvozdják & Dobiš, 1961).

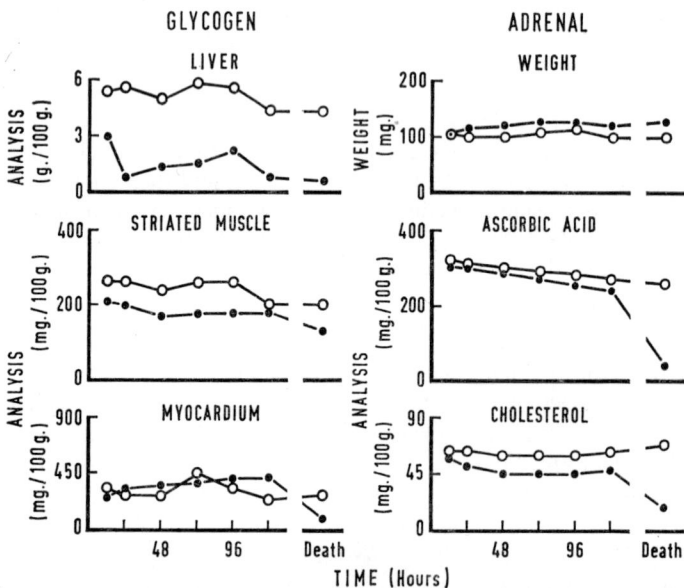

FIG. 1. CHANGES IN GLYCOGEN AND IN THE ADRENALS IN SUBACUTE EXPERIMENTS

Mean values from groups of at least nine rabbits. Sodium salicylate, 0·45 g. per kg. daily in three divided doses subcutaneously, was administered to experimental animals (closed circles). Control animals (open circles) were injected with normal saline at the same intervals.

Lipids

Fatty acid esters in the liver were increased in both peracute and acute models. The other lipid fractions were unaltered (Niederland, Dzúrik & Kovács, 1958). In the kidney there was a slight increase in fatty acid esters in the peracute model, other fractions showing no significant alteration. In the acute model there was a significant increase in fatty acid esters and a decrease in lipid phosphorus. Cholesterol was unaltered (Niederland, Dzúrik & Kovács, 1958). A steady increase of fatty acid esters, free fatty acids, and lipid phosphorus occurred in the liver in subacute experiments (Fig. 2) (Niederland, Kovács et al., 1960; Niederland, Dzúrik et al., 1961). Liver cholesterol increased on the first two days, but thereafter control and experimental values were similar. In the kidney there was a slight but constant increase in fatty acid esters, free fatty acids were unaltered, and lipid phosphorus and cholesterol decreased steadily.

After chronic administration there was an increase in fatty acid esters, which was of significant extent in the liver. Liver cholesterol increased slightly, but other lipid fractions showed no remarkable change. In the chronic-intermittent model there was no substantial change in fatty acid esters, but kidney cholesterol decreased significantly (Niederland, Dzúrik & Krajči-Lazáry, 1961, and unpublished data).

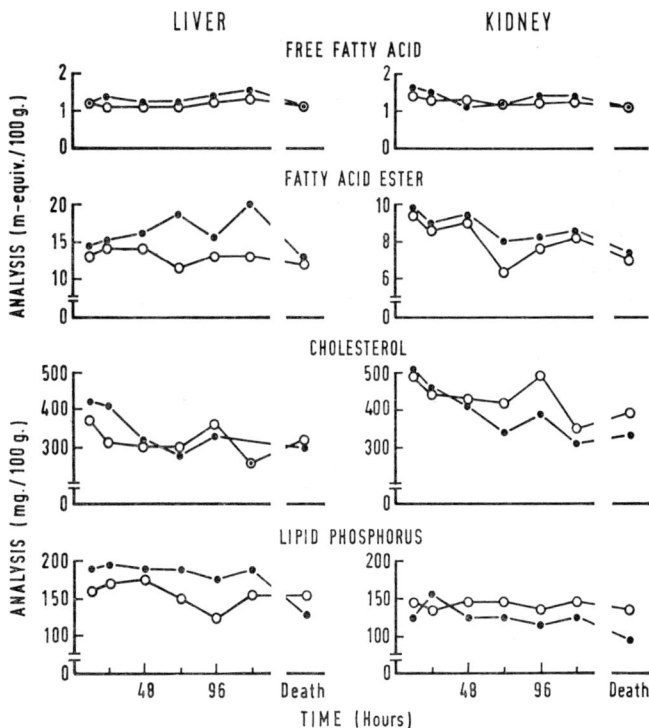

FIG. 2. CHANGES IN LIPID FRACTIONS IN SUBACUTE EXPERIMENTS
Experimental procedure as outlined in Fig. 1. Control animals depicted by open circles, and experimental animals by closed circles.

The total protein concentration in the liver and kidney did not show any remarkable change in the chronic and chronic-intermittent models (Niederland, Mézeš et al., 1958).

The adrenals

The weight of the adrenals did not alter in the peracute and acute experiments, although there was a decrease in ascorbic acid and in cholesterol (Niederland, Gvozdják & Brixová, 1957). There was a steady increase in the weight of the adrenals in the subacute experiments (Fig. 1). Ascorbic acid and cholesterol were significantly reduced, especially in the terminal stage of life (Niederland, Gvozdják & Brixová, 1960).

In the chronic model there was a decrease in ascorbic acid and cholesterol content. After chronic-intermittent administration cholesterol was reduced, but to a lesser extent. On the other hand, ascorbic acid increased in this model (Niederland, Gvozdják et al., 1961).

Large doses of salicylates thus cause the following changes:

(i) a decrease in liver glycogen, followed by a marked decrease in the glycogen content of muscle and myocardium in the terminal stages of life;

(ii) a simultaneous constant and marked increase in neutral fat in the liver and kidney, a chemical estimation of fatty infiltration in these two organs;

(iii) a decrease in ascorbic acid and cholesterol in the adrenals.

These changes also result from chronic administration of moderate and well-tolerated doses of salicylate.

The most interesting finding in these experiments is the quite different picture that follows chronic but intermittent administration of similar moderate doses. In this experiment glycogen was increased in liver, muscle, and myocardium; neutral fat in liver and kidney was unaltered; and the ascorbic acid content of the adrenals was increased.

Salicylate, as an uncoupling agent, is known to be a metabolic stimulant, producing a catabolic effect. The changes found after the administration of toxic and of chronic doses are in keeping with this action of salicylate. However, in the chronic-intermittent model the biochemical features are quite reversed. This shows that in certain conditions salicylates do not have a catabolic action. The biochemical picture we found in these experiments suggests an anabolic effect of salicylates.

SUMMARY

Biochemical changes in various organs were determined after the administration of various doses of salicylates to experimental animals. Two different biochemical pictures were found. The administration of toxic doses, or of moderate doses for a long time, produced a decrease in the glycogen content of liver, muscle, and myocardium; an increase in neutral fat in the liver and kidney; and a decrease in the ascorbic acid and cholesterol content of the adrenals.

Prolonged and intermittent administration of moderate doses of salicylates produced the reverse picture: glycogen and ascorbic acid were increased, and neutral fat in the liver and kidney was essentially unaltered.

REFERENCES

Niederland, T. R., Brixová, E., & Gvozdják, J. (1959). *Bratisl. lek. Listy*, **39**(2), 287.

Niederland, T. R., Brixová, E., Kolesár, P., & Dobiš, J. (1961). *Bratisl. lek. Listy*, **41**(1), 18.

Niederland, T. R., Dzúrik, R., & Kovács, P. (1958). *Bratisl. lek. Listy*, 38(1), 464.

Niederland, T. R., Dzúrik, R., Kovács, P., & Hostýn, L. (1961). *Čas. Lék. čes.*, 100, 85.

Niederland, T. R., Dzúrik, R., & Krajči-Lazáry, B. (1961). *Bratisl. lek. Listy*, 41(1), 140.

Niederland, T. R., Gvozdják, J., & Brixová, E. (1957). *Bratisl. lek. Listy*, 37(2), 73.

Niederland, T. R., Gvozdják, J., & Brixová, E. (1958). *Bratisl. lek. Listy*, 38(1), 385.

Niederland, T. R., Gvozdják, J., & Brixová, E. (1960). *Čas. Lék. čes.*, 99, 497.

Niederland, T. R., Gvozdják, J., Brixová, E., & Bachledová, E. (1961). *Bratisl. lek. Listy*, 41(2), 647.

Niederland, T. R., Gvozdják, J., & Dobiš, J. (1961). *Bratisl. lek. Listy*, 41(2), 415.

Niederland, T. R., Kovács, P., & Dzúrik, R. (1958). *Bratisl. lek. Listy*, 38(2), 137.

Niederland, T. R., Kovács, P., Dzúrik, R., Hostýn, L., & Marko, P. (1960). *Bratisl. lek. Listy*, 40(1), 24.

Niederland, T. R., Mézeš, V., Fedorčáková, A., Dobiš, J., & Križko, J. (1958). *Bratisl. lek. Listy*, 38(1), 513.

DISCUSSION

D. G. RUSHTON (*Department of Pathology, King's College Hospital Medical School, London*):

Post-mortem appearances

My duty is to describe, briefly, the gross changes that the morbid anatomist finds at autopsy on human subjects in salicylate poisoning. Most of the cases of which I speak were found dead at home or died within a few hours of admission to hospital.

The external findings in such cases are usually not dramatic, but occasionally a few petechial haemorrhages are found in the skin. Also, the skin is often made quite pink in colour by the bright red blood in it, presumably the result of hyperventilation. This appearance may even simulate the pink colour of carbon monoxide poisoning.

The internal findings are usually very obvious. The stomach is often almost filled with a glistening mass of disintegrating tablets. Inhaled vomit in such cases may then block the airways and cause early death by asphyxia. In contrast, the changes seen in the alimentary mucosa at autopsy are not very striking. There may be some reddening and erosion of the lining of the lower oesophagus, with desquamation of epithelium. There may also be some reddening, erosion, and haemorrhages in the mucosa of the stomach, but frequently none of these changes have been present in cases that I have examined. I have never seen such changes in the duodenum in aspirin poisoning.

In cases where death has been delayed, or treatment has been given in hospital, one usually finds only mucosal changes, but sometimes such cases may be complicated by inhalation of vomit and a haemorrhagic 'chemical' pneumonia. Occasionally, however, a large quantity of aspirin remains in the stomach, even after gastric lavage. Perhaps it might be beneficial to remove this surgically.

One complication of aspirin poisoning that is rarely seen is oedema of the larynx, causing death by asphyxia. I saw one such case which was due to an unexplained hypersensitivity to aspirin in a young man who had taken a medicinal dose to treat a cold and a sore throat. Recognition of this tragic complication was delayed, and death occurred from asphyxia.

Osorio: Was there any difference in the food intake of Niederland's rabbits? Most of the changes found after salicylate administration could have occurred as a consequence of starvation.

Niederland: No, there was no difference. Both controls and the chronic groups were given oats and turnips every day. The chronic group were very well at the forty-second day, and had gained weight as well as had the controls.

M. J. H. Smith: Niederland's paper is very welcome because it clearly shows that acute and chronic administration of salicylate may affect a whole variety of important metabolic processes in the intact animal. However, the possible effects of salicylates and other drugs on gastric emptying and ultimately on liver glycogen deposition should be remembered. Salicylate causes a delay of between six and twelve hours in the passage of barium through the stomach in the rat (Smith, M. J. H., & Irving, J. D. [1955]. *Brit. J. Radiol.*, **28**, 39), and this action may explain the initial depletion and subsequent accumulation of liver glycogen in the fed animal.

G. Cumming: Rushton attributed the pink coloration seen after death in aspirin poisoning to overventilation. I think it is understood that hyperventilation cannot change arterial saturation by more than one or two per cent, and I think it is unlikely that his explanation is correct.

Rushton: I think hyperventilation is the explanation for the pink colour. Normally, in the ordinary process of dying, there is a reduction of oxygen tension and the subject becomes rather cyanosed. The individual who dies in the early stages of aspirin poisoning hyperventilates perhaps to the last, maintains a good state of oxygenation, and thus often remains pink after death.

Collier: Are people who die of laryngeal oedema or inhaled vomitus pink? Were it a chemical action of aspirin on the blood then they, too, might be pink.

Rushton: No, they are not pink, they are asphyxiated.

MORTALITY AND MORBIDITY FROM SALICYLATE POISONING IN ENGLAND AND WALES

H. CAMPBELL

General Register Office, Somerset House, London

THE General Register Office has two principal sources of information concerning the health of the people. The first is the death certificate, which is a time honoured method for the study of vital statistics but one that is not sensitive to minor changes or to non-fatal occurrences. The second is the 10 per cent sample of all hospital in-patient records, which was started in 1949 and which has been a reasonable instrument of value in epidemiological study since 1958.

Mortality

Death from salicylate poisoning is an infrequent event in the experience of any one doctor, and the majority of practitioners outside hospitals will

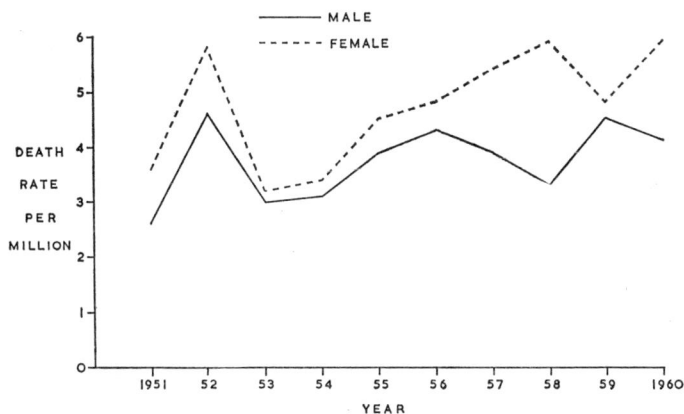

FIG. 1   DEATH RATE FROM SALICYLATE POISONING IN ENGLAND AND WALES, 1951–1960 (ICD No. N 972)

pass the whole of their professional careers without seeing a case. Nevertheless, in England and Wales as a whole there have been over 200 such deaths regularly for the last five or six years. The annual death rate is shown (Fig. 1). There has been an increase in the death rate due to this cause during the last decade. Annual rates are liable to fluctuation as the figures are small but the rate in the quinquennium 1951–1955 was 3·9 per million persons, whereas five years later in 1956–1960 it was 4·7 per million, an increase of 20 per cent in five years. The reason for the anomalous high rate in 1952 is not known.

A death from salicylate poisoning may be either accidental or suicidal, and often an accidental death due to gastric erosion may occur after only one or two five grain tablets of aspirin, whereas a suicide may fail with 50 or more. In general 80 per cent of the deaths are considered to be the result of suicide and 20 per cent due to accidents. Figure 2 shows accidental and suicidal deaths separately by sex and age. It is clear from this

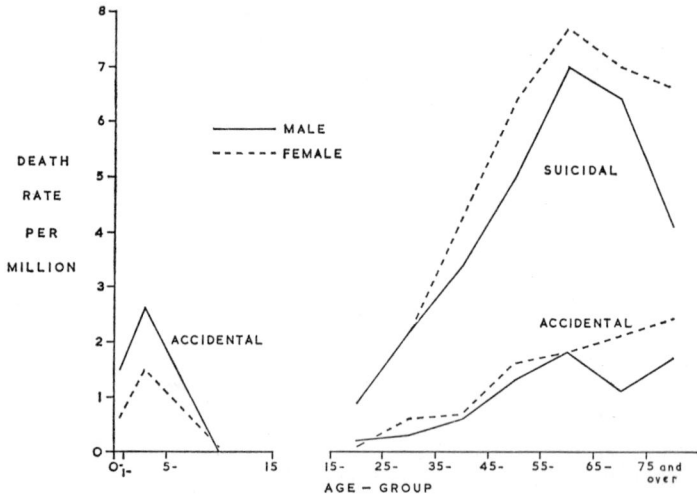

FIG. 2   DEATH RATE FROM SALICYLATE POISONING IN ENGLAND AND WALES, 1951–1960, ACCORDING TO AGE AND CAUSE OF INTOXICATION (ICD No. N 792)

figure, with its bimodal distribution, that there are various risks which differ with sex and age. Firstly, with the pre-school child there is a risk of death which is at a maximum at the toddler age and, as is to be expected, the male is at greater risk than his sister. This age is then followed by a period at school when the risk is almost nil. After adolescence the rate slowly increases, with suicides predominating and with the woman at higher risk than her husband. At ages over 65 the rates show a decline as domestic (coal) gas and barbiturates become the preferred instruments of suicide.

The aetiology of these deaths must be sought in a study of deaths from suicide, which is beyond the scope of this present paper, but it is interesting to note that the male suicide rate from all causes is higher than the female rate, so that the sex difference in salicylate poisoning is probably due to the male suicide preferring a more assured form of death.

Morbidity

The 10 per cent sample of hospital in-patients, which is organized by the Ministry of Health and the General Register Office in partnership, gives a more detailed picture of the incidence of poisoning from salicylates. It is only since 1958, however, that a true random sample of all patients has been used in reporting cases, and consequently the data in the following figures are restricted to the three years 1958 to 1960. Figure 3 gives the mean annual Hospital In-patient Rate (spells in hospital) per

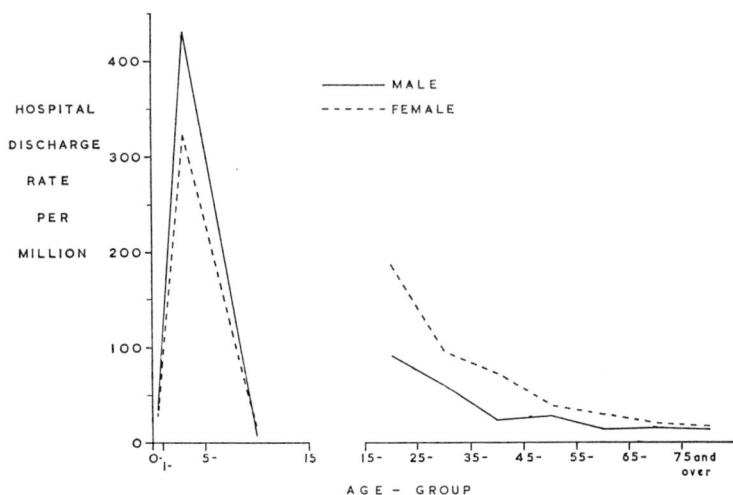

FIG. 3 SALICYLATE POISONING IN ENGLAND AND WALES, 1958–1960—
HOSPITAL DISCHARGE RATE, INCLUDING DEATHS

million population in England and Wales. It is not possible to distinguish these admissions into those that were accidental and those that were suicidal in intent, but it seems reasonable to assume that all the cases under 15 years of age were accidental and that probably 80 per cent of those over this age were suicidal.

There are some interesting differences between Fig. 2 and Fig. 3. In Fig. 3 the pre-school peak becomes very much more prominent and the boys remain at greater risk than the girls. The school-age trough is not quite so low, and it is apparent that some school-age children do suffer from salicylate poisoning, although they recover from it. The remainder of the age rates differ markedly. The morbidity reaches a second peak in the adolescent period for both males and females, although the female rate is double the male rate. After this age there is a steady decline in hospital admissions, and the female rate remains higher than the male rate at all ages. From these figures it is clear that the risk to the young child of being admitted to hospital as a suspected case of salicylate poisoning is far from negligible, and probably there are approximately 1,000 such admissions of children between the ages of one to four each year, of whom five or six cases die.

The discrepancy in the shape of the curves in Fig. 2 and Fig. 3 suggests that there are several factors operating to produce these statistics. Firstly, there appears to be a difference in the proportion of patients who succeed in reaching a hospital alive, and secondly, there is a difference in the case fatality rate when they reach hospital. There were 900 patients discharged from hospital during the three years 1958–1960 who were included in the 10 per cent sample and of these only nine died, giving a case fatality rate of one in 100. This suggests that there was only approximately a total of 90 deaths *in hospital* due to salicylate poisoning in these three years, although due to the sampling error of such small numbers these deaths might have been anywhere between 54 and 140 ($P = 0.1$). The number of deaths *registered* during these three years was 650, which means that the great majority of deaths took place before a hospital admission was possible.

Fatality rates

An attempt has been made to relate the registered deaths in the three years 1958–1960 with the 10 per cent sample of hospital cases. It should be appreciated that this can only give tentative findings. The age groupings were widened to increase the number of cases in a single group. Under the age of 15 there were 28 deaths registered, and the 10 per cent sample included three deaths, so probably all children benefited from some form of hospital treatment before death. Over the age of 15, however, there were only six deaths in the sample and yet 622 deaths were registered, so at these ages probably only one tenth of those dying had been admitted.

It is possible to calculate two series of statistics to estimate the case fatality rate. The ratio of hospital admissions and deaths gives a hospital fatality rate, but to calculate a national fatality rate it is necessary to consider the cases occurring outside hospital. We have no knowledge about the number of non-fatal cases not admitted to hospital and consequently we can only consider registered deaths plus hospital discharges as giving the total number of cases to be considered. The ratio of these total cases and registered deaths gives an estimate of the national case fatality rate. This is shown in Fig. 4. There is a remarkable contrast between the case fatality rate when based upon hospital cases and when based upon registered deaths. The hospital rate increases from 1 per cent in childhood to approximately 3 per cent at ages over 45, but the national rate increases from 1 per cent in childhood to approximately 30 per cent at ages over 45.

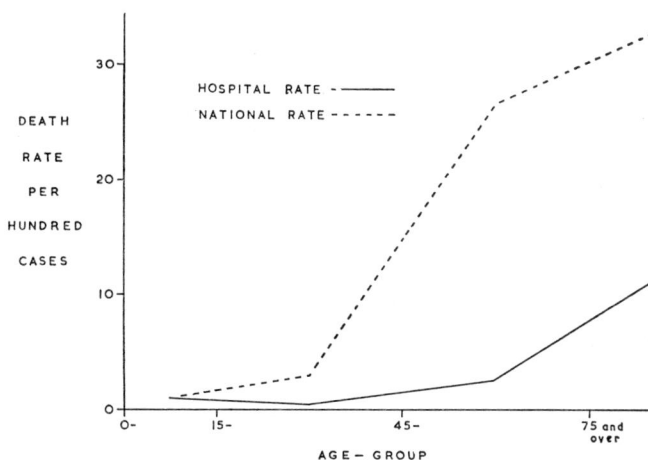

FIG. 4 CASE FATALITY RATE FROM SALICYLATE POISONING IN ENGLAND AND WALES, 1958–1960

SUMMARY

Two hundred deaths occur annually in England and Wales due to salicylate poisoning. There are two peaks in the mortality rate; the first is in the pre-school child and the second is in late middle age.

There are approximately 3,000 admissions to hospital with salicylate poisoning each year, and 1,000 of these are between the ages 1–4 years. The peak ages for admission are the pre-school child and the young adult, 15–24 years.

The case fatality rate for hospital admissions is approximately 1 per cent; the fatality rate for all cases in the country may be nearly 7 per cent and may be 30 per cent over age 45 years.

ONTOGENETIC STUDIES OF SALICYLATE INTOXICATION

ALAN K. DONE

*Department of Pediatrics, University of Utah College of Medicine
Salt Lake City, Utah, U.S.A.*

IT has long been known that infants and young children are especially vulnerable to serious complications of salicylate intoxication, particularly the acid-base disturbances. Little else is known, however, about the ontogenetic or developmental aspects of salicylate pharmacology and toxicology.

Salicylate intoxication in man

The acid-base disturbances of salicylate intoxication have been well described (Singer, 1954; Winters et al., 1959). Figure 1 is concerned with the influence of age on the pattern of acid-base disturbance in a group of patients with salicylate intoxication (Done, 1962). The expression S_0 refers to the extrapolated zero-time salicylate level, which has been found to correlate far better with the clinical severity of salicylate intoxication than do random blood salicylate levels (Done, 1960). S_0 is obtained by taking advantage of the fact that, when salicylate is taken as a single dose, its disappearance from the blood is a first-order reaction, making it possible to extrapolate to zero-time and obtain a theoretical figure that is proportional to the peak salicylate level. Older children having S_0 values greater than 130 mg. per 100 ml., indicative of extreme intoxication, are included in the graph with the children less than three years of age because they behave similarly. In this group severe hypocapnoea, frequently associated with frank metabolic acidosis, was the rule. Children over three years of age had less marked hypocapnoea and failed to develop frank acidosis except when extremely intoxicated. Adults characteristically exhibit respiratory alkalosis and virtually never develop metabolic acidosis regardless of the severity of intoxication. The arrows represent the proposed pathways followed by the three groups. In each group the respiratory stimulant effect of salicylate results in hypocapnoea and, if not influenced by other factors, would lead to the development of respiratory alkalosis. In adults, and in older children with other than extreme intoxication, this is as far as the process goes, except for compensatory reactions which may be called forth. On the other hand, very young or extremely intoxicated children exhibit an additional metabolic component which leads to the development of metabolic acidosis. The less severe hypocapnoea exhibited by the older children is probably related to two factors; the most severely intoxicated individuals were removed from the group, and while CO_2 production is probably increased more in children than in adults, in the older children without extreme intoxication this effect is not counteracted by respiratory compensation for acidosis.

In the absence of extreme or chronic intoxication the accumulation of extra fixed acid in the blood in response to salicylate intoxication is

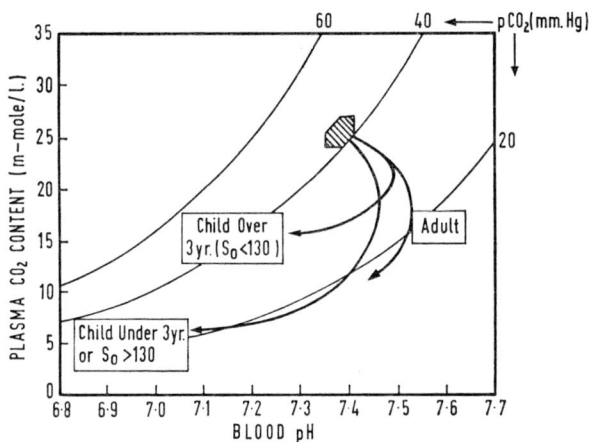

FIG. 1   ACID-BASE STATUS OF PATIENTS WITH SALICYLATE
INTOXICATION

This is a graphic representation (after Davenport, 1958) of the Henderson-Hasselbalch equation relating blood pH, carbon dioxide content, and the partial pressure of carbon dioxide (pCO_2). The shaded area represents the range of normal values, and the arrows represent the trends of the three principal abnormalities observed. The expression S_0 refers to the extrapolated zero-time salicylate concentration in the plasma.

influenced strikingly by age. All patients under one year of age had very high concentrations of extra fixed acid in the blood; the levels then tended to diminish with advancing age. Fixed acid accumulations equal to those observed in infants occurred in some children as old as four years, but only in the presence of extreme or chronic intoxication. Children beyond about seven years of age and adults had no or comparatively little accumulation of extra fixed acid, even with severe or chronic intoxication; furthermore, that amount present was entirely attributable to bicarbonate loss and therefore probably reflected compensation for alkalosis rather than a primary metabolic effect of salicylate. From these and the foregoing data, it appears that the very young child is quite sensitive to whatever metabolic effect of salicylate is responsible for the production of metabolic acidosis. This sensitivity, then, seems to diminish with

A. K. DONE

increasing maturation until the older child is relatively, and the adult almost absolutely, resistant.

However, maturation does not appear to influence response to the respiratory effect of salicylate. There is no relationship between age and the magnitude of reduction of pCO_2, which is strictly related to the degree of intoxication. To recapitulate, it appears that whereas the metabolic effect of salicylate is influenced strikingly by the degree of maturity, the central respiratory effect is not. Another and not unexpected factor that varies with age is the rate at which salicylate can be removed from the circulation. The half-life of salicylate in the blood was found to vary inversely with age among patients with salicylate intoxication (Done, 1962).

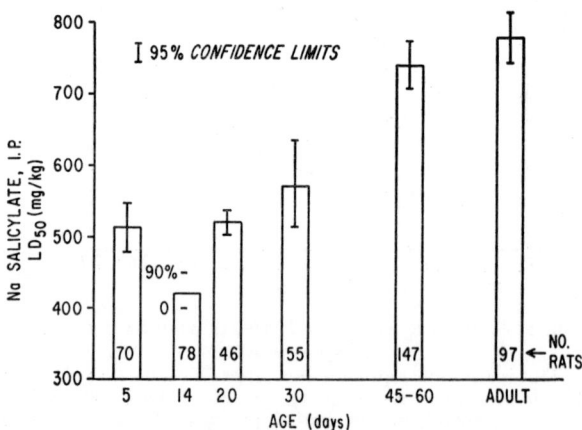

FIG. 2   COMPARATIVE TOXICITY (LD_{50}) OF INTRAPERITONEAL
SODIUM SALICYLATE IN RATS OF VARIOUS AGES
The mortality of 14-day-old animals rises abruptly from near zero at 400 mg. per kg. to 90 per cent at 450 mg. per kg., and so it is not possible to calculate 95 per cent confidence limits.

Experimental studies in animals

Turning now to some animal studies, Fig. 2 concerns the toxicity of intraperitoneal sodium salicylate in male rats of various ages (Done, 1962). The LD_{50} values were obtained by the graphical method of Litchfield and Wilcoxon (1949), after tests for significant heterogeneity or lack of parallelism among the curves proved to be negative. It can be seen that sensitivity to the lethal effect of salicylate decreases with advancing maturation beyond 14 days of age. It is noteworthy, however, that the 5-day-old rat is actually less sensitive than the 14-day-old. Even though it is not possible to calculate 95 per cent confidence limits for the

14-day-old animals, the difference is clearly significant; the LD_{90} for the 14-day-olds is similar to the LD_{30} for the 5-day-olds and is well below the 95 per cent confidence limits of the 5-day LD_{50}. It is apparent from these data that the immature rat is more sensitive than the mature to the lethal effects of salicylate, but that the newborn is relatively resistant by comparison with slightly older animals.

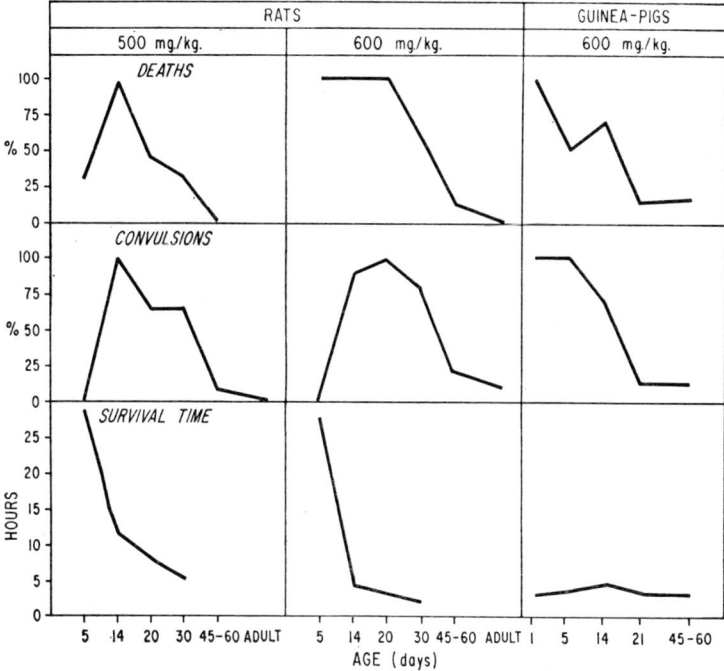

FIG. 3 INCIDENCE OF DEATH AND CONVULSIONS AND THE SURVIVAL TIME OF ANIMALS TREATED WITH SODIUM SALICYLATE INTRAPERITONEALLY

Figure 3 depicts the incidence of death and convulsions and the survival time of animals of various ages given uniform doses of salicylate. With a dose of 500 mg. per kg., the lesser sensitivity of the newborn rats can again be seen, and the mortality curve is noted to parallel the incidence of convulsions. Overt seizure activity was never observed in 5-day-old animals given this or any other dose of salicylate. The rat at this age has been shown also to be resistant to the development of maximal seizure activity following the administration of electroshock (Millichap, Balter & Hernandez, 1958) or strychnine (Pylkkö & Woodbury, 1961). This observation might seem, at first glance, to provide an explanation for the lesser mortality; in other words, the newborn animal is protected by his inability to develop seizures. In support of such a theory is the fact that the 14-day-old animal, which is most sensitive to the lethal effects of salicylate, is also the most sensitive to the convulsant effects and develops violent seizures even with relatively low doses. Against such a theory is the observation that when the dose of salicylate is increased to 600 mg. per kg., the mortality difference between 5- and 14-day-old animals disappears despite the fact that the former continue to be seizure-free. Another possible explanation for the relative resistance of the newborn rat to the lethal effect of salicylate is the markedly prolonged survival time, which averaged over 29 hours among 5-day-old animals who died.

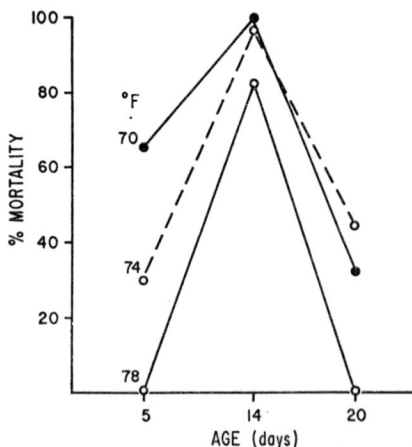

FIG. 4   INFLUENCE OF AGE AND OF AMBIENT
TEMPERATURE ON MORTALITY IN RATS GIVEN
SODIUM SALICYLATE

Sodium salicylate, 500 mg. per kg., was administered intraperitoneally.

Perhaps the markedly prolonged survival time simply allows the animals to outlive the salicylate effect. Again, however, increasing the dose to a level which obliterates the mortality difference does little to survival time, thus shedding some doubt on this explanation. Differences in blood levels of salicylate cannot be implicated because, while levels in the very young animals were somewhat more variable, they actually tended to be higher and more prolonged. We are left, then, with much speculation and no definitive explanation for the relative resistance of the newborn rat to the lethal effect of salicylate.

The developing guinea-pig behaves quite differently from the rat in its response to salicylate administration. Even when animals are studied as early as the first day of life, a similar newborn resistance is not demonstrable (Fig. 3). It is noteworthy that this animal also does not exhibit resistance to convulsions or prolonged survival during the newborn period.

Figure 4 depicts the combined influences of age and ambient temperature on the mortality rate due to salicylate intoxication in rats. It is well known that temperature may significantly influence the toxicity of a variety of drugs. It is interesting to note, however, that the magnitude of the temperature effect may vary appreciably with age, in this instance being most striking in the newborn. A dose of salicylate which kills two-thirds of 5-day-old rats at 70° F (21° C) kills only 30 per cent when the temperature is raised to 74° and none when it is raised to 78° F (25·5° C). The less striking effect of temperature on the response of 14-day-old animals is probably attributable in part to the greater overall mortality. However, the temperature effect is less in 20-day than in 5-day-old animals, despite a similar LD_{50}.

Implications

What, if any, implications these findings in experimental animals may have relative to salicylate intoxication in human beings is unknown. It can be said, however, that development poses interesting and complicated problems in relation to the pharmacology of salicylates as well as other compounds. It is perhaps of some practical interest to speculate on the possible implications regarding current proposals that drugs be tested in newborn animals before they are released for use in infants. It is becoming abundantly clear that the problem is not so simple as comparing LD_{50}'s using randomly selected animals and experimental conditions. Since the transition from the neonatal to the mature pharmacological response may not be a smooth linear progression, it is not enough to investigate only the response of the most immature animal. It is apparent also that such factors as species differences and the influences of temperature may be significantly affected by immaturity. Only after considerably more study of the problem of developmental pharmacology can we hope to provide reliable tools for predicting drug actions and toxicity in infants and children.

SUMMARY

Salicylate intoxication was studied in experimental animals and human patients at varying levels of maturity. The human infant is especially vulnerable to the serious acid-base derangements of salicylate intoxication, metabolic acidosis occurring universally and almost exclusively under two years of age, only with extreme intoxication in older children, and virtually never in adults, the latter usually exhibiting pure respiratory alkalosis. There was a parallel age relationship of the quantity of extra fixed acid, but not of carbon dioxide tension, in the blood, suggesting that immaturity increases sensitivity to the metabolic but not to the respiratory component of salicylate toxicity. Additionally, the rate of removal of salicylate from the circulation increased with increasing maturity.

Immature rats were more sensitive than the mature to the lethal effects, but 5-day-old animals were resistant by comparison with 14-day-olds. This was associated with complete resistance to convulsant effects, as well as with markedly prolonged survival, of the former. The newborn guinea-pig is not similarly protected. Between 70 and 78° F (21–25·5° C), higher ambient temperatures lessen the toxicity in rats of all ages, the differences being most marked in the newborn.

The author is a Research Career Development Awardee of the United States Public Health Service. This investigation was supported by a P.H.S. research grant (B-2952) from the National Institute of Neurological Diseases and Blindness, U.S. Public Health Service.

REFERENCES

Davenport, H. W. (1958). 'The ABC of Acid-Base Chemistry.' Chicago: University of Chicago Press.
Done, A. K. (1960). *Pediatrics*, **26**, 800.
Done, A. K. (1962). Proc. 41st Ross Pediatric Res. Conf., p. 83.
Litchfield, J. J. Jr., & Wilcoxon, F. (1949). *J. Pharmacol. exp. Ther.*, **96**, 99.
Millichap, J. G., Balter, M., & Hernandez, P. (1958). *Proc. Soc. exp. Biol. (N.Y.)*, **99**, 6.
Pylkkö, O. O., & Woodbury, D. M. (1961). *J. Pharmacol. exp. Ther.*, **131**, 185.
Singer, R. B. (1954). *Medicine (Baltimore)*, **33**, 1.
Winters, R. W., White, J. S., Hughes, M. C., & Ordway, N. K. (1959). *Pediatrics*, **23**, 260.

DISCUSSION

GORDON CUMMING (*Department of Medicine, University of Birmingham*):
One thing in CAMPBELL's paper which struck me as being important was that 200 people each year died from the toxic effects of salicylates. The bulk of these patients do not enter hospital at all, and so nothing can be achieved by modifying the method of hospital treatment. Preventive therapy must be directed towards preventing the absorption of the ingested tablets. We have with us members of the pharmaceutical industry to whom, perhaps, I should direct my remarks. I would suggest that perhaps the inclusion of an emetic agent in aspirin tablets might have a beneficial effect. I understand that experiments on these lines have been done, and I should be pleased to hear of their results.

The second point of interest was that 3,000 experiments of high dosage ingestion every year are being substantially thrown away from the investigations of the effects of salicylates. Might we not use these experiments in some way to get further information about how salicylate works? Perhaps the rheumatologists, even the Empire Rheumatism Council, might open the pathways of utilization for these experiments.

In his excellent paper on children, DONE raised in my mind the question about the term fixed acid. Can he give us any further information about what this is? Is it pyruvic acid or lactic acid, and why is the pH diminished in children? He also seemed to show (Fig. 1) that the response of the infant medulla to salicylate ion was normal, and that the ventilatory response was as it is in adults, and yet one never sees respiratory alkalosis in children. This seems to show that we are dealing with a rate phenomenon. Is the rate of formation of these acids greater in children, or is there a qualitative reason for the difference?

DONE: I do not know the nature of the extra fixed acid that is imparted to the blood of the child with salicylate intoxication. I assume that this may well consist of products of intermediary metabolism, their accumulation being due, perhaps, to metabolic interference of the type which SMITH has demonstrated. It seems likely that these are organic acids of some type. We have not found elevated levels of lactic acid in children, but we have found significantly elevated levels of pyruvate; these are not sufficient, however, to account for the acidosis or the total quantity of extra fixed acid.

With respect to the respiratory effect in children, it is true that one virtually never sees respiratory alkalosis in children, yet one invariably sees hyperventilation, which is at least as severe as it is in adults. The most likely explanation is that whatever factors tend to create acidosis operate early, so that the child immediately begins to wend his way towards acidosis. The alkalotic tendency, then, is counteracted by this acidotic factor. The child is able to compensate for a period of time but, when his buffering mechanisms are overwhelmed, he goes ahead and develops acidosis.

Extra fixed acid

WYNN: Let us give the term fixed acid a very wide berth and eliminate it from acid-base terminology. It is almost impossible to define, and it is almost impossible to get anyone interested in this field to accept a definition of fixed acid. Let us say that what DONE has demonstrated is a change in acid-base balance and a change in the anions. There is an increase in alkalis other than those normally present and normally identified in the blood plasma, and that probably many of these are buffer anions, but there is so far no evidence as to what they are.

MILNE (*Chairman*): It would be helpful if we could ask DONE to give his definition of the term fixed acid.

DONE: I am using the terminology of Davenport, who designates as fixed acids those acids which, unlike carbonic acid, cannot be metabolized directly to respiratory products. To show how the quantity of extra fixed acid is determined, an individual with metabolic acidosis must have added to his blood sufficient acid (or its practical equivalent, have removed enough base—perhaps by renal excretion) to account for the observed depression of plasma bicarbonate; there must have been a further addition of acid that titrates blood buffers in the acid direction, to account for the shift in blood pH. The total of these two is extra fixed acid. Winters uses the term R fraction to come to essentially the same thing from a different direction.

M. J. H. SMITH: DONE found that if the environmental temperature was raised, the mortality of his rats given toxic doses of salicylates declined. This must imply that uncoupling is not the main cause of death, since one would expect the reverse to occur.

OSORIO: DONE used S_0 as a mathematical index of the degree of salicylate intoxication in a patient. However, the calculation of S_0 depends essentially on the rate of disappearance of salicylate from the blood. Therefore a salicylate-poisoned patient in whom salicylate is removed from the blood at a very rapid rate must have a much higher value for S_0 than an individual in similar circumstances in whom the rate of disappearance of the drug is much slower. This implies that the individual with rapid disappearance of salicylate from the plasma is at greater risk of intoxication.

DONE: One drawback of S_0 is that it may be artificially altered by factors that increase or decrease the disappearance rate. From a practical standpoint, however, the half-life of toxic levels of salicylate does not vary greatly from one individual to another. The important point is that S_0 correlates quite well with the clinical severity of intoxication and is much more reliable than random salicylate levels.

OSORIO: For S_0 to be a reliable index of the severity of salicylate poisoning, it is necessary to assume that the disappearance rate of salicylate from the blood is the same in all individuals. It would be easier simply to relate the concentration of salicylate in the blood to the time after the ingestion of the drug.

If S_0 correlates well with the clinical severity of salicylate poisoning, whatever the rate of removal of salicylate from the blood, it could mean that a faster rate of removal, which will produce a higher value for S_0, is the consequence of a weaker binding of salicylate by the plasma proteins. This weaker binding will produce a higher concentration of free (non-protein-bound) salicylate in the blood and a higher concentration of salicylate in the tissues.

In other words, S_0 could be an index of the concentration of free salicylate in the blood.

MILNE: Many of these increased toxicities in the newly-born are due to immaturity of the so-called detoxification mechanisms of the young animal. Is there any proof that the young animal carries out the salicylurate and glucuronide conjugations less readily?

DONE: Yes, it does it less readily. I do not think that this accounts completely for the differences in toxicity, however, because older animals die at a period where this would not make much difference. They die so quickly that I do not think this would play a significant role. Whereas the newborn animal dies 29 hours after salicylate is given, the older animal dies in about 30 minutes.

ACID-BASE DISTURBANCES, AND THE TREATMENT OF SALICYLATE INTOXICATION

ROBERT W. WINTERS

Department of Pediatrics
Columbia University College of Physicians and Surgeons
New York, N.Y., U.S.A.

ACID-BASE DISTURBANCES

SALICYLATE intoxication is often associated with disturbances of acid-base equilibrium. The complexity of such disturbances is greatest in infants and small children who have been poisoned with the drug, and for this reason this paper will be confined largely to this group of patients.

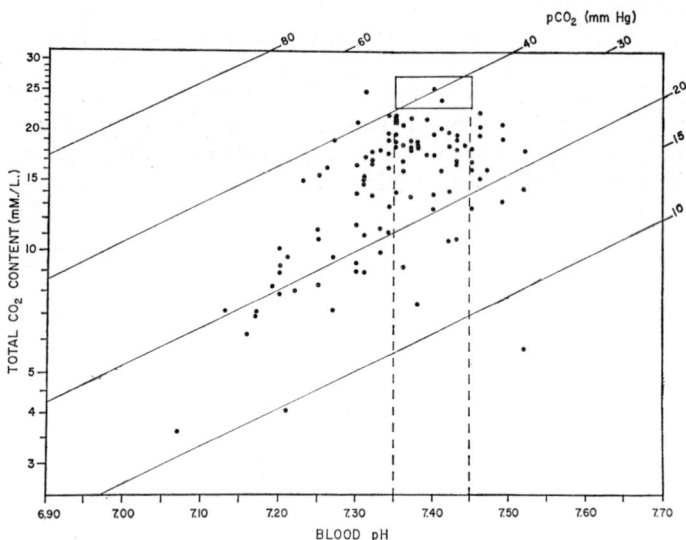

FIG. 1 INITIAL ACID-BASE STATUS OF INFANTS AND CHILDREN WITH SALICYLATE INTOXICATION

This has been compiled from the literature. The Figure is a graphic representation of the Henderson-Hasselbalch equation for the bicarbonate-CO_2 system of plasma. The ordinate, plasma total CO_2 content, is on a logarithmic scale. The advantage of this type of diagram is that the isopleths for pCO_2 are nearly straight lines, shown as diagonals crossing the basic grid. The rectangle represents a rather arbitrarily chosen range of normal values, centering about a pH of 7·40, a total CO_2 content of 25 m-mole per litre, and a pCO_2 of 40 mm. Hg.

270

Figure 1 shows a compilation of data from the literature on the acid-base status of infants and children with salicylate intoxication prior to any therapy. It is apparent from the points plotted on this figure that in nearly all instances of salicylism there is some reduction, and often a considerable reduction, in both plasma total CO_2 and pCO_2. Blood pH, on the other hand, shows no such consistent change, many patients

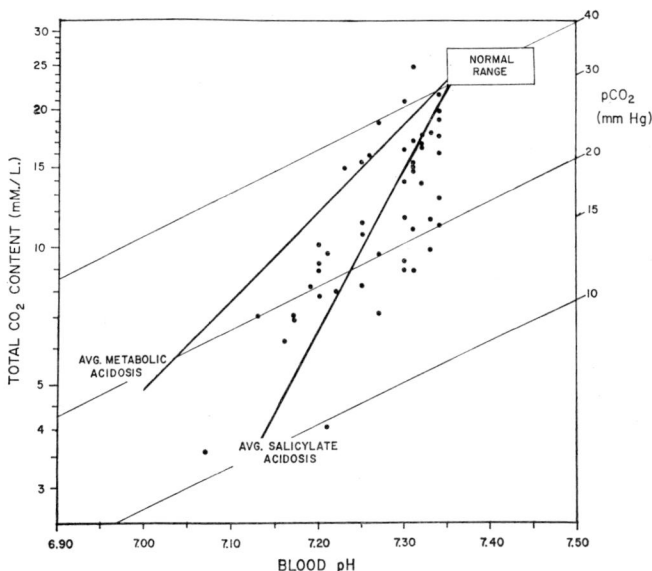

FIG. 2 COMPARISON OF PATIENTS WITH SALICYLISM AND ACIDOSIS
WITH PATIENTS WITH SIMPLE METABOLIC ACIDOSIS

Acid-base status is plotted, as in Fig. 1.

Average metabolic acidosis—regression line fitted to data from 66 infants and children with metabolic acidosis due to uncontrolled diabetes or diarrhoea (Winters et al., 1959).

Average salicylate acidosis—regression line fitted to plotted points, which represent all of the reported instances of typical acidosis in salicylate intoxication.

having acid values, a smaller number having alkaline values, while still others have normal values.

This variation in blood pH has been known for many years. It was first thought that it could be accounted for by supposing that initially all patients were in respiratory alkalosis, but that with the passage of time there occurred a transition to metabolic acidosis. An alternate view was first put forward by Singer (1954) and developed further by Winters and co-workers (1959). This hypothesis holds that the disorders of acid-base equilibrium in salicylism come about as the result of multiple simultaneous independent actions of the drug, each of which affects acid-base equilibrium in a specific manner. The final result upon blood pH then represents the balance between the intensities of these several factors and is therefore a true mixed disturbance of acid-base equilibrium.

The difference between a mixed disturbance and a simple disturbance may be illustrated with the data shown in Fig. 2, which contrasts the acid-base displacement seen in simple metabolic acidosis with the acidosis encountered in salicylate intoxication. With a very few exceptions the data on the typical instances of acidosis in salicylate intoxication fall below the line depicting the average behaviour of patients with metabolic acidosis alone. The regression curve labelled average salicylate acidosis differs significantly in slope from that representing metabolic acidosis.

One way to view these findings is to suppose that the stimulus for hyperventilation and hence for the lowering of pCO_2 in metabolic acidosis is blood pH itself or some factor directly related to blood pH. Hence as blood pH falls, ventilation increases and pCO_2 falls, and the average pathway depicting this response in a steady state is the regression curve. In salicylism, this quantitative relationship is disturbed such that at any given acid pH, pCO_2 is lower than would be expected in simple metabolic acidosis. In other words, these data suggest that in salicylate intoxication there is some factor stimulating respiration over and above that found in metabolic acidosis. This, of course, is not an unreasonable assumption since one of the well-known properties of this group of drugs is stimulation of the respiratory centre. Yet it is obvious that this action alone would not produce the observed acid shift in pH, and there must therefore be some other factors at work to account for this.

Metabolic factors

This problem was approached by a study of the anion partition of the plasma of a number of patients with salicylism; the relative contributions of bicarbonate, chloride, inorganic phosphate, salicylate, protein, and undetermined anion were assessed (Winters et al., 1959; Winters, 1959a). On the basis of these studies the decrease in bicarbonate concentration seen in patients with acidosis is accountable to a number of causes. First, there is the contribution from the foreign anion, salicylate, but this is relatively small. The principal cause for the fall of bicarbonate is to be found in the rise in the undetermined anion fraction. So far no studies have been conducted to determine the quantitative contribution of components within this fraction, although there is good circumstantial evidence that the chief offender is probably the ketone bodies, aceto-acetate and β-hydroxybutyrate. The major reason for implicating these substances is that profuse ketonuria is frequently seen in salicylism in infants and young children. There are in addition a few measurements on the plasma showing considerable increases in these anions (Erganian, Forbes & Case, 1947), although many more data are needed. Lactate, the other strong suspect, has not been adequately excluded as a possible contributor, although Barnett and co-workers (1942) presented a few measurements showing normal values for this anion.

Finally, there is some increase in the concentration of chloride in the plasma. This is called excess chloride and is computed as the increase in chloride concentration observed above that expected for the observed concentration of sodium if the usual normal relationship between these two ions obtained. The origin of this hyperchloraemia is not clear. It could be secondary to vomiting, which is a frequent accompaniment of salicylism, or to some renal adjustment either to the excretion of ketone bodies or as a compensation for a pre-existing alkalosis if that had occurred.

Hence, these disturbances in the metabolic component have multiple origins. Quantitatively the most significant abnormality is one probably associated with ketosis. When these disorders occur simultaneously with the respiratory stimulation, a mixed disturbance of acid-base equilibrium results. The occurrence of such a mixed disturbance was then sought in patients presenting with normal or alkaline values for blood pH. As shown in Fig. 1, these patients all have reductions of pCO_2 reflecting the stimulatory effect of salicylate upon the respiratory centre. Evidence for the occurrence of a mixed disturbance in these patients would then consist of identification of the disorders in the metabolic component. Indeed in many of these patients Winters and co-workers (1959) were able to demonstrate the presence of ketonuria associated with an increase in the undetermined anion fraction of the plasma, despite the presence of normal or alkaline values for blood pH. The picture was quite similar to that seen in the patients with acid pH except that the magnitude of increase of undetermined anion was less.

Not all patients in these two groups, however, showed this abnormality. There were an appreciable number who did not have ketonuria and in whom the increase in undetermined anion was rather slight or absent. Their plasma composition resembled that seen in partially or completely compensated respiratory alkalosis. Hence, in some patients in each group evidence was convincing that a mixed disturbance was present, while in the remainder the only discernible abnormality was that of respiratory alkalosis. One of the major differences between these two groups was the age of the patient. Patients with mixed disturbance were generally younger children or infants, while those with alkalosis alone were generally older children. This factor of age will be referred to again.

A mixed disturbance of acid-base equilibrium

On the basis of these studies a unified view of the pathogenesis of the acid-base disturbances in salicylism was put forward by Winters and co-workers (1959). Toxic amounts of salicylate exert three basic actions which affect acid-base equilibrium directly: they can cause an increase in fixed acids, presumed to be ketone bodies; they can cause a primary involuntary increase in alveolar ventilation (Tenney & Miller, 1955); and they can cause an increase in metabolic rate with an attendant increase in CO_2 production (Dodd, Minot & Arena, 1937; Tenney & Miller, 1955). As a pure effect the increase in fixed acids causes a fall in bicarbonate concentration. The pure effect of an increase in alveolar ventilation is a fall in pCO_2, while the pure effect of an increase in metabolic rate is a rise in pCO_2. In nearly all cases these two opposing effects upon pCO_2 are such that ventilation outstrips CO_2 production, and pCO_2 falls. It may be noted in passing that the impressive degree of hyperventilation that occurs in salicylism has its origin in these two effects, since the degree of ventilation necessary to achieve the low pCO_2 values observed in these patients must be correspondingly greater in the face of augmented CO_2 production than is the case, for example, in metabolic acidosis where CO_2 production is presumably unchanged.

The final effect of the interaction of these three effects determines the blood pH, and the direction and magnitude of deviation of blood pH represents the net effect of the intensities of the disturbances of the respiratory component on the one hand and of the metabolic component on the other. When the latter is more intense, acidosis results; when the former predominates, alkalosis results; and when the two are fortuitously balanced, a normal blood pH results.

There are a number of factors which seem to condition the intensity of the disturbance in the metabolic component (Winters et al., 1959). Of most importance is the age of the patient and the closely related factor of the method by which the intoxication is contracted. The most severe metabolic disturbances occur in infants who have become intoxicated as the result of therapeutic overdosage for some febrile illness, usually a minor respiratory infection. Most of the acidotic patients fall into this group. Other factors which seem to favour acidosis are the amount of salicylate taken and the duration of intoxication. As one proceeds up the age scale, acidosis becomes less frequent but also the mode of intoxication is different, usually being accidental ingestion of a single large dose rather than cumulative multiple smaller doses. There is another possibly important difference as well; namely, that the child who receives therapeutic overdosage is already ill and probably not receiving full caloric and fluid intake, while the child who accidentally ingests salicylate is previously healthy. It is therefore difficult to identify which of these several factors is exerting the predominant effect in allowing toxic doses of salicylate to produce such a dramatic ketosis. Certainly in older children, ketosis of the magnitude encountered in infants is rare unless the dose ingested is very large; the same seems to be true of adults. Hence, in these older subjects the metabolic component may be undisturbed, and one sees only the respiratory effects of the drug as these are reflected in the development of respiratory alkalosis.

TREATMENT

Treatment of acid-base disturbances

Only those aspects of treatment that bear directly upon the acid-base abnormalities will be discussed here. Such other important aspects as emptying of the stomach, rehydration, repletion of potassium deficits, and prevention or control of bleeding disturbances have been covered elsewhere (Winters, 1959a, b).

The question frequently arises as to what if any therapeutic measures should be taken to counter the acid-base abnormalities. This question presupposes that the nature of these disturbances in any given patient has been completely documented by measurement of plasma total CO_2 content *and* whole blood pH, and that these data have been correctly interpreted. In cases presenting with alkalosis or with the mixed disturbance with normal pH, no specific therapy need or should be given. Alkalotic tetany in salicylism seems to be uncommon unless inappropriate previous therapy has been given. Usually this comes about through administration of alkalinizing salts such as sodium bicarbonate or sodium lactate on the mistaken assumption that the patient is acidotic because of the low total CO_2 content.

The more frequent question concerning alkali therapy arises in patients initially presenting with the mixed disturbance and an acid pH. In this connection it is important to note the difference in the recovery pathways of patients treated with no alkalinizing salts compared with those receiving large amounts of these salts (reviewed by Winters, 1959a). In the first group of patients recovery to normal acid-base status was found nearly always to proceed through a transient alkalotic phase, caused by a delayed recovery of pCO_2 relative to the rate of recovery of bicarbonate concentration. This phenomenon is apparently due to some type of delayed readjustment of the respiratory centre. This pathway may be compared to that seen in patients receiving large amounts of alkalinizing salts. In these patients the bicarbonate concentration of the plasma rose faster and to a greater extent and, because of the delayed recovery of pCO_2, the alkalosis was more intense.

These findings bear directly upon the question of therapy for the acidotic patient. While correction of blood pH is clearly desirable, it is the author's belief that a relatively acute shift in blood pH from acid values to potentially dangerous alkaline values is of greater risk than the relatively modest acid values themselves. For this reason, it is our practice to attempt some correction of blood pH by administration of relatively small amounts of sodium bicarbonate, 2 to 4 m-mole per kg. body weight, and to monitor the effects of such infusions with frequent determinations of blood pH and plasma total CO_2 content.

Control of the ketosis would provide a logical way to treat the disturbance in the metabolic component. Although large quantities of carbohydrate are customarily administered the ketosis seems to clear only slowly.

Treatment designed to rid the body of salicylate

A number of measures have been suggested to rid the body of salicylate. These may be divided into two groups: measures designed to accelerate the renal excretion of the drug through alkalinization of the urine, and measures designed to remove the drug through extrarenal means. Two general questions arise in the evaluation of these proposals. Firstly, which patients should be selected to receive them and which can be managed conservatively? Second, what are the specific risks of each of these procedures?

The matter of selection of patients is difficult and ultimately it is resolved on the rather unsatisfactory basis of clinical experience. In an attempt to gain some objective information which might aid in this selection a number of reported fatal cases have been analysed (Fig. 3). While not pretending to provide perfect discrimination, this analysis does point to several potentially helpful signs which may aid in selecting patients for other than simple conservative management. The most striking feature is the large number of infants under the age of one year in proportion to the total. A second important point is that most of these fatal cases occurred as the result of therapeutic overdosage, while a much smaller proportion occurred as the result of accidental ingestion. Another interesting feature was the high incidence of hyperpyrexia; of the total of 20 patients on whom data are available, 15 had body temperatures of $104°$ F ($40°$ C) or greater. All of the reported values for total CO_2 content were reduced, and an appreciable number were less than 10 m-mole per litre.

On the basis of these findings the profile of a typical fatal case is an infant intoxicated because of therapeutic overdosage and presenting with hyperpyrexia and a considerable reduction in total CO_2 content. In addition, very severe cases often have convulsions, coma, acute pulmonary oedema, or respiratory depression.

The data on the concentration of salicylate in the plasma are of interest in that they emphasize the fact that in therapeutic overdosage the concentration of the drug correlates poorly if at all with severity of intoxication. The graph shows the large proportion of fatal cases with plasma levels of less than 50 mg. per 100 ml. In contrast, in the patients with accidental ingestion of the drug, as Done (1959) has demonstrated, the salicylate level does bear a reasonably good correlation with clinical severity when corrected for the duration of the intoxication.

Finally, it is of interest to note in passing that the duration of hospitalization of fatal cases prior to death is often only a few hours. This is probably because of a delayed recognition of the seriousness of the intoxication until it is too late and demonstrates that the real solution to this whole problem is prevention. It also means that in many instances we have only a few hours to attempt to institute one or another of the special measures to get rid of the drug.

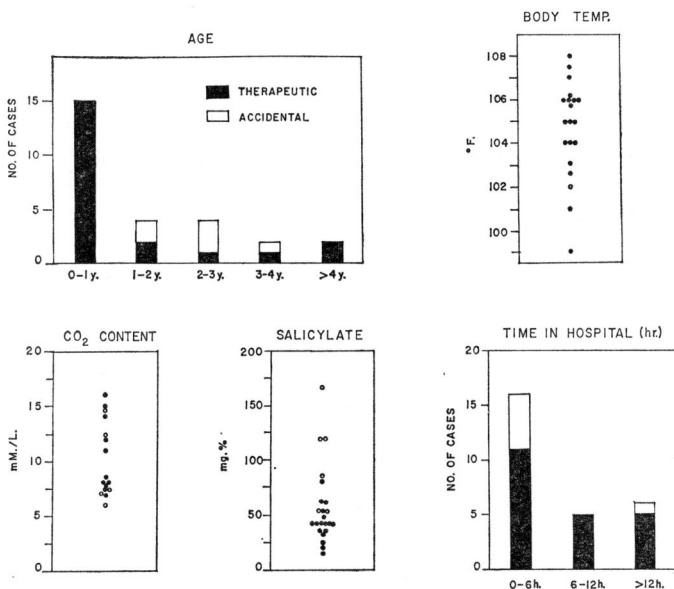

FIG. 3   ANALYSIS OF FATAL CASES OF SALICYLATE INTOXICATION IN INFANTS AND CHILDREN

Promotion of renal excretion

With respect to the first group of measures, those designed to increase the rate of renal excretion of the drug, there are several possible approaches. Firstly, there is the suggestion that sodium bicarbonate be given in large amounts so as to achieve an alkaline urine. Whitten and co-workers (1961) have used this procedure and found that the rate of salicylate excretion was indeed enhanced as urine pH rose. The predicted alkalosis, however, did occur, and in several patients blood pH values in excess of 7·60 were recorded. Since these particular patients did not manifest any symptoms referable to the alkalosis, these authors were inclined to dismiss this risk as a theoretical one. In support of this contention, they point out that there have been few published reports to document this type of risk in salicylism. Although this is true, it is hardly surprising since one tends not to publish one's mistakes. In view of the much broader body of evidence attesting to the adverse effects that alkalosis may exert, it would seem premature to dismiss this risk, particularly since the number of severely intoxicated patients treated by these authors was a relatively small proportion of the total.

A second mode of alkalinizing the urine is to administer the drug acetazolamide. This agent inhibits carbonic anhydrase in the renal tubular cells and causes the excretion of large amounts of bicarbonate accompanied by sodium and potassium. To the extent that this accelerated excretion of bicarbonate occurs, the extracellular fluid bicarbonate concentration falls and hence this agent has the effect of causing a metabolic acidosis. This effect can be countered by administration of appropriate amounts of sodium and potassium bicarbonate. Schwartz and co-workers (1959) treated three patients with severe degrees of intoxication and obtained considerable increases in the rate of excretion of salicylate. However, in two of these convulsions occurred rather late in the course but in a temporal sequence suggesting that this otherwise rather benign drug might be exerting some adverse synergistic effect with salicylate upon the central nervous system. One of these patients died, apparently of neurological complications. Somewhat in contrast to this study is that of Feuerstein, Finberg and Fleishman (1960), who treated a larger number of patients without observing any such complications, although judging from their published data few if any of their patients were as severely intoxicated as those treated by Schwartz and his co-workers. The question of possible synergism between these two agents must therefore be left open until more data, particularly on the severely intoxicated patients, are available.

A third means of alkalinizing the urine is by the administration of tris (2-amino-2-hydroxymethylpropane-1:3-diol) buffer. This agent has been shown to enhance the rate of excretion of salicylate in experimental animals (Strauss & Nahas, 1960). It has not been adequately evaluated in clinical salicylism.

The second group of measures, those designed to remove salicylate through the extrarenal route, will be considered only briefly in view of the subsequent paper on this subject. Three measures have been tried: exchange transfusion, peritoneal dialysis, and haemodialysis. Exchange transfusion has the advantage of being a familiar technique to paediatricians, and it is applicable to infants. Its effectiveness increases as the volume of blood exchanged increases (Leikin & Emmanouilides, 1960). It has inherent disadvantages which are obvious. Intermittent peritoneal dialysis, particularly when the dialysing fluid contains albumin (Etteldorf et al., 1961), is also an effective technique, and in trained hands it appears to be reasonably safe (Segar, Gibson & Rhamy, 1961). It is also applicable to infants. Neither of these techniques is as efficient as haemodialysis (James, Kimbell & Read, 1962), but this latter presents certain formidable technical difficulties when applied to infants.

SUMMARY

Acid-base disturbances. The acid-base disorders in salicylate intoxication are characterized by reductions in plasma bicarbonate concentration and pCO_2; blood pH, on the other hand, may be acid, normal, or alkaline. A physiological analysis of these disorders suggests that most infants and children with salicylism have a true mixed disturbance with simultaneous independent abnormalities in the respiratory component, reflected by a fall in pCO_2, and in the metabolic component, reflected by a fall in bicarbonate concentration. The respiratory disorder is apparently secondary to the effect of salicylate upon the respiratory centre itself and leads to an increase in alveolar ventilation which is sufficient to cause a lowering of pCO_2 in the face of an increase in CO_2 production, also effected by the drug. The metabolic abnormality is predominantly due to an increase in strong acids, presumably ketone bodies. The varying intensities of these disturbances in the two components of acid-base equilibrium determine the final effect upon blood pH. Age appears to condition the degree of ketosis in that most patients in the younger age groups show intense ketosis and are acidotic, while most older children, and adults as well, seem less likely to develop this metabolic disorder; hence, the typical acid-base disturbance in the latter groups is respiratory alkalosis.

Treatment. Most patients can be managed conservatively unless the intoxication is severe, in which case more drastic measures are indicated. Selection of patients is difficult, but attention is directed to such factors as age, mode of intoxication, body temperature, total CO_2 content of the plasma, and the presence of coma, convulsions, acute pulmonary oedema, or respiratory depression, as being of importance in selecting patients for other than conservative management.

Two groups of measures designed to rid the body of salicylate are discussed: those which are directed towards alkalinization of the urine, such as administration of sodium bicarbonate or acetazolamide, and those directed towards extrarenal removal of the drug, such as exchange transfusion, peritoneal dialysis, and haemodialysis.

REFERENCES

Barnett, H. L., Powers, J. R., Benward, J. H., & Hartmann, A. F. (1942). *J. Pediat.*, 21, 214.
Dodd, K., Minot, A. S., & Arena, J. M. (1937). *Amer. J. Dis. Child.*, 53, 1435.
Done, A. K. (1959). *Pediatrics*, 24, 800.
Erganian, J. A., Forbes, G. B., & Case, D. M. (1947). *J. Pediat.*, 30, 129.

Etteldorf, J. N., Dobbins, W. T., Summitt, R. L., Rainwater, W. T., & Fischer, R. L. (1961). *J. Pediat.*, **58**, 226.

Feuerstein, R. C., Finberg, L., & Fleishman, E. (1960). *Pediatrics*, **25**, 215.

James, J. A., Kimbell, L., & Read, W. T. (1962). *Pediatrics*, **29**, 442.

Leikin, S. L., & Emmanouilides, G. C. (1960). *J. Pediat.*, **57**, 715.

Schwartz, R., Fellers, F. X., Knapp, J., & Yaffe, S. (1959). *Pediatrics*, **23**, 1103.

Segar, W. E., Gibson, R. K., & Rhamy, R. (1961). *Pediatrics*, **27**, 603.

Singer, R. B. (1954). *Medicine (Baltimore)*, **33**, 1.

Strauss, J., & Nahas, G. G. (1960). *Proc. Soc. exp. Biol. (N.Y.)*, **105**, 348.

Tenney, S. M., & Miller, R. M. (1955). *Amer. J. Med.*, **19**, 498.

Whitten, C. F., Kesaree, N. M., & Goodwin, J. F. (1961). *Amer. J. Dis. Child.*, **101**, 178.

Winters, R. W. (1959a). *Pediatrics*, **23**, 255.

Winters, R. W. (1959b). *Pediat. Clin. N. Amer.*, **6**, 281.

Winters, R. W., White, J. S., Hughes, M. C., & Ordway, N. K. (1959). *Pediatrics*, **23**, 260.

THE USE OF THE ARTIFICIAL KIDNEY IN SALICYLATE POISONING

F. M. Parsons

Renal Research Unit, The General Infirmary, Leeds

Although Abel and co-workers (1913) showed that haemodialysis removed salicylate from the plasma of dogs, clinical trials were not possible until the development of safe procedures (Doolan et al., 1951).

As dialysis removes salicylate from plasma or saline at about the same rate (Schreiner et al., 1955), protein binding of salicylate in the plasma is of little consequence during a haemodialysis (Doolan et al., 1951). However, addition of albumin to the irrigating fluid, as in peritoneal dialysis, allows a greater clearance of salicylate (Etteldorf et al.,1960). This is probably unnecessary during a haemodialysis; Doolan and co-workers found that the same quantity of salicylate was removed by a three-hour dialysis as was excreted by the kidneys in 24 hours, and 60 per cent of the salicylate was removed from the plasma during one passage through the dialyser. The volume of distribution of salicylate approximates to that of the extracellular fluid volume (Schreiner et al., 1955) rather than to the total body water, a factor that enhances the total body clearance rate. During a haemodialysis any electrolyte disturbances are corrected because sodium, potassium, chloride, and bicarbonate ions are transported rapidly across the Cellophane membrane (Wolf et al., 1951). At the same time water deficits can be made good.

We have used a modified rotating Kolff-Brigham machine (Parsons & McCracken, 1958). As all the cases of salicylate poisoning that we have dialysed were assessed to have a normal red blood cell picture, the dialyser was primed with reconstituted dried plasma. This allowed a dialysis to start within one hour of admission if necessary. The majority of patients were dehydrated and fluid was administered during the dialysis. Potassium depletion was treated by increasing the potassium in the bath fluid to 5 m-equiv. per litre. When this failed to correct a deficit oral supplementation was used.

Indications for dialysis

No single clinical or biochemical test is available to indicate the necessity for dialysis. Schreiner and co-workers (1955) found no correlation between the clinical state and either the plasma salicylate level or the quantity of drug taken. However, Guest, Rapoport and Roscoe (1945) found that primary hyperpnoea and the fall in CO_2 tension were pro-

DETAILS OF SEVEN CASES OF SALICYLATE POISONING THAT WERE TREATED BY HAEMODIALYSIS

All were adults who had attempted suicide, and all recovered

Case	Sex and age (yr.)	Drugs taken (and number of tablets)	Plasma salicylate levels (mg. per 100 ml.)		Dialysis	
			Maximum	Before and after dialysis	Duration (hr.)	Indications
1	M 54	Aspirin	84	84 / 40	4	Coma for 12 hours
2	M 21	Aspirin (100) Meprobamate	73	66 / 47	2	Coma for 9 hours
3	F 29	Aspirin Barbiturate Anticonvulsants	140	96 / 35	3	Coma for 12 hours; Cyanosis and pulmonary oedema; Plasma barbiturate 5·1 mg./100 ml.
4	F 61	Aspirin Chlorpromazine	118	83 / 23	5	Disorientated 24 hours; Clinical deterioration; Hypotension
5	M 28	Aspirin (300)	110	66 / 29	3	Disorientated 24 hours; Cyanosis; Haematuria
6	M 52	Aspirin (500)	100	52 / 28	5	Increasing drowsiness 24 hours; Hypotension
7	F 61	Aspirin (200)	52	39 / 19	4	Semi-coma; Severe oliguria; Plasma urea nitrogen 85 mg./100 ml.

portional to the dose swallowed. Deaths from salicylate poisoning have been reported with a plasma level of 20 mg. per 100 ml., but recovery has been reported when the level had reached 70 mg. per 100 ml. (Rentsch, Bradley & Marsh, 1959). We have observed one patient with a plasma level of 93 mg. per 100 ml.; consciousness was retained and recovery occurred without the need for haemodialysis.

The main indications for haemodialysis are therefore clinical. We have dialysed seven patients (Table), in whom the indications were:

(i) *In the presence of coma.* Three patients were transferred to the Artificial Kidney Unit less than 24 hours after ingesting salicylate. In two of these patients coma was the main indication for dialysis. In case 3 the level of barbiturate in the plasma was high enough to cause coma, although the severe cyanosis and pulmonary oedema were thought to be due to salicylate poisoning; thus there were two separate indications for dialysis.

(ii) *In the absence of coma.* Three patients had been under observation in another hospital for more than 24 hours, and clinical deterioration was continuing despite a fall in the plasma salicylate level. In cases 4 and 6 progressive hypotension developed, resulting in a diminished excretion of salicylate. In case 5 respiratory embarrassment and cyanosis were increasing; there was haematuria and haematemesis.

(iii) *In the presence of renal failure.* Salicylates may cause acute renal failure (Scott & Hanzlic, 1916; Bywaters & Joekes, 1948; Bracey, 1951; Miller, 1955; Campbell & Maclaurin, 1958). One such patient was dialysed, in whom there was no marked toxic manifestation of salicylism. As 70 per cent of salicylate is excreted in the urine (Rentsch, Bradley & Marsh, 1959), dialysis was resorted to fairly early in the course of renal failure when the plasma urea nitrogen was 85 mg. per 100 ml.

This series is too small to justify firm conclusions. Furthermore, few observations were possible as cases 1–6 were considered to require immediate dialysis at the time of their admission. Nevertheless it is quite clear that haemodialysis is an effective form of treatment, and is often more economical on man-power than more conservative procedures. A relatively short dialysis of two to four hours restored cerebration and respiratory function to normal, even though the level of salicylate in the plasma was still high. It is suggested that once the plasma salicylate level has been reduced to 40 mg. per 100 ml. and the patient has regained consciousness, further specific treatment is unnecessary unless renal function has been disturbed.

In two patients one indication for dialysis was pulmonary oedema and cyanosis (cases 3 and 5). Granville-Grossman and Sergeant (1960) have suggested four possible causes of pulmonary oedema in salicylate poisoning: a high sodium intake, probably not applicable when aspirin is taken alone; a sensitivity reaction; an increase in protein breakdown, with a secondary increase in plasma volume; and retention of sodium and water. The rapid clearing of pulmonary oedema that occurred during the dialysis of these two cases, without any significant change in sodium and water balance, suggests that pulmonary oedema is due to a reversible sensitivity reaction.

More recently the buffering agent tris (2-amino-2-hydroxymethyl-propane-1:3-diol) has been used by Clark (1960) to correct the acidosis of a 17 lb. baby admitted with salicylate poisoning, sufficient drug being given to return the pH of the blood to normal. The child's colour and breathing improved and consciousness returned within two hours. This may also enhance the renal clearance of salicylate (Strauss & Nahas, 1960). If these results are confirmed, this agent might be of value in paediatrics and in some adult cases, reserving haemodialysis for the severe case and for those with acute renal failure.

SUMMARY

Haemodialysis corrects the symptomatology of salicylate poisoning faster than normal renal function is able to. It should be considered seriously in all patients whose clinical condition is deteriorating despite appropriate therapy and in those who have other serious disease. It is valuable when other drugs also have been taken, even if these drugs are not dialysable.

In our experience cases probably are referred for dialysis too late. The procedure can be commenced rapidly if the artificial kidney is primed with reconstituted dried plasma rather than waiting for cross-matched blood. In infants it is always technically difficult or even impossible to institute an extracorporeal circulation; peritoneal dialysis or exchange blood transfusion (Rentsch, Bradley & Marsh, 1959) should be considered as an alternative. In this series the cause of salicylate poisoning was attempted suicide; subsequent psychiatric care was necessary.

REFERENCES

Abel, J. J., Rowntree, L. G., & Turner, B. B. (1913). *Trans. Ass. Amer. Phycns*, **28**, 51.
Bracey, D. W. (1951). *Brit. J. Surg.*, **38**, 482.
Bywaters, E. G. L., & Joekes, A. M. (1948). *Proc. roy. Soc. Med.*, **41**, 420.
Campbell, E. J. M., & Maclaurin, R. E. (1958). *Brit. med. J.*, **i**, 503.
Clark, L. C. (1960). *Trans. Amer. Soc. art. intern. Org.*, **6**, 253.
Doolan, P. D. Jr., Walsh, W. P., Kyle, L. H., & Wishinsky, H. (1951). *J. Amer. med. Ass.*, **146**, 105.
Etteldorf, J. N., Montalvo, J. M., Kaplan, S., & Sheffield, J. A. (1960). *J. Pediat.*, **56**, 1.
Granville-Grossman, K. L., & Sergeant, H. G. S. (1960). *Lancet*, **i**, 575.
Guest, G. M., Rapoport, S., & Roscoe, C. (1945). *J. clin. Invest.*, **24**, 770.

Miller, M. R. (1955). *Lancet*, **i**, 596.
Parsons, F. M., & McCracken, B. H. (1958). *Brit. J. Urol.*, **30**, 463.
Rentsch, J. B., Bradley, A., & Marsh, S. B. (1959). *A.M.A. J. Dis. Child.*, **98**, 788.
Schreiner, G. E., Berman, L. B., Griffin, J., & Feys, J. (1955). *New Engl. J. Med.*, **253**, 213.
Scott, R. W., & Hanzlik, P. J. (1916). *J. Amer. med. Ass.*, **67**, 1838.
Strauss, J., & Nahas, G. G. (1960). *Proc. Soc. exp. Biol. (N.Y.)*, **105**, 348.
Wolf, A. V., Remp, D. G., Kiley, J. E., & Currie, G. D. (1951). *J. clin. Invest.*, **30**, 1062.

DISCUSSION

VICTOR WYNN (*Department of Human Metabolism, St. Mary's Hospital, London*):

WINTERS and PARSONS have given us a masterly account of the treatment of salicylate intoxication. I would like to point out that, as has happened so often in the past, these major findings in clinical science have come to us from paediatricians, and American paediatricians at that.They have shown us what a magnificent tool clinical measurement can be in the elucidation of these complex acid-base disorders. I would like to thank WINTERS particularly for telling us that the method of treatment of these patients depends upon precise biochemical measurements, but I doubt whether more than a handful of hospitals in this country can carry out such treatment. Acid-base disorders have been well understood for more than thirty years, and hardly anything really new has been added to the knowledge of them since the first textbook of Peters and van Slyke in 1931. The measurement of acid-base disorders has been effective since about 1920. Is it right or fair that patients can come in to hospital suffering from gross salicylate intoxication, which can produce life-threatening metabolic changes, and yet the hospital laboratory may be unequipped to undertake the measurements upon which the success of the treatment may largely depend? This is a call to treat any form of intoxication by means of measurements such as we have just been shown; without these simple measurements one has nothing except clinical judgement and the possibility of a fatal result.

The whole acid-base spectrum in the patient can now be measured in a fraction of a cubic millimetre of blood in roughly three to four minutes. It need not be arterial blood, it can be capillary blood, and I think there is no justification for delaying any longer the introduction of clinical acid-base measurements into this type of case. Haemodialysis, in the hands of people like PARSONS and other trained teams, is a safe and magnificent procedure. Here I think we have been a bit more enterprising in this country, we have something like twenty artificial kidney units. I will only amplify PARSONS's plea not to send patients when they are moribund, but to get them into hospital in the vicinity of an artificial kidney at the earliest possible moment.

M. J. H. SMITH: WINTERS's results on the increased amounts of undetermined anions found in the plasma of children suffering from the mixed acid-base disturbance in salicylate poisoning are particularly interesting. A possible mechanism may be as follows, if the metabolism of glucose is considered as an example. The uncoupling action of salicylate will tend to stimulate glycolysis, leading to an increased formation of pyruvate. The conversion of pyruvate to either alanine or lactate will be inhibited because salicylates interfere with the transaminases and lactic dehydrogenase. Therefore more pyruvate will be metabolized to acetylcoenzyme A. Some of this will enter the tricarboxylic acid cycle, but salicylate inhibits transaminase and dehydrogenase enzymes in or associated with the cycle, notably malic and isocitric dehydrogenases. This may cause, firstly, an accumulation of organic acids such as malic, citric, and α-ketoglutaric acids, and secondly, tend to decrease the entry of two carbon compounds into the cycle. If acetylcoenzyme A metabolism via the cycle is depressed, then aceto-acetylcoenzyme A may be formed at an increased rate, leading to a superimposed ketosis.

Amount of salicylate removed by dialysis

BYWATERS: I would like to ask PARSONS two questions. First of all, could he give an estimate of the amounts of salicylate that he has been able to remove? Secondly, would he comment on the pathological types of renal failure, and on sub-clinical evidence of renal failure, in these poisoning cases? When Joekes and I were using one of the original artificial kidneys in this hospital, one of the cases was an aspirin suicide who ultimately died five days later of renal failure (Case IX). We did remove 5 g. of salicylate in a three-hour dialysis. We are particularly interested in the renal aspects of salicylate overdosage, and would be interested to know if there is any evidence of renal disorder or irritation in these cases who develop renal failure.

PARSONS: I cannot answer about the amount removed. The amount is relatively of no significance, because we do not get down to zero levels of salicylate in the plasma. Once consciousness has been restored and the plasma level has fallen below 40 mg. per 100 ml., the dialysis is stopped.

G. CUMMING: Perhaps I can give some idea. In a recent case a man of 62 years took 65 g. of aspirin by mouth. Some three hours later, when he arrived in hospital, his serum salicylate level was 128 mg. per 100 ml. Polyuria was induced, and after this the level fell to 65 mg. per 100 ml., the pre-dialysis value. A four-hour dialysis reduced the level to 26 mg. per 100 ml. In the first four hours 5·5 g. were excreted in the urine, dialysis removed 6·8 g., and the final plasma salicylate level presumably represents the remainder of the dose distributed in the body water.

PARSONS: Doolan and co-workers give precise figures.

Tubular necrosis must be rare, considering the number of tons of salicylate which are consumed, but when it does occur it is rather shattering. Of other types of damage I do not have any specific information because I only see cases referred for dialysis. I do not look specifically for signs of residual damage, but hypotension might be a factor prior to dialysis. On ordinary routine examination after dialysis there was no change found.

I wonder if anybody has worked out the stimulus of salicylates on the respiratory centre. We see stages similar to diabetes in some patients with severe metabolic acidosis, including accumulation of ketone bodies. One has seen this following uretero-colic anastomosis. Is salicylate acting in a similar manner? The alkalosis and the secondary changes are those associated with intracellular acidosis and may be interfering with carbohydrate metabolism. Clark demonstrated a very rapid return of respiration to normal, and I suggest that this was due to correcting intracellular acidosis in the respiratory centre.

CONCLUSION

Chairman W. S. C. Copeman

CONCLUDING REMARKS

J. J. R. Duthie

Rheumatic Diseases Unit
Northern General Hospital, Edinburgh

Many of the papers we have heard have been of a highly technical nature, and I am sure I speak for the clinicians among us when I express our gratitude for the lucid exposition of much intricate experimental work. Nevertheless, in spite of an immense expenditure of energy and skill, it seems to me that the central question of how salicylates act in reducing the symptoms and signs of inflammation remains unanswered. An immense amount of ground has been covered, and much of the material presented I am in no position to assess, and so I propose to consider briefly a number of matters of special interest to me as a clinician.

In the first session Bywaters remarked on the fact that, although much time had been devoted to many aspects of the action of salicylates, little attention appeared to have been paid to their ability to relieve pain. I would add that no tribute has been paid to an even more remarkable property of this group of drugs, their ability to relieve the disabling stiffness that is such a prominent feature in rheumatoid arthritis. Levy made the important point that gastrointestinal irritation and erosion can be correlated with dissolution rate, and that gastrointestinal bleeding can be reduced by using rapidly dissolving solid forms or salicylate solutions. This promoted considerable discussion, but I think he ably defended his thesis.

In the second session we were reminded of the extraordinary variety of metabolic changes that may follow the administration of salicylates. Smith reviewed their effects on intermediary metabolism, due, in part at least, to three distinct actions on enzyme systems, and other speakers dealt with changes induced in connective tissue, on thyroid function tests, on cholesterol metabolism, on blood sugar levels, and on membrane permeability. We were warned of the dangers of attempting to elucidate the mode of action of salicylates in disease by experimenting on normal tissue. It has always seemed rather extraordinary to me that we clinicians see so little objective evidence of these profound changes in our patients who have been taking fairly large doses of salicylates for many years.

Anti-inflammatory effects

I have long felt that the elucidation of the mode of action of this group of drugs in modifying the inflammatory reaction might provide valuable information about the mechanism involved in the response of tissues to injury, and might lead to a better understanding of some of the pathogenetic factors in disease. Aspirin has little influence on the erythema and oedema induced by the intradermal injection of bradykinin, in contrast to its ability to suppress the initial reaction to thurfyl nicotinate. It seems likely that the anti-inflammatory action of aspirin is more closely related to its ability to suppress the reaction to SRS-A, a material that COLLIER has shown can be released by injury and that is capable of causing an inflammatory reaction. I was interested in the demonstration by SPECTOR and WILLOUGHBY of a suppressive effect of salicylate on the delayed vascular response following the injection of turpentine into the pleural space, in contrast to the failure of aspirin to influence the late development of erythema following exposure to UV light or the application of thurfyl nicotinate. ADAMS's observations, and our own, illustrate the fact that tests for anti-inflammatory activity in animals, such as the UV erythema technique, may not provide a reliable guide to the likely clinical effects of compounds shown to be effective by this method. The almost unique property of aspirin in suppressing the initial erythema and oedema of the thurfyl nicotinate reaction is of particular interest, especially in view of the failure of sodium salicylate to have any appreciable effect. In my opinion, sodium salicylate is certainly less effective clinically. This striking difference implies that acetylsalicylic acid has properties not possessed by other forms of salicylate. I think we have heard too much about salicylates, rather than the particular forms used.

BYWATERS raised the basic question as to whether the suppression of the signs and symptoms of inflammation was a desirable objective, and whether the marked exacerbations following withdrawal of salicylates and steroids might not be an index of some weakening of the body defences. It is certainly true clinically that cases of rheumatoid arthritis starting acutely with severe local signs of inflammation often have an excellent prognosis, in contrast to those starting insidiously, which tend to run a progressive downhill course.

AUSTEN's review of the immunological effects of salicylates was timely in view of the current interest in the possibility of auto-immune reactions being concerned with the pathogenesis of diseases of connective tissue.

11*

Site of action of anti-inflammatory drugs

In considering the problem of drugs and their possible sites of action, I have found it useful to think of inflammation as being made up of three components:

(i) hyperaemia and increased vascular permeability—cellular exudates;

(ii) proliferation of connective tissue cells, with the production of granulation tissue;

(iii) the exogenous or endogenous primary damaging factor which initiates the whole process.

In the case of bacterial infections this last is the infecting organism or its products, but in many other situations, particularly those rheumatic conditions characterized by widespread inflammation in connective tissue, the factor or factors responsible remain unknown.

With regard to the action of anti-inflammatory drugs such as salicylates, I think they exert their effect primarily on the vascular component; they reduce hyperaemia and exudation, and may thereby achieve their analgesic effect. They may even have some effect in inhibiting the proliferation of cells. I believe the corticosteroids affect both the vascular and the proliferative phases. On the other hand, gold and the antimalarial drugs, which have no immediate analgesic effects, may exert their beneficial effects only on the proliferative phase, and clinical benefit may be delayed for weeks or even months. None of the drugs available at present appear to have any influence on the unknown factors which initiate tissue damage. I do not believe personally that any living organism is directly concerned in connective tissue diseases, although in the case of rheumatic fever the haemolytic streptococcus plays an essential part in the aetiology. Nevertheless, whether the basic cause is a genetically determined metabolic defect or disorder of the immune reaction, I am hopeful that eventually we may discover a remedy that will exert its effects at this basic level and render the search for new and more potent anti-inflammatory drugs less urgent.

There is one other concept of inflammation and drug action that I should like to mention briefly. Enzymes in the cell are contained within small structures called lysosomes, from which they are no doubt released in normal circumstances in a controlled fashion. The addition of vitamin A to suspensions of these particles *in vitro*, or exposure to UV light, leads to a release of these enzymes. The addition of hydrocortisone will prevent this (Fell, H. B. R., & Thomas, L. C. [1960]. *J. exp. Med.*, 111, 719; Dingle, J. T. [1961]. *Proc. roy. Soc. Med.*, 55, 109; Weissman, G., & Dingle, J. T. [1961]. *Exp. Cell Res.*, 25, 207). If inflammation in the living animal is related to an abnormal release of lysosomal enzymes, then the action of the corticosteroids and perhaps salicylates may be related to their ability to stabilize lysosomes.

Toxic effects

In the fourth session we heard a great deal about the gastrointestinal bleeding and anaemia that may follow the ingestion of salicylates. MUIR painted an alarming picture of potential exsanguination and death following a single tablet of aspirin taken to relieve a headache. It is right and proper to pay due attention to these complications, but in my opinion it would be a pity if their importance were overrated. Patients soon get to know about such matters and may come to regard aspirin, the most useful single remedy in the treatment of rheumatic diseases, as a dangerous drug. It may well be so on occasions, but I do not think we should over-emphasize this aspect. Many other drugs used in treatment without much criticism carry far more serious risks than aspirin. If a knowledge of these undesirable effects stimulates our colleagues in the drug industry to produce other equally effective anti-inflammatory agents free from them, so much the better.

Of the other toxic effects of salicylates I need say little. It is reassuring to know that haemodialysis is now regarded as a safe and effective method of treatment, and that artificial kidney units are available in most areas for the treatment of acute salicylism. It has occurred to me that the thurfyl nicotinate reaction might occasionally serve a useful purpose in a diagnostic sense. In a comatose patient in whom aspirin poisoning was suspected, a positive skin reaction would almost certainly rule this drug out. A negative reaction, on the other hand, would be less helpful as we have heard that potential suicides often take a mixture of drugs, and this might include a few aspirins.

DISCUSSION

M. J. H. SMITH: DUTHIE remarked that he was surprised that the widespread effects of salicylates on enzymes and metabolic processes were not more evident in the patient. How does he know this? Until the metabolic implications of these effects in whole animals and man have been studied in more detail it is difficult to know if either the observed signs and symptoms are a reflection of biochemical disturbances at the cellular level, or whether one should look more closely for additional symptoms in salicylate poisoning.

DUTHIE: I think the non-biochemical part of the audience did appreciate my point.

VAN CAUWENBERGE: One aspect which has not been discussed in this symposium is the effect of salicylates on the pituitary-adrenal axis. This is a substantial area of salicylate research in which a number of people have been interested for many years (e.g. Roskam, J. [1956]. *Bull.*

schweiz. Akad. med. Wiss., **12**, 120; Done, A. K., Ely, R. S., & Kelley, V. C. [1958]. *Metabolism*, **7**, 52). Our findings have differed from those of some other workers, but the explanation of this difference may be due to the fact that we have used different techniques, and also to the higher doses we administered (Roskam, J., van Cauwenberge, H., Vivario, R., & Vliers, M. [1955]. *Presse méd.*, **63**, 1105).

Wood: In our discussions we have been subjected to a certain amount of confusion between the analgesic effect of aspirin and this drug's effectiveness as an anti-inflammatory agent. In practice it is difficult to sort out how much of the action of aspirin is due to its pain-relieving properties, and how much is due to its action in reducing such complaints as stiffness, which may be due to a separate anti-inflammatory action. We are aware that in severe cases aspirin is effective perhaps for only two hours. It has been suggested that this duration of action may be related to Mandel's demonstration that after two hours all the acetylsalicylic acid in plasma has been hydrolysed (Mandel, G., Cambosos, N. M., & Smith, P. K. [1954]. *J. Pharmacol. exp. Ther.*, **112**, 495). However, salicylic acid will also relieve stiffness in such cases, and also for a similar two-hour period, and therefore Mandel's findings are unlikely to be relevant. If the relief of stiffness can represent a distinct anti-inflammatory action of aspirin, then in this context aspirin and sodium salicylate appear to be equally efficacious.

Duthie: Like everyone else, we have been cooperating with the drug industry for a long time, trying to find a substitute for aspirin. I would not care to say how many promising drugs we have screened that the industry had already assayed using the standard tests for anti-inflammatory activity. In clinical trials none of them have come up to the level of effectiveness of aspirin.

Holt: Presumably in therapeutics we are interested in the concentration of salicylate in the tissues. In man we have to assess this from levels in the blood. I am still uncertain what is the best measure of serum levels in future studies for clinical and experimental purposes.

Osorio: I still think that what will be meaningful is to measure free, non-protein-bound, salicylate in blood. This is not difficult, and can be done by measuring the binding power of the plasma proteins by a dialysis technique, and relating it to the total salicylate concentration.

Adams: A simpler method for the determination of acetylsalicylic acid in blood might be of considerable value. Perhaps we should be interested in acetylsalicylate as well as salicylate.

Copeman (*Chairman*): I think perhaps we had better leave the discussions on that note of doubt. I am sure you will feel that by and large this symposium has been worth while; it may have raised as many questions as it solved, but that gives all the more material for our next meeting.

INDEX OF CONTRIBUTORS

Numbers in bold type indicate a contribution in the form of a paper or a prepared introduction to a discussion.

INDEX OF SUBJECTS

Proprietary names are not indexed, unless no alternative is available (See p. vi. for synonyms).

The following abbreviations are used in this index:

S :   Salicylate
ASA :   Aspirin (acetylsalicylic acid)
SA :   Salicylic acid

Printed by Spottiswoode, Ballantyne & Co. Ltd., London and Colchester